Healing Collective Trauma Using Sociodrama and Drama Therapy

EVA LEVETON, MS, MFT

Editor

SPRINGER **PUBLISHING COMPANY**

New York

Springer Publishing Company, LLC
11 West 42nd Street
New York, NY 10036
www.springerpub.com

Acquisitions Editor: Sheri W. Sussman
Senior Editor: Rose Mary Piscitelli
Cover design: Steve Pisano
Composition: International Graphic Services

Ebook ISBN: 978-0-8261-0487-8

10 11 12 13/ 5 4 3 2 1

The author and the publisher of this Work have made every effort to use sources believed to be reliable to provide information that is accurate and compatible with the standards generally accepted at the time of publication. The author and publisher shall not be liable for any special, consequential, or exemplary damages resulting, in whole or in part, from the readers' use of, or reliance on, the information contained in this book. The publisher has no responsibility for the persistence or accuracy of URLs for external or third-party Internet Web sites referred to in this publication and does not guarantee that any content on such Web sites is, or will remain, accurate or appropriate.

Library of Congress Cataloging-in-Publication Data

Healing collective trauma using sociodrama and drama therapy / Eva Leveton, editor.
    p. ; cm.
  Includes bibliographical references and index.
  ISBN 978-0-8261-0486-1 (alk. paper)
  1. Drama—Therapeutic use. 2. Sociodrama. I. Leveton, Eva.
  [DNLM: 1. Stress Disorders, Post-Traumatic—therapy. 2. Psychodrama—methods. WM 170 H4332 2010]
  RC489.P7H43 2010
  616.89'1523—dc22
                                2010008763

Printed in the United States of America by Hamilton Printing

For my family, who endured the long absences (mental and physical); to all those sociodramatists and psychodramatists who travel the world in an effort to make it better; and to my students, who teach me something new every day.

I also dedicate this book to the many unsung heroes who travel the world facing groups beset by the consequences of war, disaster, and political oppression. Their courage, their imagination, their heartfelt dedication, and their willingness to endure hardship in order to help others is an inspiration to us all.

Contents

Contributors

Mario Cossa, MA, RDT/MY, TEP
Trainer, Safe School Ambassadors Program of Community Matters,
Santa Rosa, CA; Founding Member,
Bay Area Moreno Institute; SF Bay Area, CA;
Director, Post Traumatic Stress Center, New Haven, CT

Pam Dunne, PhD, RDT/BC
Director, Drama Therapy Institute of Los Angeles, Los Angeles,
CA; Professor, California State University, Los Angeles, CA

Antonina Garcia, EdD, TEP, RDT/BCT, LCSW
Associate Professor, Drama Therapy Program, New York University, New York, NY

David Read Johnson, PhD, RDT/BCT
Assistant Clinical Professor, Yale University School of Medicine,
New Haven, CT; Staff Psychologist, Veterans Administration Medical Center, West Haven, CT; Director, Institute for the Arts in
Psychotherapy, New York, NY

Jon P. Kirby, PhD
Social Anthropologist, Teacher, Consultant in Human Development/Culture Drama, Tamale Institute of Cross-Cultural Studies,
Ghana, West Africa; Facilitator and Professor, Boston University
School of Theology, Boston, MA; Consultant, The Paulist Center,
Boston, MA; African Studies Association, Researcher, Northern
Ghana, Africa

Alan Leveton, MD
Consultant, Community Institute for Psychotherapy, San Rafael, CA; Private Practice, San Rafael and San Francisco, CA

Martin Newman, MA, MFT
Private Practice, San Francisco, CA; Adjunct Faculty, Wright Institute, San Francisco, CA

Leticia Nieto, PsyD
Tenured Full Professor, Psychology and Counseling, Master Program, Saint Martin's University, Lacey, WA; Director, Acting for Change, Director, Teatro de la Vida Real/True Story Theatre, Faculty Member, Escuela Europea De Psicodrama Clásico En México, Faculty Member, International Trauma Treatment Program

Herb Propper, PhD, TEP
Trainer, Psychodrama Therapist, and Consultant/Supervisor, Montpelier, VT; Foreign Advisor and Lead Trainer, Celebration of the Soul, Bangladesh Therapeutic Theatre Institute, New Delhi, India; Recipient: Fulbright Grant: Bangladesh 2009–2010

Thomas Riccio, MFA
Professor of Performance Studies and Arts and Technology, University of Texas at Dallas, Dallas, TX

Gong Shu, PhD, ATR, TEP, LCSW
Founder, Center for Creative Development, Founder, International Zerka Moreno Institute, St. Louis, MO, Taipeh, Taiwan

Armand Volkas, MA, MFA, MFT, RDT/BCT
Associate Professor, Drama Therapy Program, California Institute of Integral Studies, Director, Living Arts Counseling Center, Oakland, CA

Sabine Yasmin Saba, MA
Instructor, Bangladesh Therapeutic Theatre Institute

Preface

Collective trauma is a "blow to the basic tissues of social life that damages the bonds attaching people together and impairs the prevailing sense of community."

—K. Erikson

Current newspapers, books, stories, magazine articles, and essays contain a plethora of themes dealing with victims of war, oppression, sexual mistreatment, and natural disasters. The *San Francisco Chronicle* (Hefling, 2008) reports that by 2007—4 years into the Iraq war—the rate of suicides per year in the U.S. Army was the highest in 26 years of record keeping, currently up to 12 per day. At the same time, homicides increased unexpectedly among Iraq War veterans (Soltz, 2008). The demand for mental health services exceeds records set in previous wars (Dao, 2009), and the symptoms of post-traumatic stress disorder and depression can last for years (Barnes, 2008). Whether we are asked to read about Iraq, Bangladesh, the Sudan, Ghana, South America, China, or our own internal problems with Katrina victims, Native Americans, immigrants, or the gay population, we are struck by the sheer numbers of victims and the poor quality of help available to individuals and groups (Erikson, 1995; Hefling, 2008; Soltz, 2008). Not only are we confronted by the present, but the past also refuses to leave; the historical legacy of Jews under Nazism and Japanese Americans during World War II, for example, has left traces into the third generation (Hoffman, 2004; Kellerman, 2007). In other regions, such as Africa, ancient tribal conflicts have increased dramatically (Kellerman, 2007).

Our title suggests healing. Let the reader be warned: Healing is not curing. This volume, replete as it is with practical advice and voices of deep experience, promises neither "cookie-cutter" methods nor "sure-fire" solutions. Healing is a process. Participants in the groups led by our adventurous pioneers will have an opportunity to regain lost vitality and to experience new ways of dealing with old problems. Healing consists of all kinds of changes, big and small. Where one participant begins to heal through an initial development of trust in the group, another gains an altogether new perspective, and a third is unable to cite a clear result. The theories and methods in the following chapters serve as an orientation and a challenge to future healers; with application, a degree of healing can be achieved.

When large groups of people are involved in political upheavals, social crises, and natural disasters, it is difficult to allocate the personnel and financial resources to deal with the stress that ensues. Government agencies as well as nongovernmental organizations lack staff and funds necessary for the many people they seek to serve. Of the methods employed to address these problems, often referred to as post-traumatic stress syndrome, sociodrama (Sternberg & Garcia, 2002) and drama therapy (Johnson & Emunah, 2009) have been used successfully in many parts of the world. Because both methods have always focused on the entire group, not just the individual, support, expression of the problems, and renewed community can be achieved for many, not just one client at a time.

Drama therapists and sociodramatists have an advantage in delivering services to populations affected by collective trauma (Hudgins, 2002; Kellerman, 2007). Their application saves time and money that would otherwise be spent on individual or family interviews. However, their success is more than economical: The techniques described here have been successful in reducing pain, improving communication, and suggesting solutions for oppressed and victimized groups.

Moreno (1959), the founder of psychodrama, realized something that eluded many of the early psychiatric theorists. A great thinker and theoretician himself, he came to the conclusion that talking and thinking alone were insufficient stimuli for producing change. Concentrating on discovering processes that produce psychological health, rather than focusing on overcoming pathology, he suggested that the healing process should activate the client through "spontaneity training" that would enable the protagonist to access a spontaneous, flexible, appropriate response to a new challenge instead of falling back on learned habits that no longer apply. His metaphor of the fountain—the Latin root of spontaneity is *sponte*—with its dancing, life-giving waters illuminates his method, developed to help not only the protagonist, but all of those in the group, from the other role-players to the audience. Like the authors represented in this volume, Moreno also realized that there are issues that affect an entire group, whether it is a group of oppressed individuals like the prostitutes he worked with in Vienna (Marineau, 1989) or much larger groups, like prison populations, deaing with collective trauma. He developed sociodrama to address issues confronting general, cultural, and political roles, from parents and children, to teachers and students, to victims and oppressors.

It is often said that Americans remain provincial in relation to the world's problems, that we don't want to hear about the problems of others, traumatized or oppressed, even in our own country (Erikson, 1995). We are known to have a foreign office that lacks Arabic speakers. Our professional associations pay little attention to work done abroad. Kellerman (2007) writes:

> Major traumatic events such as war, terrorist bombings and natural disasters, transcend the realms of individual suffering and enter the universal and collective sphere....In the long run, collective trauma...needs a group setting for its proper exploration and resolution. (p. 9)

The authors in this book are individuals who understood, early on, the importance of the views Kellerman advocates and responded to Moreno's call to make the world a better place (1959). They are among the many motivated individuals who have taken it upon themselves to pioneer in reaching out to traumatized and oppressed populations the world over.

At a recent psychodrama conference, one of the attendees remarked, "It's just amazing how much your work is based in your personal biographies." In my experience, this is particularly true of the sociodramatists and drama therapists who appear in this volume. Their immense outlay of personal energy, often without adequate financial support, is evidence of an unusual personal commitment. I am convinced that the passion to reconcile groups with deep historical conflict, or groups suffering from a current trauma, has its basis in deeply personal experiences and motivations. Because those who wish to follow in their footsteps will learn both from their professional and their personal stories, we have included both in these chapters.

All of the techniques discussed enlarge the topic of sociodrama with original work developed by the authors. In the panoply of techniques culled from the theater, from socio- and psychodrama, from Playback theater and from drama therapy, the reader will find new ways of warming up groups, of conducting enactments, and of sharing. A discussion of the difficulties of developing trust in victimized or opposing groups and the necessity of developing realistic goals will aid the directors of prospective sociodramatic work. The application of a wide range of auxiliary arts—music, artwork, poetry—will be illustrated. New ways of developing roles as well as new role constellations will be explored. Several of our authors talk about the continuation of their work by encouraging the members of their groups to become social activists. One, Herb Propper, has developed an entire institute in Bangladesh to train Bangladeshis in the use of psycho- and sociodrama. Without ignoring the depths of these conflicts or providing false hope, the authors demonstrate a variety of ways to approach collective trauma.

The following chapters will illustrate that drama therapists and sociodramatists work both with individuals and with groups, large and small. After covering the broader aspects of our discussion, the authors in Part I will discuss problems of marginalized groups occurring in the United States, where problems in groups of returning veterans, teenagers, immigrants, and homosexuals are addressed; the intergenerational problems of post-Holocaust Germans, Poles, and Jews are also considered; as well as work with traumatized women in the Middle East. Part II covers work done far afield—in Africa, where the work concerns Ghanians, Tutsis, and Hutus; in Bangladesh; and in China, where the one-child family has been legally mandated. We will be dealing with the reconciliation of opposing groups, the change in family roles during and after times of crisis, and the historical legacy of trauma.

Throughout the book, our authors provide practical examples the reader can adapt. Although each of the chapters is a mixture of theory and practice, each of the two parts of this volume will begin with a more theoretical chapter, followed by case studies that demonstrate the work. The volume is completed by an Afterword that discusses the implications of these new developments and their possible application in a wide variety of social problems.

We begin with sociodrama. Antonina Garcia, one of the most widely published and recognized authors on the subject (Sternberg & Garcia, 1997), in her opening chapter reviews theory, techniques, and applications as they relate to work discussed in this volume. These techniques also demonstrate one of the roots of drama therapy, a discipline that enlarged on the earlier work of psychodrama and sociodrama by widening its theoretical base and adding performance and ritual components to its repertory (Johnson & Emunah, 2009).

J. L. Moreno (1959), the founder of psychodrama and sociodrama, began with a creative career that included an improvised theater form, the *Stehgreiftheater*, using some of Hollywood's best known actors (Marineau, 1989). As a physician, Moreno soon integrated his understanding of improvisation with healing by developing a type of group therapy in which spontaneous action on the stage—theater—was the main component: psychodrama.

A side-remark may be relevant here. When David Johnson (1997, personal communication), one of the authors of this volume, suggested to Zerka Moreno, J. L.'s coworker and spouse, that, were he alive today, Moreno would be a drama therapist, she agreed that might well be the case, as the use of theater to bring about change had always interested him. Present-day drama therapists have closed the circle, reconnecting theatrical performance to the compendium of improvisation and widening the theoretical base of action techniques (Johnson & Emunah, 2009; Landy, 1986).

The Trauma in America section continues by exploring Narradrama, with Pam Dunne, its originator. This form integrates narrative therapy (White, 2007) with drama therapy and explores the use of all the creative arts (music, photography, drama, poetry, and art). In addition to a comprehensive theoretical orientation, the reader—whom we hope will excuse the inclusion of Middle Eastern women in this chapter—will learn new techniques using spontaneous writing, photography, collage, song, and puppetry, combined with role-playing and performance techniques, culminating in ritual. Problems of self-esteem addressed in Dunne's work with American teenagers in a group home, and, later in the chapter, their grown Middle Eastern sisters, demonstrate the universality of these techniques. Dunne's use of Narradrama demonstrably includes a much-debated subject, the psychiatric patient. Her work shows, as J. L. Moreno (1959) once did, that hospitalized psychotic patients can often access socially appropriate roles without repetition of psychotic content in spontaneous role-play.

David Read Johnson, a pioneer of drama therapy, who developed a form of drama therapy called "Transformations" (2009), acquaints the reader with a range of uses of theatrical performance with veterans. The veterans begin with improvised enactments that serve to help the men communicate with each other and with other groups of veterans using improvisational role-play. Then the veterans rehearse selected scenes to be performed in public. The form remains improvisational—the words are not set—but the scenes proceed in a known and rehearsed order, like acts in a play. As his title, "Performing Absence," suggests, these forms can help veterans to express and communicate—not erase—their painful experiences. The "absence" experienced in war—the absence of expected meaning, more than anything else, composed of all the lesser absences, such as family, home, reliability, predictability, safety—cannot be "worked through." Traces of this "absence" remain in the psyche, a traumatic experience easily re-stimulated.

Mario Cossa's chapter acquaints the reader with the trauma of HIV, for both victims and helpers. His innovative work combines Kate Hudgins' Therapeutic Spiral Method, developed specifically for trauma work, with other sociodramatic methods.

We continue with Leticia Nieto's work with Americans of ethnicity, using an example of a psycho-sociodrama with a Philippina-American. A section based on the theoretical background of the Rank system (Mindell, 1995) and Target and Agent roles (Hays, 2001) describes Nieto's anti-oppression approach. As this work represents the most recently developed area in the field, the reader may find that the terms used are unfamiliar. Their use provides an entirely new way of viewing and working with problems of racism and offers new strategies and possible ways of "re-training" those who have internalized oppression.

Finally, Eva Leveton and Armand Volkas discuss their work with several generations of post-Holocaust Germans and Jews, based on Volkas' *Healing the Wounds of History*, a process he developed as he began his work of reconciliation between first-, second-, and third-generation Germans and Jews living in the United States and in Europe. In this chapter, we encounter yet another combination of sociodrama, the arts, and performance, used to abreact trauma, discover new ways to regard old roles through role reversal, familiarize ourselves with the oppressor present in all of us, and help heal the deep and serious wounding by the Holocaust.

We begin Part II with a theoretical orientation by Thomas Riccio, a theater director and actor, who has taught in the Drama Therapy Department at San Francisco's California Institute of Integral Studies and is currently a professor at the University of Texas, Dallas. He is the ultimate theatrical traveler, having taken his work from the American theater to Canada, where he helped Yup'ic Eskimos recover their sense of pride and honor their native rituals; to Africa, where he helped create dances and peaceful encounters between warring tribes; and back again to Western and European theater, helping theater groups to recover some of the vitality of their original commitment. His orientation to "place, body, and space" will introduce the reader to novel and active ways of entering and working with indigenous populations who rediscover their pride of origin, tradition, and unity in activities that use movement, breath, and the circle, combining past and present cultures with the familiar rhythms of the heart.

The following chapter, by Herb Propper and Sabine Yasmin Saba, adds a detailed explication of the use of sociodrama into the mix, with examples from their innovative Bangladesh Therapeutic Theatre Institute, which is currently providing training for Bangladeshis working with problems of poverty, oppression, and regularly occurring natural disasters. Their work, both with adults and children, in the aftermath of Cyclone Sidr, and some of the religio-political problems caused by Osama bin Laden in the Bangladesh Muslim community, offers a window into working with another language—sometimes with and sometimes without a translator. Saba, one of the members of the Bangladeshi Therapeutic Theater Institute, also provides an example of the far-reaching effects of working with one of the most underprivileged groups in the world, the Indian transvestite prostitutes, for whom simple sociometric exercises provided a basis for joining, sharing, and addressing the deeper problems affecting them all.

Jon P. Kirby (2007) and Gong Shu also traveled to Africa, combining Abrams' experience as an anthropologist with Gong Shu's (2004) internationally recognized sociodramatic work to address a serious tribal conflict in Ghana. Their example of "culture drama" illustrates an approach to one of the root causes of war everywhere: territoriality. New ways to use both art and sociodramatic techniques address the long-held wrongful projections each tribe has of the other.

In the final chapter of Part II, Leveton, Leveton, and Newman address one of the least discussed problems in China: the consequences of the one-child family rule (Hesketh, Lu, & Xing, 2005), which caused a pervasive sense of abandonment and alienation in those generations affected by it (Becker, 1996). In our teaching at Sichuan University in

ChengDu, China, we found that our students commonly cited a problem that affected three generations: grandmothers (and, to a lesser extent, grandfathers), parents, and children. The grandmothers are scarred by the oppressive experience of the Cultural Revolution and hold authoritarian disciplinary values. The parents, the first educated middle-class generation in China, hold more liberal values and are likely to have an affectionate relationship with their children. However, they usually find work in a city away from their village, and, even if they live in a city, work long hours. The children, now in their 20s, have painful memories of being raised by harsh, resentful grandmothers, of longing for the absent parents. Presently, they strongly reject traditional family values for those of the materialistic West. The group work helped them to form a closer community, to share their pain—many for the first time—and to support each other in formulating strategies for the future.

In this important and emerging field, we hope that the reader will be challenged by theoretical material and inspired by the case examples. Marginalized and oppressed groups everywhere are in need of help and support. They present their own sets of problems of trust and hope. We hope that our readers will see enough commonalities with their particular approaches to create their own ways of helping similar groups, reassured by the repetition of the rule that there are no set rules for doing this work. Each group is unique; each method and process works at a particular time for a particular set of problems. All of our authors emphasize the necessity of flexibility and constant co-creation. It is not easy to work in a new country, possibly with a new language, with translators, with new institutions and new cultural beliefs and customs. For that reason, we want to bring the reader along on our often-distant journeys, and to present a "hands-on" approach. Each chapter includes more than one detailed illustration of workshop activities, the problems encountered by the leaders, and the effects of the work.

Active therapies—beginning with Fritz Perls' Gestalt Therapy (Perls, 1969), based on learning in Moreno's workshops—have been developed using role-playing as their base. In addition, we hope that clinicians with other therapeutic backgrounds, such as family therapy, Jungian analysis, or behavior therapy, continue to adapt role-playing and various art-forms in their work. Combined, we now have a large number of sociodramatists, psychodramatists, and drama therapists who have been trained and continue to be trained in the use of active techniques. It is our hope that our authors' efforts will serve to inspire future generations of group therapists to use active techniques in addressing collective trauma.

REFERENCES

Barnes, J. E. (2008, April 18). 20% of Iraq, Afghanistan veterans have depression or PTSD, study finds. *Los Angeles Times.*

Becker, J. (1996). *Hungry ghosts: Mao's secret famine.* New York: Free Press.

Dao, J. (2009, July 13). Veterans Affairs, already struggling with backlog, faces surge in disability claims. *New York Times.*

Erikson, K. (1995). *A new species of trouble.* New York: W. W. Norton.

Hays, P. A. (2001). *Addressing cultural complexities in practice: A framework for clinicians and counselors.* Washington, DC: American Psychological Association.

Hefling, K. (2008, February 13). Iraq War vets suicide rates analyzed. *San Francisco Chronicle.*

Hesketh, T., Lu, L., & Xing, Z. W. (2005). The effect of China's one-child family policy. *New England Journal of Medicine, 353,* 1171–1176.

Hoffman, E. (2004). *After such knowledge: Memory, history, and the legacy of the Holocaust.* New York: Public Affairs TM, a member of the Perseus Book Group.

Hudgins, K. (2002). *Experiential treatment for PTSD.* New York: Springer Publishing Company.

Johnson, D. R., & Emunah, R. (Eds.). (2009). *Current approaches in drama therapy.* Springfield, IL: Charles C Thomas.

Kellerman, P. F. (2007). *Sociodrama and collective trauma.* London: Jessica Kingsley.

Kirby, J. P. (2007). Ethnic conflicts and democratization: New paths toward equilibrium in northern Ghana. *Transactions of the Historical Society of Ghana, New Series, 10,* 65–108.

Marineau, R. (1989). *Jacob Levy Moreno, 1889–1974, father of psychodrama, sociodrama, and group sociometry.* New York: Routledge.

Mindell, A. (1995). *Sitting in the fire: Large group transformation using conflict and diversity.* Portland, OR: Lao Tse Press.

Moreno, J. L., & Moreno, Z. T. (1975). *Psychodrama, second volume.* Beacon, NY: Beacon House.

Perls, F. S. (1969). *Gestalt therapy verbatim.* Moab, UT: Real People Press.

Shu, Y. (2004). *The art of living with change.* St. Louis, MO: F. E. Robbins and Sons Press.

Soltz, J. (2008). *PTSD and murder among newest veterans.* Retrieved August 15, 2009, from votevets.org

Sternberg, P., & Garcia, A. (2000). *Sociodrama: Who's in your shoes?* Westport, CT: Praeger.

Acknowledgments

Many cooks have stirred the pot in preparing the present volume. I want to thank the authors—many of them traveling the world as we worked on this volume—who put in many hours and revisions to achieve the final result. I am grateful to Sheri W. Sussman, my patient and helpful editor at Springer Publishing, and to Kerry Vegliando at Springer Publishing, and to Pamela Lankas, who took care of the editing and the technical aspects of putting this complex work together.

Healing Collective Trauma Using Sociodrama and Drama Therapy

Trauma in America

1 Healing With Action Methods on the World Stage

ANTONINA GARCIA

Author's Profile

My interest in sociodrama started in the 1970s when a local police trainer asked me to come to the county police academy and lead role-plays so that the police could learn experientially how to handle domestic violence. Soon after, I was invited to do the same for the State Police. Over a 12-year period, I conducted role-plays and sociodramas to train police in sex-crime investigation and a variety of other crisis-intervention situations, such as safely handling motor vehicle stops and dealing with mentally ill or suicidal people. Currently, I train people in how to use sociodrama and do inservice trainings at a variety of agencies in which sociodrama is the modality used to explore many topics, for example, how to resolve conflict on the job.

Antonina Garcia, EdD, TEP/BCT, LCSW, is one of the best known sociodramatists working today. She trains psychodramatists nationally and internationally and maintains a private practice. She is co-author, with Patricia Sternberg, of *Sociodrama: Who's in Your Shoes?* (2nd ed.), published by Praeger Press, a book widely accepted as the leading text for sociodrama. She is featured demonstrating psychodrama in a DVD titled *Three Approaches to Drama Therapy*. She is past Executive Editor of the

Journal of Group Psychotherapy and Psychodrama and past Chair of the American Board of Examiners. Formerly Coordinator of the Creative Arts in Therapeutic Settings Option and a full professor at Brookdale Community College, she currently teaches at NYU in the Drama Therapy Program. She is certified as a Trainer, Educator, and Practitioner by the American Board of Examiners in Psychodrama, Sociometry, and Group Psychotherapy and is a Fellow of the American Society of Group Psychotherapy and Psychodrama (ASGPP). She is also a recipient of ASGPP's J. L. Moreno Lifetime Achievement Award as well as their Scholar's Award and is a two-time winner of the Collaborator's Award.

MORENO'S LEGACY: SOCIODRAMA AND PSYCHODRAMA

It is axiomatic that action methods have been used to heal since the dawn of history. Early tribes co-created enactments to ward off evil, heal trauma, and return participants to harmony. They knew that the very act of embodying painful experiences in a metaphorical way and transforming those experiences to hoped-for, wished-for futures allows for profound positive shifts in perspective and experience.

In modern times, the grandparents of all enactive educational and therapeutic modalities are sociodrama and psychodrama. They have been in the world's cultural context since 1921. Sociodrama and psychodrama are branches of the same tree. Jacob Levy Moreno created both as a way to heal both individuals and groups (Sternberg & Garcia, 2000).

Jacob Levy Moreno, MD (1889–1974), was a visionary thinker who was born in Romania and raised and schooled in Vienna. Moreno germinated and initiated many of his early ideas and projects in Vienna. He spent most of his professional life in the United States, arriving in 1925. During his years in the United States he further developed his theories and methods, and his work spread throughout the world (Moreno, 1953).

Moreno had a tremendous interest in social action in favor of oppressed peoples. The first class of people with whom he worked were prostitutes in 1913. Having discovered that prostitutes in Vienna had no legal rights and were not allowed access to public hospitals, he engaged an attorney to advocate for them, a newspaper editor to publicize their plight, and a doctor to see to their medical needs. Having acted on behalf of some of their human rights, Moreno organized the women into a kind of guild that met weekly to discuss their issues and difficulties. As they spoke, Moreno began to develop some of his theories about roles and about how groups work. He noticed that the prostitutes, though individuals, had very much in common. It was through revealing their commonality that they were able to come together around a common purpose. He noted that every role we play in life has a private and a collective component and that each member of a group is a potential therapeutic agent of the other members.

Moreno acted also as the chief medical officer at a camp for Italian refugees in Mittendorf, Austria (Marineau, 1989). He was appalled that the refugees were not only suffering the trauma of displacement, but were also separated from loved ones and comrades who were at the camp. He proposed to reorganize the camp along lines of choice, to offer more options to these beleaguered people. Although it is uncertain whether the plan was carried out, the fact that Moreno sought to improve the lot of those traumatized tells us of his commitment to helping those who were underserved and lacking in options. It was at this time that Moreno began to develop his ideas about the science of sociometry. Sociometry is a science that focuses on the choices people make and the nature of those choices.

Still deeply interested in social action, Moreno started a socio-political theatre group called the Theatre of Spontaneity in Vienna in 1921 (Sternberg & Garcia, 2000). He organized a group of professional actors whom he trained in spontaneity techniques and social research regarding the issues of the time. Members of the general public were invited to attend and explore with the actors the current events of the culture. Moreno directed the "performances" and interacted with the actors and audience, and issues were explored in action spontaneously. Through this method, sociodrama was born.

Briefly, a sociodrama is an unscripted enactment of a social situation in which various techniques are used to help a group explore the social context in which the members live. The focus of sociodrama is the group, the *socius*, society. The focus of psychodrama, on the other hand, is on the individual and his or her personal story. Psychodrama also emerged from Moreno's Theatre of Spontaneity (Garcia & Buchanan, 2000). Here's how it happened.

One of Moreno's leading actresses was married to a playwright who came to see Dr. Moreno for marital help. "George" complained that his wife, "Barbara," was a shrew at home, although she seemed an angel at the theater. To help them, Moreno suggested that "George" bring up the issue at that evening's performance. When it was addressed, Moreno asked the couple to come up onstage, set the scene, and re-enact an argument that had occurred in their apartment earlier that day. Moreno, who was a psychiatrist as well as director, used the opportunity to engage in action marriage counseling. Thus was psycho-drama born. In addition to helping the couple through psychodrama, Moreno helped them in another way.

It seems "Barbara" was frequently called upon to play ingenue roles in the company. Moreno hypothesized that she had developed role fatigue by being typecast as a sweet young girl and, at home, was enacting the counter role, that of shrew, in an effort to find balance. He made his first therapeutic role assignments with "Barbara" by re-casting her in a wider variety of roles, rather than keeping her in the fixed role of ingénue. As a result of these therapeutic role assignments Barbara's behavior at home was more balanced.

An essential substructure of both psychodrama and sociodrama is sociometry. Sociometry is the science that explores people's choices and provides direction in helping them make choices that enhance their life experience. After emigrating to the United States, Moreno put his ideas about sociometry into action when he used sociometry to organize the prison population at Sing Sing. He and Helen Hall Jennings surveyed the population according to many variables, such as, age, immigration history, neighborhood experiences, language, behavior, etc., and re-organized groups according to each member's social quotient so that the prison would operate as a more harmonious social community (Marineau, 1989).

Moreno and Jennings turned their attention to another underserved and traumatized population, at the New York Training School for Girls, a home for delinquent girls in Hudson, New York. Moreno served as Director of Research at the School from 1932-34. It is here for the first time that Moreno actively interwove sociometric study with sociodrama and psychodrama. Moreno studied the girls' preferences in classmates, study mates, task mates, and house mothers. He also asked for their preferences of which cottage in which to live. Further, he surveyed the house mothers regarding with which girls they felt they would work best. Having completed this complex research (there were no comput-ers, remember), he reorganized the entire community and began offering both group psychotherapy and retraining for the girls. He utilized psychodrama, sociodrama, and spontaneity training, filming some of the sessions. The films show the girls involved in role-plays, learning to improve their social skills.

In succeeding years, Moreno continued to develop psychodrama, sociodrama, sociometry, and group psychotherapy. He and his wife, Zerka Toeman Moreno, wrote extensively (Marineau, 1989; Z. T. Moreno, 2006). They lectured and trained people around the world. J. L. Moreno administrated a psychiatric hospital and psychodrama training center in Beacon, New York. He also founded the Moreno Institute in New York City. Moreno died in 1974.

Moreno believed that all human beings have enormous potential for spontaneity and creativity, that we are co-creators of our reality and that we are all interdependent from the moment of conception until our last moment on the planet. As a result of this philosophy of life, he devised a series of theories and methods that dovetail each other and form a coherent expression of his desire to heal all of humankind. He created a theory of spontaneity and creativity. He developed a theory about roles we play in life and how we engage or disengage regarding others. He also developed the science of sociometry to explore how groups work and what can be done to help them function more adequately.

SOCIOMETRY

With the growth of global communications systems, we have all become acutely aware of the many places on the planet where oppression is widespread. The questions many of us ask are, "What can I do about it? How can I contribute to the solution? How can I contribute to the healing of wounded hearts? How can I help an oppressed person to trust again in goodness and hope? How can I help to heal the effects of trauma?"

Jacob Levy Moreno was deeply sensitive to such issues. Growing up a Jew in Victorian Vienna, he knew firsthand about prejudice and injustice foisted upon a minority. He knew well the many pogroms in Jewish history. From his early adulthood he asked himself how to help people move past intolerance and into acceptance of a basic tenet of his belief system: that we are more alike than we are different. Moreno believed that if we could come to realize this fact, we would be more tolerant, less judgmental, and kinder to ourselves and others. As a result he developed the science of sociometry (J. L. Moreno, 1953).

According to Moreno, sociometry is the science that studies the choices people make. Moreno noticed that each of us is continually engaged in the choice-making process when we are not hindered from doing so. For example, we choose with whom we want to dine; with whom we prefer to work; with whom we share confidences; with whom to laugh; with whom to love. When someone reciprocates our positive choice, we have the greatest opportunity for satisfaction. When outside forces drastically restrict our choices as happens in times of war, oppression, famine, and other natural disasters, our dissatisfaction and dysfunction grow exponentially.

Regarding the choices we make, they are based on either positive, negative or neutral feelings. For example, although we may enjoy chatting with one of our neighbors, we may avoid another because we don't like his political views and experience neutral feelings towards another neighbor who is completely off our radar screen.

There are various configurations of choice. Based on a specific criterion, two people can positively choose each other (+ +), positive choice. They can reject each other (− −), negative choice. Someone can choose another, while the person rejects him (+ −), incongruous choice. Or a person can choose no one and be chosen by no one. A person who is unchoosing and unchosen is called an isolate. In a group situation, the person who receives the most positive choices is said to be the sociometric or positive star. The person who receives the most negative choices is said to be the rejection star. There are positive and negative aspects to being either the positive star or the rejection star. Although it is gratifying to be positively chosen, for example, much is expected of a sociometric star. This can cause undue pressure to perform in particular ways. Although it is unpleasant to experience rejection, less is expected of a rejection star and, as a client once noted, "I'd rather have negative attention than no attention at all." It is said that the positive star belongs to the group, and a negative star belongs to himself. The reason for this is that the positive star often sacrifices his/her own wants and needs to accommodate to the group's wants and needs. The rejection star, on the other hand, puts a higher priority on his/her own wants and needs rather than those of the group.

In addition to the sociometric star and the rejection star, there are the star of incongruity and the role of isolate. As an example of incongruity,

Antonio chooses to partner on a work detail with Raimundo. If Raimundo doesn't want to partner with Antonio, an incongruous choice exists. What each of us seeks is mutuality. If there are many examples of incongruous choices in a group, members express dissatisfaction and feel disconnected. It is essential that a group leader make interventions to increase mutuality. This is particularly important in working with groups of displaced persons.

Finally we come to the role of isolate. The position of isolate is a bit complicated. There are certainly times in our lives when we prefer and/or need to be alone. We may isolate for a day. No one contacts us, and we contact no one. However, when a person routinely chooses to isolate himself and is unchosen by others, he may be a true isolate. Such people are rare and we don't know much about them because of their persistent avoidance of others. These people are in danger of depression, anxiety, suicide, and other deeply dysfunctional behavior. The type of isolate that we see most frequently is the near isolate. An example of a near isolate would be a homeless person to whom a homeless shelter reaches out during a winter storm but who insists upon staying on the street alone.

Isolation is a particular problem for those who have been traumatized and oppressed. Sometimes feelings of isolation occur because a person is displaced from home and loved ones, as can happen in times of revolutions, wars, and natural disasters. Sometimes feeling isolated comes from the depression or shame that arises from experiencing the horror of violence, such as that which occurred in Rwanda. The leader using sociometric techniques can do much to reduce feelings of isolation. Dr. Cecilia Yocum (2008) in an unpublished monograph describes a simple yet elegant exercise she used in Rwanda. For this self-care and inner strength exercise, the group is divided in two and sits in concentric circles facing each other. The leader asks a question and each member of the duo facing each other has time to tell the partner the answer to the question. After the dyad has answered the question, people on the outer circle move one seat to their right and the process begins again and continues until each member of the outer circle has shared with each member of the inner circle and vice versa. Some of the questions asked are: "When you feel sad what do you do that helps you? What wisdom have you learned from the things that you have been through in your life? When you feel like giving up, what gives you strength to continue? Even though life can be difficult, we all have things that bring us joy. What brings joy in your life today, and why does that bring you joy?" This exercise helped the participants to shed isolation, fear, and shame. They connected with each other and told elements of their stories in a context of hope. The process of speaking one's truth, being heard and witnessed by another, and reminding each other of inner strength provides powerful healing.

Healthy groups provide access to many roles so that no one is role locked into any single position. When working with traumatized peoples it is essential for a leader to assist members to share coveted roles and diminish the need to place members in roles they experience as negative, for example the role of scapegoat. It is helpful for the leader to find ways to allow the gifts of each group member to emerge and be enacted and appreciated by the group.

Our choices are also based on specific criteria. We don't choose in a vacuum. For example, if a person wants to engage in a project at work, if permitted, she may elect to work with someone who would complement her skills and would be committed to the project. If she knows of a coworker who seldom follows through on projects, she is likely to reject working with that person. The criterion upon which she based her choice was, "Who could best help me complete this task adequately." When people are displaced, frequently they are stripped of their ability to choose with whom to engage.

Oftentimes, choices are also based on specific categories, for example, "people like me" and "people unlike me." Although we may be willing to disclose feelings of inadequacy with close friends, we may not be willing to do so with an acquaintance. Choice is based on cultural and personal expectations as well, such as race, ethnicity, religion, and social status. This is an area that has the potential to bring about enormous dysfunction in the choice-making process, particularly when the person choosing polarizes his/her views and resists information that would allow him/her to expand the view. For example, a man hates Palestinians because he is a Jew and believes that Jews "should" hate and mistrust all Palestinians. Or a Palestinian woman hates all Jews because she's been told they are all infidels and worthy of annihilation. These people may be following what they have heard at home (subculture) or what they have introjected from their culture at large.

Racial and ethnic intolerance is an area of sociometry that many seek to redress. What is interesting to note is that recent research finds that the problem may not be as difficult to resolve as one might think if sociometry is utilized. Benedict Carey (2008) reports in a *New York Times* article, "Tolerance Over Race Can Spread, Studies Find," that over the past few years there have been research studies demonstrating how quickly people from diverse backgrounds can build trust when the circumstances are right. The article describes one such program in which two strangers from different ethnic groups come together and interact in 4-hour-long sessions developed by Art and Elaine Aron, two social psychologists from Stony Brook University. In the first session, the pair share their answers to a variety of questions, ranging from the impersonal to the more personal.

In the second session, the dyad competes against other dyads in several games that are timed. In the third session, they discuss several things, not the least of which is why they are proud to be a member of their ethnic group, whether they are Asian, Latino, Black or White. In the last session, they perform a familiar trust exercise. Each takes turns wearing a blindfold, while the other verbally guides him/her through a maze. What is compelling is that relationships built through engaging in these dyadic exercises may last months or longer. They also reduce participants' scores on a test that measures prejudice. How heartening it is to see proven again that acceptance and tolerance emerge when we come to see that we are more alike than we are different, as Moreno hypothesized so many decades ago.

Sociometry can be used both descriptively and prescriptively. It can be used to study what current choices the members of a particular group are making. It can also be used to help a group to function more adequately and harmoniously as was described above. In times of trauma and oppression, sociometric choices are often stripped from the victims, leaving them bereft. They may be torn from their homes, villages, families, social networks. A skilled group leader can use sociometry to address their needs. The leader can facilitate an increase in access to roles, reduce isolation, increase tolerance and acceptance of differences, and promote greater spontaneity and creativity in a group. The leader can also help those traumatized to trust their ability to choose again.

Moreno observed that there are hidden currents of choice in every group. In new groups hidden currents abound. For example, Micah may not know that he and Joe attended the same high school. Keisha may not know that three other members of her group have lost a child. It is the work of the group leader to facilitate bringing pertinent currents of choice into the open. In working with oppressed or traumatized people, for example, feelings of isolation and shame are common. Gently helping these feelings to come to the surface allows group members to see that they are not alone in their pain. It can also serve to normalize the complexity of the emotions members experience.

John Donne, in his *Meditations XVII*, said, "No man is an island." Moreno agreed. In fact, he felt that the smallest unit of study of an individual is the person in his social atom. The social atom consists of all those whom a person considers significant. Our family, friends, work partners, and even our enemies are all members of our social atom. Our social atom changes over time, as we ourselves grow and change. When we think back over our lives, we may notice that some people who were important to us when we were children are still important. However, some people who were important then may no longer be significant today. In fact, we may have drifted away from them over the years; had arguments that separated us; have moved to a different place; or death has intervened to shift the importance of the relationship.

Awareness of the social atom and the shifts that can occur is especially germane when dealing with people who have lost significant people and/or role relationships because of trauma or oppression. When tragedy strikes and an individual sustains many losses, great holes appear in a social atom that was formerly full. Grief and dysfunction easily ensue. The psychodramatist/sociodramatist works to help the person reweave a social atom that will offer sufficient support.

Moreno conceived of the social atom test as a way to diagnose social dysfunction, plan a course of treatment, and evaluate that treatment's effectiveness (Buchanan, 1984). All of this is done in cooperation with the person completing the atom. In a first session one could ask the individual or group members to complete a current and a future social atom. The future social atom would consist of sociometric changes toward which the person is working. The initial social atom of a battered woman indicates to her that she has isolated herself from her friends because of shame. She asserts that she wants to overcome her shame and resume a past friendship. At the end of treatment, the woman completes a social atom of her present world. Since she has in fact resumed that friendship, the goal has been achieved. Through charting each social atom, the woman can clearly see that she has empowered herself to rebuild her life.

The social atom can also be used to explore and recover aspects of one's pre-trauma world. A person forced to flee the village during a revolutionary assault could construct a social atom of the time before the assault, another atom post-assault, and a future (wished-for) atom. In addition to mourning what was lost because of the trauma, the person can work psychodramatically to restore feelings of innocence and personal power and to forgive himself for fleeing to safety and surviving though others died.

In addition to personal social atoms there are also cultural social atoms. The cultural atom depicts the groups to which one belongs, for example, religious, work, family, interest, and social. Often rectangles are used to represent these groups. Cultural social atoms are particularly useful in working with sociodrama groups where the focus is on collective experience. When working with those who have been culturally traumatized or oppressed, it is essential to focus on the changes that have taken place in the cultural and personal atoms. Even if participants have not charted their social atoms on paper or in action, it is important that the leader bring those aspects of the persons' sociometry to the surface.

Although the presence of our interconnections exists within us, Moreno devised a written exercise in which a person can depict his social atom on paper, thus externalizing the connections. There are many types of social atoms and directions for constructing one (Hale, 1986). Here's an example of one set of directions that the author has modified over the years.

The person is given a piece of paper that says the following:

> Your social atom is composed of you and those who are important to you in your life. You are now going to construct a picture of your social atom. Imagine that the piece of paper in front of you is your life space today. Using a triangle if you are a male or a circle if you are a female, locate yourself on the page. Then, using triangles for males and circles for females, arrange in relation to you those who are significant in your life. If they feel close to you, place them close. If they feel far away, place them far away. If they feel big in your life, make them big. If they feel small in your life, make them small. Put a name or initials in each figure so that you will remember who is who after you've completed the process.

After completing the social atom, discussions or action can occur. Group members can sculpt their social atoms in action or focus on a particular relationship in the atom. In working with trauma over time psychodramatically, it is useful to ask the person or group members to draw a pre-trauma social atom, a post-trauma social atom, and a future (wished-for) social atom. Aspects of these atoms can be concretized in action in many ways. Here are just a few examples: to mourn losses; to recapture positive aspects of the former self; to project into a hopeful future; to express unexpressed emotions from the time following the trauma; to gather resources for coping in the present.

ROLE THEORY

Moreno viewed people as being composites of the roles they play. He viewed role as a specific group of behaviors that society recognizes and labels in a particular way. He felt that each of us plays roles from the moment we take breath (J. L. Moreno, 1946). Our first roles are somatic—sleeper, eater, crier. Through the interactions we have with our caregivers we begin to develop our social roles. The social roles are reciprocal and are most satisfying when the person whom we choose chooses us. Developing concurrently with the social roles are the psychodramatic roles which are our intrapsychic roles, such as imaginer, dreamer, solitary thinker. Dr. Natalie Winters (2000) has proposed that there is a fourth role category: psychospiritual roles, which comprise our transpersonal role relationships.

For each role that we play, both we and our subculture and culture have expectations regarding how the role is to be played. Differing role expectations among people can easily lead to strife, particularly if each person rigidly holds to his or her own expectation. For example, religious, ethnic, and racial wars in part have to do with differing role expectations and the belief that one's own expectations are the only correct ones.

The power of role expectations cannot be overestimated by those who go to cultures other than their own to work. Clearly it is important to find ways to access what the role expectations of the particular group are. This is where using action sociometry is especially valuable in that it can provide an opportunity for the leader to learn group preferences and customs in action.

Some other aspects of role that are helpful to consider are role conflict and role stripping. In situations in which a person is ordered to commit violence on a neighbor to protect their own family from violence as happened in the Rwandan crisis, the role conflict is intense and traumatizing. Role stripping occurs when one is removed from a role, without consent and usually without much notice. It is clear to see how dramatically this occurs for oppressed peoples who may be stripped of many roles all at once.

J. L. Moreno (1946) underscored the importance of role reciprocity. In each social role we play, we have necessary partners. A mother needs a child to be in the role of mother and vice versa. A teacher and student need each other to perform their roles. When we highly value a role and lose our reciprocal role partner, grief and its attendant emotions ensue. This horror can be seen in the faces of people who lose family and friends in earthquakes, fires, and tsunamis. Although lost people cannot be replaced, it is essential to assist survivors in grieving the losses, finding techniques to cope with them, and building new and satisfying role relationships.

SPONTANEITY/CREATIVITY THEORY

J. L. Moreno (1946, 1953) believed that we are potentially spontaneous, creative geniuses. He felt that spontaneity and creativity are essential to get us through every day of our lives. Loosely defined, creativity is the idea, the inspiration for something new, and spontaneity is the catalyst that gets us to put our ideas in action. He pointed out that people have many great ideas that they never put into action. It is spontaneity that spurs us to get into action. He also noted that people sometimes feel the unrest of wanting to change aspects of their lives but not having a clue of how to go about doing that. Thus, spontaneity and creativity are necessary partners.

Moreno also underscored the importance of warm-up in his theory. Warm-up is a readying process. We ready ourselves to play the roles we play. We ready ourselves to take actions to change situations with which we're dissatisfied. Moreno observed and did research showing that in emergency situations, it was far more difficult for people to be spontaneous and creative than it is when they have an opportunity to warm up to new situations. In emergency if we have little time to think, our judgment is often impaired. We fight, flee, or freeze, with any of these responses possibly being inadequate to the situation. Trauma and oppression can wreak havoc with our spontaneity and creativity. People who have been imprisoned for years find it difficult to re-enter a world of choices, a world where they must be spontaneous and creative. Michelle Hoff (personal communication, April 23, 2009), a social worker in New Jersey, works in a halfway house where she uses socio-drama to prepare prisoners to return to the world outside prison. She helps them to role-train how to navigate interactions they may encounter.

Operationally, all of Moreno's theories interweave. Spontaneity and creativity are necessary for making choices (sociometry) toward people with whom we want to interact (role theory). Based on his theories, he devised the following interventions to heal mankind: sociometric exercises, spontaneity training exercises, and sociodrama and psycho-drama.

SOCIODRAMA

Sociodrama (Sternberg & Garcia, 2000) is an action method in which people spontaneously enact social situations as a way to understand the situations more fully. For example, a group of aid workers might enact a scene offering aid where people seem reluctant to receive aid. The workers may come to realize that they need to approach the recipients in a different way than they had planned to do. People also enact such situations to explore various levels of feelings about an event or events. For example, a group of people from two tribes might explore how healing would help them to trust members of a neighboring tribe. Groups also enact various solutions to social problems. For instance, a group may rehearse how to manage anger in more effective and non-violent ways. A group may enact a future projection at the time of completion of a plan they have made to share goats in a village. A group may also explore an issue that has no current resolution so that they may express feelings about the issue and speak their truth.

After each sociodrama, a group has an opportunity to debrief the enactment and to note what has been learned. It is also a time for brainstorming other options, if the action has focused on problem solving, and for reaching closure for the session.

Like role-play, sociodrama is a spontaneous, non-scripted enact-ment. Unlike role-play, there are many techniques used in sociodrama to expand and deepen the learning coming from the action. Some of hundreds of techniques are role reversal, doubling, future projection, magic screen, soliloquy, freeze frame, and aside. Simply stated, role-play is a lot easier to do, needs vastly less training but is less effective.

Sociodrama focuses on the collective aspects of the roles we play. Because it does this, sociodrama can help a group to explore cultural roles and how they feel about them. An enactment can occur in which group members play roles of cultural leaders interacting with each other or with members of the community regarding a specific issue. Thus, in a sociodrama, a person is not acting out his/her own life story. He is playing a role as it is codetermined by group members. In the enact-ment of the role of a hurricane victim approaching FEMA, the person playing the role shifts it so that it is not identical to his own life experience. If, in fact, he had been rescued in a boat, perhaps in the enactment, instead he would have retreated to an evacuation center before the hurricane hit. If, in fact, he had no children, perhaps for the enactment the group decides he's the father of four. One might ask why not enact the true life story of this person? The answer is connected with the contract the leader has with the group. If the contract is educational rather than therapeutic, the person's anonymity should be preserved. Further, people are often less fearful of moving ahead with enactments delving into difficult issues when they are safely dis-tanced enough.

The emotional distancing aspect of sociodrama allows for many positive results. Participants express feelings they might not otherwise express if the drama were more personal. They can have a greater perspective when viewing an issue, because the issue is not expressly theirs. They are frequently able to examine challenging emotional or sociopolitical topics because they're not directly exploring and exposing their own personal lives in a group of people whom they may not know well or trust.

PSYCHODRAMA

The question of enactment of a person's life story leads us to a discussion of psychodrama. Psychodrama is a deep action method developed by Moreno to allow people an opportunity to enact scenes from their lives, from their day and night dreams, and from their fantasies and wishes.

They enact these scenes so as to express feelings they had not previously been able to express and to contain expression of feeling that is out of control. They may also gain insights through the actions they perform and practice new behaviors so that their world can run more smoothly.

In psychodrama, the traumatized person enacts his own story. That is not to say that he/she re-enacts the traumatic events. Instead, scenes of hope and coping are enacted to rebuild spontaneity and creativity. Lauren Shpall (personal communication, 2009) works with adolescent male prisoners and with female prisoners ranging in age from 18 to 70 on Riker's Island. In her women's group, the women enact psychodramas in which they create and interact with "resource figures" to help them cope with current challenges. A resource figure may be a Higher Power, a woman's grandma, or Oprah. The enactment of these dramas helps the women to experience and see that they already have internal resources of which they were not previously aware.

The person who is enacting his/her story is called the protagonist. All other characters in a drama are played by other members of the group, who are chosen to play specific roles. These people are called auxiliary egos. In Colombia, Dr. Cecilia Yocum (personal communication, August 24, 2008) worked on a project with Friends Peace Teams "to bring trauma healing and reconciliation programs to displaced persons, who have fled their rural homes because of violence and moved to the outskirts of large towns or cities in that country…"(p. 2). These programs are experiential, empower participants, and help in rebuilding the community by renewing trust, encouraging solidarity, and sharing of experiences among participants. After asking people to draw a picture of a loss and discuss it, Dr. Yocum led the group in healing rituals in which they sculpted a meaningful moment that occurred during that loss. Each protagonist chose members of the group to become people, animals, or objects that were essential to that meaningful moment. Thus, the group members acted as auxiliary egos to co-create the healing with the protagonist. In her correspondence, Dr. Yocum (personal communication, August 24, 2008) shares two participant reactions:

> I will always remember the tragedy, which was fatal, but now I will also remember the person and how beautiful they were. Now I can remember the person and not just the tragedy. When we dramatized things out it was like a housecleaning. We started addressing things and leaving some things behind. We can take steps toward healing.

Although there are hundreds of techniques used in psychodrama to facilitate healing, there are two techniques that are particularly helpful. One of the most profoundly moving and powerful techniques of both sociodrama and psychodrama is role reversal. The way the technique works is this: the person playing the prisoner in a drama switches roles and physical positions with the person playing the warden. When each plays the role of the other, many opportunities arise: one can develop empathy for the other's position; one can develop a deeper understanding of the situation at hand, a perspective on the situation; one can develop compassion; one can become unstuck; one can gain insight into new ways to solve a problem; one can see oneself as others see her. Finally, through role reversal a person can begin to see ways that we are more alike than different. The other person may actually feel similarly to how I feel.

Although we are capable of reversing roles with people in our minds, actually changing places and stepping into the other's shoes provide us with information and empathy in an even more profound way. Role reversal is the most valuable technique that Moreno developed to maximize the chances of helping each of us realize that we are more alike than we are different, a factor necessary in establishing a truly peaceful co-existence on the planet.

The other extremely helpful technique is doubling. The double is an auxiliary ego who is a kind of inner voice that expresses one's heretofore unexpressed thoughts and feelings. For example, if the double notices that the protagonist is speaking with a calm voice but has his fists clenched, he might say, "I'm speaking to you calmly and controlling my feelings but I'm really angry." If the double is accurate, the protagonist repeats or puts in his own words what was said. If the double is inaccurate, the protagonist corrects the statement. Sometimes in a drama a protagonist has a permanent double, and sometimes group members or the director spontaneously come up and make doubling statements to assist the protagonist's expression or containment.

David Moran (personal communication, 2009), a social worker, administrates an outpatient substance abuse and co-occurring disorders program. Most of the people with whom he and his employees work suffer from PTSD. Many of the social workers utilize doubling with their clients to help them access emotions beneath their denial and to learn containment techniques. They also help them to contact and embody inner strengths of which they were previously unaware.

Here (Table 1.1) are some of the similarities and differences between sociodrama and psychodrama (Garcia, 2006):

Both sociodrama and psychodrama have been utilized with people suffering from trauma since their inception. They continue to be used in this way. They are ideal modalities for working with children and adults, with the able and disabled, with those who are similar or different, and with people suffering from personal and/or cultural trauma. Currently sociodrama and psychodrama are being used globally to heal trauma in such places as India, Bangladesh, Ghana, Rwanda, Burundi, and Colombia, and many other countries as well. Here in the United States, they have been or are currently being used in prisons, to help Katrina victims, and to help Cambodian refugees.

One insidious aspect of trauma is that it promotes isolation and feelings of isolation. Enactment in community normalizes the feelings participants have. After a psychodramatic enactment, as people share similar emotions, one can almost feel a collective sigh of relief from the group. Enactment allows us to speak the unspeakable and experience comfort, compassion, and support from others. In sociodrama, where people are sharing and practicing coping mechanisms, interdependence is fostered and hope is restored.

J. L. Moreno (1953, p. 1) felt that "the only true therapeutic goal was all of mankind." Through use of sociodrama and psychodrama he sought to encounter and heal people on the streets and in the consulting room, to find and help them wherever they were.

In addition to sociodrama and psychodrama, other enactive modalities have emerged since the 1920s. Among these are Playback Theater (Fox, 1994; Salas, 2000), Narradrama (Dunne, 2000), Role Method (Landy, 1993), Developmental Transformation (Johnson & Emunah, 2009), Theatre of the Oppressed (Boal, 1992), and other forms of Drama Therapy (Johnson & Emunah, 2009).

J. L. Moreno (1946) once said that each of us has innumerable stories to tell and moments to enact. He believed that important stories should be enacted twice: once in life and once in psychodrama. Jonathan Fox and Jo Salas developed Playback Theater in the 1970s (Fox, 1994; Salas, 2000). Playback Theater offers a representative psychodrama enactment in which a person from the audience tells a story, and members of a troupe of spontaneity players enact the person's story in its essence. In this way, many stories may be told and witnessed in a given session.

Table 1.1

SIMILARITIES AND DIFFERENCES BETWEEN SOCIODRAMA AND PSYCHODRAMA

SIMILARITIES ONLY BETWEEN SOCIODRAMA AND PSYCHODRAMA

Each session has three components: the warm-up, the action, the sharing.

Open tension systems (themes) and act hungers (need to complete an action) guide the director.

The director must build the positive sociometry (connections) of the group and assist the group in the warming-up process.

The same production techniques are used.

DIFFERENCES ONLY BETWEEN SOCIODRAMA AND PSYCHODRAMA

SOCIODRAMA	PSYCHODRAMA
Sociodrama is primarily educational and sociocultural in intent.	Psychodrama is primarily therapeutic and psychological in intent.
The director contracts with the group.	The director contracts with the protagonist regarding the issues to be explored in the drama.
The participants are called enactors because many sociodramas are group-centered.	The participants are called auxiliary egos or protagonists because psychodramas are protagonist-centered.
Enactors volunteer for roles.	The protagonist chooses auxiliaries and defines the way the auxiliaries will play the role.
During the enactment, the director often freezes the action and asks the audience how they feel, what they think, what ideas or suggestions they have for resolution of problems emergent in the drama or for opinions about what is occurring.	The protagonist may ask for help from the audience if he/she is stuck.
There are times when group members return to an enactment after it has concluded to try out various alternatives that the group has generated in the sharing.	The protagonist doesn't enact additional scenes after the drama has ended. If the protagonist is rehearsing a new skill, he may ask for advice or suggestions during the drama. At that point, he may replay the scene, incorporating the suggestions.
Sometimes an enactor will return to the audience, and other members of the audience will step into the role and try alternate solutions to the problem being explored or explore various ways to play the role.	Auxiliaries remain in the roles for which they were chosen by the protagonist until the drama is completed.

In Playback Theater two chairs are set onstage, one for the teller of the story and one for the Conductor of the Playback troupe. The Conductor acts as emcee and warms the audience up to the telling of pertinent stories. Someone from the audience emerges to tell a story. After the person tells his story, he chooses members of a trained troupe of actors to play different roles in the story. Troupe members, without discussion, spontaneously enact the story. Musicians are also present to transition from telling to action, to accompany the action, and to assist in the conclusion of the action.

Members of Playback Theater troupes are highly trained in spontaneity playing. They are attentive listeners who are comfortable with role, story, and metaphor and have become intuitively sensitive to each other and each other's gifts. Their training enables them to hear a story, immediately embody a role, and move to enactment. After hearing the story, there are no lengthy discussions among troupe members about who will do what. Rather, the members move to collect available props as music plays beneath, and the action begins with the Conductor saying, "Let's watch."

Once the story has been told in action, the Conductor asks the teller if the enactment captured the essence of the story. If anything needs changing, the troupe re-enacts the story making the necessary adjustments. If the enactment has satisfied the teller, he returns to the audience and another teller emerges. The reactions of the tellers demonstrate again and again how wonderful it is to see one's own story in action and to have one's truth witnessed by others.

An alternate method of performing Playback Theater involves the entire group. One person tells a story to the Conductor, and members of the group enact the story. This has particular benefit when a trained troupe is not available but a Conductor is. Although the result may not be as aesthetically pleasing or as artistic in performance terms as would be the case with a professional troupe, there is certainly therapeutic value in group members participating in the telling of each other's stories. When group members co-act, each becomes a therapeutic agent of the other and personally and deeply connected with each other's stories and each other's healing.

Psychodrama, Sociodrama, and Playback Theater have the same theoretical roots, deriving from Moreno. Narradrama, Theatre of the Oppressed, and some other forms of Drama Therapy have their own theoretical bases, emanating from those who created them. Briefly,

Narradrama was created by Pam Dunne (see chapter 2 in this volume). Based on the principles of narrative therapy and theatre, Dr. Dunne devised a way for people to heal through action exploration of the narratives they construct to guide their lives. You can read of Dr. Dunne's methods and theoretical base later in this volume and in Garcia and Buchanan's (2000) *Current Approaches to Drama Therapy*.

Theater of the Oppressed began to be developed by Brazilian Augusto Boal in the early 1970s (1979, 1992). Originally designed to help people to resist oppression through upheaval and rebellion, his later work seems more devoted to how groups and society at large can move toward greater peace and harmony. Boal developed various theatre games and exercises to achieve his goals.

Drama Therapy is distinguishable from Psychodrama in that psychodramatic interventions spring from the theoretical underpinnings of Morenean thought, whereas Drama Therapy historically emerged from several theoretical bases and activities. Although psychodramatists may utilize additional theories that help inform their work, all psychodramatists are required to learn Moreno's theoretical base since psychodramatic interventions arise from the theories. In recent years, this author has observed a lot of cross-fertilization between psychodrama and drama therapy, and the lines of division in some areas have become blurred. Although perhaps confusing to those who seek to delineate one from the other, the interweaving of psychodrama and drama therapy offers myriad opportunities for exciting and meaningful cocreation of new and profound ways to heal ourselves, each other, and our precious planet.

REFERENCES

Boal, A. (1992). *Games for actors and non-actors*. London: Routledge.

Boal, A. (1979). *Theatre of the oppressed*. New York: Theatre Communications Group.

Buchanan, D. R. (1984, November 6). Moreno's social atom: A diagnostic and treatment tool for exploring interpersonal relationships. *Arts in Psychotherapy, 27,* 173–183.

Carey, B. (2008, November 6). Tolerance over race can spread, studies find. *New York Times.*

Dunne, P. (2000). Narradrama: A narrative approach to drama therapy. In P. Lewis & D. R. Johnson (Eds.), *Current approaches in drama therapy* (pp. 111–128). Springfield, IL: Charles C Thomas.

Fox, J. (1994). *Acts of service: Spontaneity, commitment, tradition in the non-scripted theatre*. New Paltz, NY: Tusila Press.

Garcia, A. (2006). *Differences and similarities between sociodrama and psychodrama.* Unpublished training papers.

Garcia, A., & Buchanan, D. R. (2000). Psychodrama. In P. Lewis & D. R. Johnson (Eds.), *Current approaches in drama therapy* (pp. 162–195). Springfield, IL: Charles C Thomas.

Johnson, D. R., & Emunah, R. (Eds.). (2009). *Current approaches in drama therapy* (2nd ed.). Springfield, IL: Charles C Thomas.

Landy, R. (1993). *Persona and performance.* New York: Guilford Press.

Marineau, R. F. (1989). *Jacob Levy Moreno, 1889–1974, father of psychodrama, sociometry and group psychotherapy.* London: Tavistock/Routledge.

Moreno, J. L. (1946). *Psychodrama—first volume.* Beacon, NY: Beacon House.

Moreno, J. L. (1953). *Who shall survive?* Beacon, NY: Beacon House.

Moreno, J. L., & Moreno, Z. T. (1959). *Psychodrama—Second volume.* New York: Beacon House.

Moreno, Z. T. (2006). *The quintessential Zerka.* New York: Routledge.

Salas, J. (2000). Playback theatre: A framework for healing. In P. Lewis & D. R. Johnson (Eds.), *Current approaches in drama therapy* (pp. 288–302). Westport, CT: Praeger.

Sternberg, P., & Garcia, A. (2000). *Sociodrama: Who's in your shoes?* Westport, CT: Praeger.

Winters, N. L. (2000). The psychospiritual in psychodrama: A fourth role category. *International Journal Action Methods, Psychodrama, Skill Training and Role Playing, 52*(4), 163–171.

Yocum, C. (2008). *Burundi to Bogota: Healing communities after war.* Available: asgpp. org/10conf/Saturday%20Workshop.pdf

2

Narradrama With Marginalized Groups: Uncovering Strengths, Knowledges, and Possibilities

PAM DUNNE

Author's Profile

My interest in people from different races and cultures began with one of my best girlfriends, an African American girl who lived in our primarily Caucasian neighborhood. The experience of seeing her shunned and excluded has stayed with me and is probably one of the roots of my later exploration of other cultures. In the 1980s, I became interested in Michael White's Narrative Therapy and found, in his emphasis on reaching out to marginalized groups throughout the world, a way to contribute to alleviating oppression. My way of working with marginalized populations was strongly influenced by Michael White's work.

Pam Dunne, PhD, RDT/BC, the originator of Narradrama, is known in many parts of the world for her teaching and her work with marginalized groups. Dr. Dunne has served as president of the National Association of Drama Therapists, was an original member of the Founding Board, and served for years as a Board member. Currently she spends her time as a Professor at California State University and Director of the Drama Therapy Institute of Los Angeles. Her film *Exploring Narradrama* is widely used by teachers of drama therapy. Her books *The Narrative Therapist and the Arts* and *Narradrama: Integrating Drama Therapy, Narrative and the Creative Arts* are widely distributed.

Narradrama, an action-oriented therapeutic approach, integrates narrative therapy with drama therapy and also invites the use of the creative arts—music, drama, poetry, and the visual arts. It borrows freely from psychology, sociology, anthropology, and experimental theater. Narradrama engages all the core processes of drama therapy, including roles and impersonation, distancing, empathy, witnessing by others, playing/creativity, and embodiment and transformation, thereby addressing the wisdom not only of the mind but also of the body and the senses. Narradrama, like traditional narrative therapy, focuses on post-modern thinking, particularly semiotics and deconstruction. It draws significantly from the work of narrative pioneer Michael White (Dunne, 2004; White, 2004, 2007).

Narradrama occurs in community, educational, and clinical settings. To illustrate Narradrama techniques I will use three case examples of marginalized groups: a group home in Los Angeles, trauma survivors from the Middle East and long-term patients in a psychiatric hospital. With a theoretical grounding in narrative therapy, Narradrama has developed its own process, utilizing some of the known psychodramatic techniques, such as the warm-up and enactments, and developed new techniques as well.

AN INTRODUCTION TO NARRATIVE THERAPY

Narrative therapy bases its foundations and epistemology on the concept that objectivity in the post-modern age fails to reflect the experience of our society because it speaks a dead language. In our rapid, worldwide electronic age, we are exposed to many widely diverging cultures and belief systems. White (2003) believes that, to survive in a postmodern age, people continuously construct and reconstruct their lives and identities in relationship. A relational self consists of a collection of evolving stories and views. Narrative therapy focuses on the way personal stories are told. White's methods include re-authoring conversations, in which communities and individuals learn to shed the stories and qualities that have led to their problems and discover alternative stories and new descriptions of their identities.

The reader will encounter some new terms, to be defined briefly here, and used in the the Narradrama examples. Most important, perhaps, is the concept of "externalization," which refers to the practice of looking at the external causes of a problem by creative means—placing it outside of the person—in order to separate it from the identity or identities of the tellers. Second, Narradrama facilitators refer to the concept of "doubly listening," so that both the message's content and its relational meaning are heard. When a Narradrama facilitator hears a child say, "I never do anything right" (the visible story), she is looking for even the smallest example from that child's life that contradicts the message. In the moment, this other story appears invisible—it is not explicit—and requires doubly listening on the part of the facilitator. Michael White refers to that process as "absent but implicit." When the child, in another moment, talks about a shirt that he created with fabric paints and a logo he really liked, then this story (which was not visible before) becomes visible with the meaning "I did something right," and illustrates the process of doubly listening. Narradrama facilitators also use the term "definitional ceremony" to talk about a way of alleviating the invisibility often experienced by members of marginalized groups and creating a ritual that allows them to take pride in being who they are. "Re-membering conversations" are formed on the basis of the conception that identity is based on "an association of life" rather than a core self. The membership in this association is composed of significant figures whose voices are influential in constructing that person's identity.

NARRADRAMA

This chapter focuses on Narradrama work with marginalized groups with respect to the social issues and beliefs thought to contribute to their members' "diminishment." Patriarchy, racism, lack of privilege, sexual discrimination, oppression, and poverty all contribute to marginalization. Narradrama approaches offer opportunities to deconstruct, question assumptions, and/or protest against the processes that objectify people and communities and result in marginalization and loss of self.

The Narradrama facilitator actively engages with the participants, not as the all-knowing leader, but as a collaborator, co-discoverer and/or co-constructor of solutions. Narradrama takes the view that facilitators need to take an open and spontaneous posture, inviting group members to step out of problem-saturated descriptions of their identity.

Their task, as the process unfolds, is to watch for unique outcomes or alternative stories to emerge. As group members attend groups over time, they often advance to becoming helpers as scribes or photographers and learn to become assistant facilitators themselves, coordinating small group work.

Narradrama uses one group member to serve as scribe and another as a photographer to record group strengths and "special knowledges"—referring to the group's positive attributes and achievements—as these emerge. Transparency, openness, and a willingness to be vulnerable are preferred qualities of Narradrama facilitators.

The first time the marginalized group meets, members state their reasons and hopes for the gathering and key members introduce themselves. In small groups, there is one facilitator. If the group is large, a team of leaders will facilitate the meeting. To enlarge the social context, messages of hope in the form of a letter, song, or dramatic presentation from another similarly marginalized community may be presented through live presentations, audiotapes, or video or digital pictures.

Interactive warm-ups require the use of the group's preferred forms of cultural expression, such as dance, music, etc. We note that although the suggestions provided in this chapter are informed by Western culture, they can be adapted to other cultures as well. Like the warm-ups used in sociodrama and drama therapy (see chapter 1), Narradrama uses a variety of activities that allow group members to become acquainted and learn to interact without having to risk much in the way of personal disclosure. One example of a Narradrama warm-up is the "cluster formation." This exercise works well in a very large group. The facilitator uses a gong or drum to get the attention of the group and calls out a statement such as: "Find the people with your same eye color." One minute is allowed for the participants to join others with the same eye color. The drum sounds again and a new cluster idea is given. Moving around and meeting people briefly helps to enliven the group and encourage participation.

After the interactive warm-ups, group members share important common stories from their community and, together, draw a visual image to represent their community on very large and long sheets of paper. They will talk first—decide on what image to use, for example, a map, or a metaphorical representation such as a beehive—and draw together, while consulting about the process. At times, collages and photographs can be added to these images. Group members of the small groups share these images with the whole group and speak about them briefly. At a later time, Narradrama team members may divide the participants into smaller groups again to share brief stories from their own lives that relate to the themes shown on the murals. For example, one mural created by teens showed angry images of gangs, domestic violence, sadness (tears and grey clouds) and isolation (a hunched-over figure in a corner). The same mural also contained positive traces, such as a heart and the sun. From these images came stories of despair, rejection, broken dreams, and betrayal, but also stories of sticking together, and hoping for a better life. Narradramas usually end with a culminating ceremony, which will be demonstrated in the Group Home Example.

A FIVE-PART PROCESS BASED ON NARRATIVE THERAPY AND NARRADRAMA ACTION TECHNIQUES

After warming up, the group will begin a five-part process based on White's (2006) work and involving: (1) discovering and honoring of special knowledges through definitional ceremony, (2) discovering and honoring of special knowledges through re-membering conversations, (3) externalization of problems, (4) developing group rituals, and (5) inviting a contribution.

Discovering and Honoring of Special Knowledges Through Definitional Ceremony

Barbara Myerhoff (1986), a cultural anthropologist who influenced White, coined the term "definitional ceremony" to describe a creative process that centers around the performer's presentation of his/her desired way of being seen or defined. In Myerhoff's (1986) words, "Definitional ceremonies deal with the problems of invisibility and marginality; they are strategies that provide opportunities for being seen and in one's own terms, garnering witnesses to one's worth, vitality and being" (p. 266). White (2006) sees identity as a "territory of life," as described in his own words:

> When people experience trauma (or silencing) and particularly when this is recurrent, there is very significant shrinking of this territory of identity.

> When their territory of identity is so reduced it becomes very difficult for people to know how to proceed in life; to know how to go forward with projects, to realize their plans for living. In these circumstances, all of the things in life that people usually give value to are diminished or reduced in presence and significance. (p. 27)

Marginalized groups usually experience a loss of voice, rendering their "special knowledges" invisible. To begin to restore a lost sense of pride, the Narradrama facilitator begins by inviting the expression of "special knowledges," meaning the communication of the strengths and abilities of a particular group. Marginalized individuals, usually left with negative views of their own group through oppression by the larger society, learn to diminish or modify these effects by recovering what they hold as precious, and tracing the development of their values and skills through the stories passed from personal, family, and social history. In listening for values in the marginalized group, the multi-layered nature of responses is revealed, which can be acknowledged and honored by the group. The facilitator is trained to listen for traces of positive skills and memories in the stories of oppression.

These stories, which are multiple rather than single stories, can be revealed through conversations, enactments, and storytelling. For example, a group home member discussed a strong conflict with another teen who had invaded her privacy and looked through her things. The angry girl argued, "Why would you do that?! Those are my personal things!" Storming out, she retreated to her room to take a breath and compose herself. Although she didn't realize it herself, the ability to refrain from calling the girl names, as well as the ability to walk away, demonstrated a trace of alternative behavior that, once aware of, she could learn to use more consistently.

Returning to the art mural created at the opening ceremony, the facilitator then expands the images further, either verbally or through enactment, living sculpture, dance, song. The appointed photographer takes photos of important moments and the scribe records the process, emphasizing the newly discovered knowledges and skills.

Definitional Ceremony Process

The leader works with the group's stories, using the following process: (1) The telling: Group members tell their stories; (2) the re-telling of the telling (the outsider witnesses responding to the story); (3) the re-telling of the re-telling (the community responding to the responses of the outsider witnesses).

Group Home Example

The first step in the development of a definitional ceremony requires that the marginalized group tell its own story. In a group home, the girls created a scene showing their experience of living there. In the enactment, one of the new girls, Shelby, demonstrated a series of frustrating experiences. First, she was refused permission to go to the corner store, without explanation. Later, when she asked for a snack, she was told there were no snacks before meals. The other girls seemed unfriendly. When Shelby asked if she could call her mom, she was told that her phone privileges had not been approved. She went to her room, only to find her roommate going through her things, and complained to the staff. The scene ended as Shelby began unpacking her suitcase and putting her things away.

Doubly Listening

This technique asks the facilitator to listen not only to the content of the story, but to what it says about Shelby's ability to relate, always mindful of possible traces of positive qualities. Through *doubly listening* in the telling of the story, the facilitator recognized Shelby's ability to continue to define and ask for what she needed in the face of repeated rejection. The facilitator and the group participants could tell Shelby that "knowing what you need and asking for it" represents an important knowledge of life, as did Shelby's ability to forego retaliation.

The second step in developing a definitional ceremony involves inviting a group of outsider witnesses, called a *reflecting team*, to reflect upon what they have just seen in order to give feedback to the group through conversation and through drama. Outsider witnesses may include people from other groups who have experienced similar struggles. Other members might be therapists, social workers, teachers or members of the larger group. A group facilitator will instruct the witnesses ahead of time to teach them their special role, namely, to discourage giving advice, making judgments, rendering interpretations, or formulating healing strategies. Instead, the observers are there to connect personally to the stories that they have witnessed and to validate and honor the experience of the story tellers or enacters.

Myerhoff (1986) suggests that "outsider witnesses serve as reflecting and amplifying tools, thus rendering the unseen, seen" (p. 283). The marginalized group observes these witnesses as they share verbally or through Narradrama action techniques. Outsider witnesses do not speak or look directly at the marginalized group members, as they need to observe without having to respond.

The facilitator begins by interviewing the outsider witnesses with the following questions:

- What captured your attention and imagination in the story you have just witnessed?
- What were you drawn to?
- What struck a chord?

Outsider witnesses reacted to Shelby's story by creating a sculpture of a person who had the power to give something that was needed (hands outstretched) while several others tried to crowd in with pushing movements. The third witness portrayed Shelby's ability to ask for what she needed, standing calmly and tall with her hand reaching out, unphased by the pushing. A second set of questions by the facilitator follows:

- What images were evoked when looking at the marginalized group's resourcefulness?
- What does the story say about the marginalized group?

The facilitators may continue the work by asking the group to sculpt an image or create an imagined scene which demonstrates the group's strengths. The third set of questions concludes the interview with the outsider witnesses:

- What images were created that touched on the history of your own experiences?
- Where has that experience taken you?

One outsider witness reflected on Shelby's story by enacting a past scene in her own life. She had responded impulsively to an unfair situation by lashing out, unable to do what Shelby did. She created a moving sculpture depicting Shelby walking down a long walkway, hearing many negative sounds along the way, but bravely continuing down the pathway to the end.

The last step, called the re-telling of the re-telling, occurs when the group responds to the outsider witnesses. The facilitator asks the following questions:

- What have you heard that strikes a chord in you, what you were drawn to, what captured your attention?
- What mental pictures were evoked by the re-telling/sculpture of the outsider witnesses?
- As you listened or observed the sculptures, what images came to mind?
- Do you have a sense of how this reflects what your group stands for?
- What does it reflect about your hopes for your life?
- Were there moments you just witnessed that you want to hold onto?

Group members are encouraged to respond verbally or through active techniques.

Observing an outsider witness deeply and emotionally connect to their story may be a new and unexpected experience for marginalized group members who have lost confidence in the possibility of touching and influencing others in their culture.

Group Home Example (continued)

Research provides us with the dark facts facing our group home girls. According to national statistics the total number of children in group homes and foster care system in the United States is 492,727. The national mean average age of children entering foster care or group homes is 8.2 years of age. "Nearly all children entering foster care," observes Wertheimer (2002), "are victims of sexual or physical abuse, neglect or abandonment, or have a parent who is incarcerated or otherwise unable to care for them" (p. 3). There is a higher level of risky behaviors with children living in foster care. These children often have "compromised development," and problems in school adjustment or in physical or mental health are common.

Working with a number of group home communities in South Central Los Angeles, one observes many commonalities in the self-images of children and teens. Perceiving themselves to be trapped at the bottom of society's totem pole, these children often respond to the stigma attached to living in a group home by keeping it secret.

The case example from a Narradrama research project in a group home for girls will demonstrate Narradrama's process sequentially. Participants ranged from ages 10 to 18. Although they represented a mixed cultural and racial group, the strongest representation was African American and Hispanic.

Step One: Definitional Ceremony: Telling of the Story by the Group

During the first steps of a definitional ceremony, the following statements were recorded from over one hundred children, ranging from the age of 10 to 18. All of the children in this research project completed a sentence-completion measure and were interviewed. Children from two group homes (same director) took part in the community Narradrama program.

Statements of negative self-image abound. The children often disparaged their looks with statements like, "My looks are not so pretty....My looks are very ugly." Describing the reactions of others, they made statements like, "Most people dislike me....Most people are all about their money....Most people do not understand who I am....Most people think I'm a liar....Most people be mean to me....Most people are different from me....Most people aren't the type you think they are....At school people don't like me."

They described their living experience as, "I hate group homes....My main worry is that I won't get out....I eat a lot....I go to sleep on my bed." They enumerated their fears: "My greatest fear is to fail in life....My greatest fear is being alone....My fear is to be badly injured....My greatest fear is death....My greatest fear is dying fat and alone....My main worry is being alone."

The night provided a stimulating theme. "At night, I cry because I miss my mum and family....At night, I can't sleep....At night, I watch television."

Hates were vividly expressed: "I hate the system....I hate when people judge me and they barely met me....I hate people who pick on little kids....I hate my adopted mom."

The children commented on their needs: "I need help going to sleep....I need love....I need help in math....I need money, food and a place to stay....I need to step up my game."

They described their greatest troubles as follows: "My greatest trouble is letting go of my depression....My greatest trouble is my mouth.... What bothers me most is being here....What bothers me most is not having a life."

Asked to describe happy times and dreams, the children responded with: "I have never had a happy time....My happiest time is with my family....My happiest time is when I was five....My happiest time is with my boyfriend/girlfriend....Many of my dreams deal with unhappiness....Many of my dreams deal with death....Many of my dreams deal with wishing....Many of my dreams don't come true." A few described themselves as good-looking and resilient.

The children then enacted personal stories of living in the group home. Their stories were short and terse. The following excerpts of stories reveal their life in the group home:

Hungry by Janessa: "When I first got to the group home I came from JUVI (juvenile detention). They didn't tell me much. I had never lived in a group home before. I was hungry. When I came, I noticed locks on the cabinets in the kitchen. I hate my life."

Boring by Rikki: "It was boring most of the time. When I didn't have homework all there was to do was watch TV. I really wanted to go home."

Phone Call to Mom by Franshay: "I wanted to call my mom. But I was told no calls until I talked to my social worker. Even when I finally got permissions to call my mom, I could only call at certain times. I wanted to talk to my mom. I missed her."

Rap by Janisha: "I liked rapping, but nobody knew this. I used to go in my closet at the group home when nobody was noticing and use that like a sound studio. I began rapping. I like the way my voice sounded in the closet."

Step Two: Definitional Ceremony: Retelling of the Story by Outsider Witnesses

Phone Call to Mom by Franshay:

Facilitator: What were you drawn to?
Outsider Witness: Franshay, the girl who wanted to talk to her mom.
Facilitator: What did the story tell you about Franshay?
Outsider Witness: It tells me that she values family. She wanted to talk to her mother. She could have been mad at her mom, negative about the environment or closed down, but she chose to talk to her mom.
Facilitator: Where does that transport you?
Outsider Witness: I realized I take my family for granted. Franshay held onto her mom and wouldn't let go of wanting to talk to her. I wanted some of her passion in my life with my mom. It really moved me.

After the interview, the outsider witness shared a living sculpture in which she placed two other outsider witnesses with hands reaching toward each other (representing Franshay and her mom), overcoming many obstacles (chairs and other people trying to keep them apart), while the hands continued to reach out.

Boring by Rikki:

Facilitator: What did you connect to?
Outsider Witness: I connected to Rikki. It tells me that she wants more for her life. Many kids veg out by watching TV, but she said she didn't like being bored. It made me wonder what kinds of things she would like to do. I was very curious about that.
Facilitator: How did that transport you?
Outsider Witness: I really saw in my life, how I fill in cracks of time with small things that are important to me. Where others read movie magazines or watch TV or play video games, I like reading a good book or I might jot down an idea for something that I would like to write. I never saw these little things I did as particularly important, but she inspired me to see this in a different way. It made me wonder how she was able to say no to the other things that kids do to fill time yet to want more for herself.

After the interview, this outsider witness created a sculpture of a teen watching TV and another playing a video game. She also placed black fabric in piles around the sculpture representing other distractions. The third participant in the sculpture, representing Rikki, was holding a red cloth and looking up, symbolizing her search for something different.

Story About Rap by Janisha:

Facilitator: Was there a particular girl you connected to?

Outsider Witness: I connected to Janisha, the girl who started rapping in the closet.

Facilitator: What did you connect with?

Outsider Witness: I loved the way that she used her imagination to create a sound studio out of a closet. I wondered what other places her imagination could take her.

Facilitator: Where did that transport you?

Outsider Witness: It was inspiring. I began to think of where my imagination could take me. I remembered as a child making up a card game and drawing images on the cards. The game was called Teli. Teli was an Indian maiden and that was the special card that in this game all the players were trying to get. I remember playing this game with my father and the delight I felt when I got the Teli card. That made me think of ways I would like to go with my imagination today, in the present.

The outsider witness enacted a TV interview to illustrate her response. She played Janisha and one of the other outsider witnesses played the interviewer. In this interview, the outsider witness, as Janisha, spoke about how she used to practice her raps in a closet.

Step Three: Definitional Ceremony: Re-Telling of the Re-Telling by the Group

The facilitator asked the group home girls whether any particular comment or enactment from an outsider witness touched them. Or did a particular comment or image stand out? Rikki, whose story was *Bored,* commented: "Everyone always said being bored was bad, I never saw it as wanting more for myself. That surprised me." Janisha, who had told the *Rap* story, reacted by volunteering to do a skit in response to the outsider witnesses. In a scene about a successful audition, Janisha chose staff members to become a band and play simple musical instruments. As Janisha began to rap, the group applauded and contributed lines of their own. In an after-audition interview, Janisha spoke about her hopes for her future as a rap artist. A child videographer took video of the moments of strength.

Closing a Definitional Ceremony

To close the definitional ceremony, a large mural was created with images and verbal representations, drawn by the scribe, reflecting the special knowledges and skills of the group. Some participants also wrote wisdom statements. The group photographer continued to take digital or Polaroid pictures, some of which were also attached to the mural. The scribes and photographer continued their function throughout this entire process. These paper murals, changing as group members added words and symbols describing themselves and their significant others, continued to be displayed throughout the meetings. The end of this meeting marked the conclusion of the definitional ceremony. However, it was not the end of the process.

Discovering and Honoring of Special Knowledges Through Re-Membering Conversations

Re-membering conversations involves a different process to attain the same goal. The process of re-membering conversations illustrates purposeful engagement with the significant figures of one's own community or individual history, the figures that affect one's identity—real or fictional, past or present, close or distant (White, 2005).

First, the facilitator focuses on the way that the significant figure has influenced and valued the group member. Then, in order to bring the group member's own power to awareness, the facilitator asks how the significant figure would describe the effect of the group member on his/her life.

Action techniques enhance these processes. The first action technique is an interview. The group member identifies a significant figure—real or fictitious, past or present—who can recognize some of his/her strengths. The leader interviews the group member playing the role with questions such as:

What is your relationship with _____?

How long have you known _____?

What is one thing about him/her that you most admire? _____

If you were to describe the strengths of _____, what would you say?

Next, the facilitator turns the frame around and asks questions about the person's impact on the significant figure. The group member describes ways in which their relationship shaped the figure, with questions like: How did your relationship with this person make your life different? How did knowing this individual affect your life? How did your relationship with this person enrich your life?

After the first interviews, the representative members of the marginalized group reverse roles to become their significant figures and are, in turn, interviewed.

Dialogue With Significant Person

A member of the marginalized community may be chosen to create a dialogue between himself/herself and one of the significant figures. A second member from the group, chosen to play the role of several people, could become multiple voices, if preferred. A significant figure, such as the grandmother or elder of the community, also represents many other members of that community and, gradually, a picture of the entire context is revealed. The significant figure begins a dialogue with the participant.

Other ways of representing significant figures include using simple art materials like pipe cleaners, clay, or colored tissue paper. Group members place figures made from these materials on a table representing their support structure in the whole community. In another technique, "Hall of Fame," group members each take the role of the significant figure, using fabric to create a costume. Photographers take pictures of these figures for display in a Hall of Fame where a participant in the role of guide can help other community members to identify each of the significant figures, explaining what the figures have to offer as holders of special knowledges and skills. Second, the community creates a memorial written by the significant figures, which represents the knowledges and skills of the community in the form of a song or a written memorial to be posted in the Hall of Fame.

Rikki, whose story was *Bored,* identified Mary, a staff member in the group home, as someone who respected her, and whom she could trust as her significant person. Rikki took on Mary's role herself. Other group home members agreed with Rikki's positive view of Mary, so that, in playing her, Rikki represented not only her own choice but also the group's:

Facilitator: Mary, Rikki told me that you are a person she can trust and she respects you very much. How did this relationship happen?

Mary (played by Rikki): Well, I always saw Rikki as a very open person. She shared her feelings with me and so it was easy for us to talk.

Facilitator: How do you suppose she was able to hold onto her openness?

Mary (played by Rikki): Well, it wasn't easy. There were times she almost gave up, but she seemed to pull herself back up.

Facilitator: I wonder how she was able to do that?

Mary (played by Rikki): I don't know.

Facilitator: Okay, well, these qualities that you observed in Rikki, of being open and trusting and believing in something better? If you made a guess, how do you think that happened? How could she hold onto those beliefs when others gave up?

Mary (played by Rikki): Because Rikki is stubborn, just like a lot of kids. Especially when it's something you believe in, it's important to be stubborn, not give it up.

Facilitator: It sounds like she has an ability to stand up for herself.

Mary (played by Rikki): Definitely.

Facilitator: I also understand that Rikki is not the only one who feels that they can trust you.

Mary (played by Rikki): That's true, I have a close relationship with many of the girls.

Facilitator: How does this ability to have a close relationship with you inform you about them?

Mary (played by Rikki): They know how to relate.

Facilitator: So they have the skills and knowledge of how to develop a relationship with another person?

Mary (played by Rikki): Yes.

In the next phase of a re-membering conversation, in an interview with Rikki in the role of herself, her own strengths were revealed:

Facilitator: Rikki, you told me before of how Mary influenced you and that you were able to talk to her. That she didn't talk down to you and respected you.

Rikki: Yeah, we used to go on walks and she trusted me to go to the store and come back. None of the other staff trusted us to go out by ourselves.

Facilitator: So what kind of influence do you think you have had on Mary's life?

Rikki: What do you mean influence?

Facilitator: How has Mary's life been enriched because of you?

Rikki: I never thought of it that way. I don't know.

Facilitator: How has Mary's life been better because of you?

Rikki: I don't know. Maybe I gave her something important because I respected her. I know how hard it is to work here. Staff don't usually stay very long.

Facilitator: This ability to respect, have you noticed this in other aspects of your life?

Rikki: No, not really. My mouth usually gets me into trouble.

Facilitator: So seeing your ability to respect, is this something new for you?

Rikki: I guess so.

Facilitator: If you were to take your ability to respect with you one day for the whole day, how might that day be different?

Rikki: I don't know. I might listen more so I could hear what others are saying.

Facilitator: If you thought of creating a club of people who might appreciate and support these qualities you have of respect and standing up for yourself, who would be in your club?

Rikki: Well, Mary for sure. And my best friend, Jasmine. And my grandma who died. She would be in that club.

Culmination Ceremony

One way of culminating the definitional ceremony and re-membering conversations involves the use of the daily murals. A wisdom book of the special knowledges, strengths, and skills of the group can be created utilizing the knowledge learned from the murals. The group decides on a way to present the book, the kinds of images to show, and how to make it. A printed copy of the book becomes part of the final honoring ceremony and each member receives a copy. A community song may be created to illustrate the stories and strengths of the community, and this song becomes documented in the wisdom book as well and sung at the culminating ceremony. In the group home example, Janisha and the others created a rap, recounting the stories of the group home:

Hood Home Rap
It's a bummer
You're on the lowest level
At restriction city!
It's cool, girl
I'll be your friend
I'll always have your back
At the Hood Home
The drama queens shout
A fight breaks out
Police break in!
It's cool, girl.
I'll always be your friend
I'll always have your back
At the Hood Home
Behind locked doors
No way to call
No one to come.
It's cool, girl.
I'll always be your friend
I'll always have your back
At the Hood Home
We can make it out
Don't give up the dream
We'll help each other.
Diploma time!
We're cool girls!
We'll have each other's back
In the Hood Home

Externalization of Problems

Once group members realize and envision more possibilities, the externalization of a problem can be successfully completed. At this point
the first descriptions, which reflected a lack of skills, knowledge, and
hope, have taken a back seat to newly recognized skills and knowledges,
which create hope for the future.

Through externalizing conversations, the problem of marginalization
becomes disentangled from the identity of the group and is perceived
as something external. As the externalizing continues, groups revise
their self-sabotaging identification with the problem, and new, more

Figure 2.1. Rikki tells her story.

positive perceptions of their life experience begin to emerge. Rikki, Maria, Janisha, and Franshay created a living sculpture by arranging fabrics to tell a story. They put brightly colored fabrics—magenta, orange, and royal blue—on the floor and placed a large piece of heavy black fabric, representing the system, on top, rendering all the beautiful colors underneath invisible. Rikki, the spokesperson for the group, told a story about the girls at the group home, with all their colorful qualities and personalities, being held down by the system. Other group members accompanied her story, using the visual image of the fabrics (Figure 2.1).

Rikki continued, saying, "Now, one at a time, start coming out to be recognized for the strengths that you have." Each girl took a colored fabric out from behind the black fabric and placed it in front. At the end of the sculpture, the black fabric was hidden beneath an array of colors.

Marginalized Group Example: Middle Eastern Women

The variables of gender and culture are discussed in a study of a group of Middle Eastern women (Stronger Women Stronger Nations, 2008).

Women for Women International gathered information from interviews with 1,513 Iraqi women about their top economic, social, and political priorities. A number of women's organizations in Iraq contributed to these interviews, including the Unified Women's League in Baghdad, Asuda for Combatting Violence Against Women, Wassit Handicapped for Human Rights, and other organizations, which needed to remain anonymous for security reasons.

Regarding gender, 73.3% of respondents stated that they felt their rights were valued differently because they are women. Primarily, these women felt their gender affected their rights to security and to participation in public affairs. In the same study, 45.3% of women described their access to opportunities as poor and 26.6% felt they have no opportunities at all. In another study of 310 women in Lebanon (Usta, Farver, & Zein, 2008), information was gathered from six different locations after the 2006 armed conflict. Negative mental health scores of women were significantly higher in war zones, where women suffered from loss of property, family income, uncertainty about the future, and difficulties in managing their daily lives—all factors that have been shown to affect mental health significantly. In Kuwait (Lindberg & Drechsler, 2008):

> women face discrimination with regard to parental authority: Islamic law views the father as the natural guardian of his children, and the mother as the physical, not legal guardian. In Kuwait, women's freedom of movement is limited, as they must request permission from their male guardian or parents if they want to travel abroad or go out at night. (p.1)

White's concept of externalization is illustrated by this group from the Middle East, with participants who had been traumatized by war and its aftermath. There were 18 women in the group and 2 men. The focus of the 3-hour meeting was the exploration of gender and marginalization. Asked to name a problem the group could explore, one woman expressed her desire to have the freedom to make small decisions without asking her husband's permission. Going to the store to buy food or clothing, for example, or leaving the house for an hour with a friend, needed her spouse's approval. To see how this idea resonated with the whole group, the facilitator suggested a spectogram: "All those who feel that personal freedom in little things is very important, stand at this end of the room. Those who are in the middle stand in the middle, and those who do not think that this issue is important stand at the other end." All 18 women immediately crowded together at the farthest end of the spectogram, leaving no doubt as to the critical importance of this issue.

The two men, on the other hand, occupied the opposite end of the spectogram, showing the women that they didn't consider this issue important at all. The facilitator then asked whether a few people would be willing to switch positions in a role reversal. One of the men went to the other end of the spectrogram to join the women, while one of the women went to stand with the other man.

The two new groups began conversations with the people standing by them from their role perspective, including a voicing of their hopes and desires, which led into a scene of a wife approaching her husband asking for the freedom to make small decisions. The man who had participated in the role reversal in the spectogram took the role of the husband. The woman who had originated the idea played the wife in the scene. When asked to externalize the problem using language, she used the words "restraining freedom." Handcuffs (represented by fabric) were placed on her wrists.

The externalization technique continued to be explored by inviting each participant of the group to create a "problem" mask and a "personal agency" mask.

Interviews with each of the masks and the creation of living sculptures showed the relationship of a group member to the problem mask when the influence of the problem was strong and a second sculpture when the mask began losing power. A third demonstrated their preference. Both the personal agency masks and the sculptures showed participants moving forward in their lives.

In another use of externalization, group members chose a "found object" from the environment to represent a strength. For example, one woman brought a shell, representing the calmness she regarded as her greatest source of power (Figure 2.2).

Marginalized Group Example: Patients With Chronic Mental Illness

These patients are categorized as having a chronic mental illness, resulting in long hospitalization. To someone with a mental illness, the

Figure 2.2. A shell represents calmness for this Middle Eastern woman.

consequences of stigma can be devastating—in some cases, worse than the illness itself. A newspaper article (Reading, Sweet, & Young, 2006) reported that people with mental illnesses feel excluded from society. This study also showed that others tend to categorize those with mental diseases as "all the same."

In working with a group of mentally ill clients who had been in the mental health system for a number of years, the facilitator used both written and visual material. Posters created by the group contained phrases of public response to those with ongoing psychiatric problems. After contributing their writing and imagery, the patients progressed to responding to the posters by creating living sculptures or improvisations. One man, who experienced a lack of empathy from a doctor, enacted a scene titled *Unseen,* in which, instead of talking with him, the doctor read a variety of diagnoses to him. Another group member created a scene titled *Medication Madness,* in which a doctor, whom he directed to keep walking around him in a circle, kept changing his prescriptions. Every time he came back to his starting point, a bell rang and he received a new prescription.

These four case examples demonstrate different ways to approach externalization. In each case, the fabric, object, mask, or poster represented the original externalization and made it easier for the group to view the problem as external rather than internal and to develop ways of creating a solution.

Developing Group Rituals

Within sessions and as part of a closing session, the ritual is particularly valuable in working with marginalized groups. Rituals honor a group by representing their stories, strengths, and special knowledges. In addition, these rituals can be observed by an audience that can serve as a support structure for the group.

In creating a ritual, a new role needs to be filled, that of the Master of Ceremonies or MC. An MC, played by a facilitator, introduces the group members to the audience, explains why they met and how the ritual was developed. The MC also keeps the ritual going and moves it along towards its conclusion.

Blatner and Wiener (2007) suggest different components to be included in each ritual. First is the invocation, a calling out to a greater, perhaps unseen, audience such as gods or ancestors to create a sense of significance and commitment. Second, he stresses the use of silence for mental focus. Prayer may serve as affirmation. Specific imagery, meaningful to each group, is central. He emphasizes mindful creation of the ritual space, including the setting, props, costumes, masks, and symbols. Burning candles, lowering the lights, using masks or other visual means support the unique, sacred importance of this event.

Talking-Stick Ritual

The group members create a "talking stick" and decorate it with symbols of the group strengths and knowledges, using colors and decorations. As the stick is passed, each member shares a cherished moment he/she wants to take away, or tells a story that expresses something learned in the group.

Call-and-Response Ritual

The facilitator plays the MC in this ritual, and group members represent community voices in unison. The group decides together what questions or statements the facilitator needs to ask (or make) while the community gives a choral response describing new discoveries.

Ritual Incorporating Poetry, Painting, and Song

The group decides what to include in this ritual and how to display the visual objects. For example, pictures or masks created in previous sessions may be placed in the center of the group circle. The group then moves together in a celebratory dance, symbolizing newly found strengths.

Ritual Song

This is a song which represents through music the story of the group. A facilitator who plays the guitar, piano, or drum can improvise music to accompany the ritual. If there are no musical instruments, the group can sound and clap in accompaniment. Some of the words for the song may be inspired by murals created during the work or by stories and notes recorded by the scribe. The song usually follows a journey from marginalization to the new, more positive story and uses the special knowledges gained in the group work. Typically, this song becomes a part of the final closure ceremony.

Honoring Group Ceremony

The group members form a circle and each member of the group, one at a time, makes an honoring statement about another, citing something that they recognize or appreciate, and draping an honorary scarf around his or her shoulders.

The group home girls, for example, created a closing ceremony in which both staff and children were honored. The tone was set as the group sat in a circle on the floor and the lights were dimmed. Memorable moments included one of the staff members moving to Nikki and draping a red scarf on her shoulders, saying, "I want to honor Nikki. For a person of her age, I was amazed at her clarity." Then Maria placed a purple scarf around Franshay, saying, "I want to honor Franshay for her not giving up." Then one of the staff placed a blue scarf around Maria and said, "I want to honor Maria. I know she doesn't like doing group participation things like this, but she participated and I know that took courage." Then Franshay placed a yellow scarf around Mary's shoulders, saying, "I want to honor Mary. When I was having a very hard time and didn't think I would make it, you were there and talked to me. If it wasn't for you I wouldn't be here now." The giving of the scarf and the honoring statements continued as the feeling of love, caring, and a bond between the girls and the staff became evident in the room.

A community dinner ended with a cake decorated with everyone's name. For their closing ritual, the Middle Eastern group wanted to place their artistic representations of masks, puppets, drawings, and clay sculptures on an altar they created. One of the men placed the two masks on the altar. One was dark and the other was made of brighter colors, with a lightness in the face. He explained that the masks represented two sides of his personality—a darker, aggressive side and a more open, peaceful side. Next, one of the women pinned two masks on the board as well as a puppet character. She said that these external objects had given her new hope. Another woman created puppets representing significant characters in her life and placed the puppets on the altar. One by one, each member placed their significant objects on the altar. To end the ritual, the whole group walked around the altar in a large circle, acknowledging these special objects.

Inviting a Contribution

Unlike most forms of sociodrama and drama therapy, the Narradrama process widens the arc of social connection and action. For marginalized groups, experiential work can become the impetus for social action. Group members learn that their experience of marginalization can offer help to others in similar or related situations. The sense of possibility, once sparked, is like a seed that begins to grow and develop into a large plant, changing the ecology of their lives. Ways in which marginalized groups can reach out and help other marginalized groups include the following:

Group Letter

Group members write a letter to another group undergoing similar struggles. This letter recounts the knowledges and skills of the first group and describes the transformation of the group. A series of letters and communication can be encouraged between groups.

Group Song

A CD recording memorializes a group song. This song recounts the struggles and experiences of a marginalized group and their discovery of special knowledges and skills. This CD can be sent as a gift to other groups going through similar struggles.

Group DVD or Digital Picture Story (CD)

During meetings, photos and video may have recorded some of the experiences of the group. From these records of important moments, a short digital presentation, scrapbook, or video can be made, which recounts the skills and knowledges of the group and how they have honored their strengths. These DVDs or CDs can be sent to other groups.

Group Volunteers

Group members often volunteer to help others in need and work with organizations in their community, giving time and putting their newly discovered skills and knowledges to use.

Group Presentations

With the help of the facilitator, group members create theatrical pieces that recount both their struggles and the discovery of new skills and knowledges. These informal pieces may combine poetry, drama, music, and dance and dramatize different stories or consist of a series of scenes that recount the journey from marginalization to being seen. Each group member participates in the writing, staging, and development of this piece and performs it for others, followed by an after-presentation discussion that allows opportunities for sharing.

In the group home, the girls got special permission to host a welcoming party for new residents at another group home. The group jointly wrote a letter, which they all signed, expressing how they had felt when they first entered a group home. They also showed the new girls their wisdom book, presented them with a copy, and taught them their group song. The party was a success.

The group of psychiatric patients chose a more formal presentation, assisted by my associate, Michelle Ebert Freire. Calling themselves *Mental in Black*, they developed a performance piece called "Scrambled Eggs" that recounted their struggles with long-term psychiatric hospitalization, using the poster exercises explored earlier and showing a journey from stigmatization into a fuller, more expressive and satisfying life. All of the members of the group expressed their appreciation of the opportunity to participate in the writing and performing of this piece. One participant said:

> If I had a chance to go back 20 years in my life, if there was anything like this program, I would take advantage of it in a minute. When we created *Scrambled Eggs*, I was expressing feelings that I was actually feeling at the same time. I've never, ever, ever experienced that in my entire life. It was more than a counselor could do.

The play represented a way to give back to others what they had received in the process.

CONCLUSION

The marginalized case groups represented here, the Hood Home girls, the Middle Eastern Group, and *Mental in Black*, are united by the discovery of their strengths and skills as a result of their Narradrama work. They became more connected, more supportive, and helpful. Their growth was noted in their personal statements, murals, enactments, rituals, and wisdom books. Through the Narradrama process, these groups experienced change and, as their strengths and living skills became more visible in their lives, these changes created growth. Their growth, in turn, began affecting others in their community, who in turn transformed their roles from victim to those of facilitator, helper, and healer.

REFERENCES

Blatner, A., & Wiener, D. (2007). *Interactive and improvisational drama*. Lincoln, NE: iUniverse.

Dunne, P. (1992). *The narrative therapist*. Los Angeles, CA: Drama Therapy Institute of Los Angeles.

Dunne, P. (2004). *Exploring Narradrama* (DVD). Los Angeles: Drama Therapy Institute of Los Angeles.

Dunne, P. (2006). *Narradrama: Integrating drama therapy, narrative, and the creative arts*. Los Angeles, CA: Drama Therapy Institute of Los Angeles.

Dunne, P., & Rand, H. (2006). *Narradrama: Integrating drama therapy, narrative and creative arts* (2nd ed.). Los Angeles: Possibilities Press.

Lindberg, C., & Drechsler, D. (2008). *Gender equality in Kuwait*. Retrieved March 22, 2009, from http://www.wikigender.org/index.php/Gender_Equality_in_Kuwait

Myerhoff, B. (1986). "Life not death in Venice": Its second life. In V. Turner & E. Bruner (Eds.), *The anthropology of experience* (pp. 263–275). Chicago: University of Illinois Press.

Reading, P. A., Sweet, P., & Young, M. (2006). Methods change in the treatment of mentally ill: Even more must be done to meet the needs of people with mental disease and their families, advocates say. *Knight Ridder/Tribune Business News*, p. 1. Washington, DC. Retrieved March 23, 2009, from http://www.highbeam.com/landing/journals.aspx

Usta, J., Faver, J., & Zein, L. (2008). Women, war and violence: Surviving the experience. *Journal of Women's Health, 17*(5), 793–804. doi;110. 1089jwh 2007,0602.

Wertheimer, R. (2002, December). Youth who "age out" of foster care: Troubled lives, troubling prospects (Publication #2002-59, pp. 1–8). *Child Trends Research Brief*. Retrieved March 24, 2009, from http://www.childtrends.org/files/FosterCare RB.pdf

White, M. (2003). Part three: Community consultations and the principles that inform them. *International Journal of Narrative Therapy and Community Work, 2,* 30–38.

White, M. (2004). *Narrative practice and exotic lives: Resurrecting diversity in everyday life.* Adelaide, Australia: Dulwich Centre Publications.

White, M. (2005). Re-membering conversations. In *Michael White Workshop Notes* (pp. 13–14). Retrieved April 3, 2009, from http://www.dulwichcentre.com.au/Michael% 20White%20Workshop%20Notes.pdf

White, M. (2006). Working with people who are suffering the consequences of multiple trauma: A narrative perspective. In D. Denborough (Ed.), *Trauma: Narrative responses to traumatic experience* (pp. 25–28). Adelaide, Australia: Dulwich Centre Publications.

White, M. (2007). *Maps of narrative practice.* New York: W. W. Norton.

Women for Women International. (2008). *Amplifying the voices of women in Iraq* (Stronger Women, Stronger Nations Report Series: 2008 Iraq Report). Washington, DC/London, UK: Women for Women International. Retrieved March 23, 2009, from http://www.womenforwomen.org/news-women-for-women/files/IraqReport.03.03. 08.pdf

3 Performing Absence: The Limits of Testimony in the Recovery of the Combat Veteran

DAVID READ JOHNSON

Author's Profile

I graduated from Yale College with a double major in theater and psychology and have combined the two fields throughout my career. As a psychologist, I worked for 17 years at the Veterans Affairs Hospital in West Haven, Connecticut, where the work I report in this chapter was done. My years there gave me the privilege to learn much about the complexities of the veterans' experiences, and to struggle with their healing from the war and, in turn, our country's healing. I will always cherish their creativity and courage.

David Johnson, PhD, RDT/BCT, one of the foremost theoreticians and practitioners of drama therapy, is a recipient of the Lifetime Achievement Award from the National Association for Drama Therapy. He is an Associate Clinical Professor at the Yale University School of Medicine, Co-Director of the Post Traumatic Stress Center, New Haven, Connecticut, and Director of the Institutes for the Arts in Psychotherapy, New York, New York.

INTRODUCTION

Armed conflict is the scaffolding of history: it creates, transforms, and destroys nations; its victories raise up great leaders, its defeats bring them down; it gives rise to grand memorials, precious holidays, simmering fears, and deep resentments. Borders are redrawn, peoples displaced, and economies shattered. Woven throughout are the great debates over right and wrong, the glorious Cause, and the often demeaned and objectified Other.

Armed conflict injures all participants, combatants and non-combatants alike: in the first case, physically, through death, wounding, torture, beatings, and rape; in the second case, economically, through loss of home, income, employment, and possessions; in the third case, psychologically, through fear, trauma, hopelessness, and helplessness. The details of each conflict are important: whether it is a civil war, where people who formerly knew each other or were part of the same social grouping fight each other; whether the conflict takes place on home soil or foreign soil; whether one is the invader or defender; how long the conflict goes on; and whether one wins or loses (Z. Solomon, 1993). Each detail influences the resulting effects upon individuals and particular groups of individuals: There are the soldiers and politicians, the innocent civilians and the refugees, the third parties (press, peacekeepers, non-governmental organizations [NGOs], diplomats), and the collaborators, spies, bystanders, perpetrators, and victims. All are scarred.

At heart, our sympathies lie with the innocent victims. Our feelings for the innocent victims are pure, for they bear no responsibility for the war. What comes to mind are the iconic images of the dead baby in the arms of a starving peasant in Darfur, the skeletal remains of the Holocaust survivor, or the poignant photos of the office worker who died in the World Trade Center. These, indeed, are the innocents. Unfortunately, in practice it is very hard to find victims who are entirely innocent. In war, the women and children who stay home may be working hard in factories producing weapons for their loved ones. In some countries, the young boys are recruited to be soldiers (Rosen, 2005). In others, such as was the case in Vietnam, the children are strapped with explosives and used as weapons. In most wars, the civilian population is forced to collaborate with whoever has power over them. In recent conflicts, journalists and NGO personnel have been used to provide information to enemy forces and have been accused of being spies. While prior to 1900, attacks on civilians were restrained, increasingly through the 20th century this restraint has been abrogated, whether in the bombing of London, Dresden, and Japanese cities, or now in terrorist attacks (Johnson, 2003). All is fair game.

I raise this issue because, in helping combat soldiers recover from the wounds of war, we are not dealing with innocence, for they are hardly innocent. If we can understand how to help the combatants recover, then perhaps we will have ways to help others along the gradient of innocence. What does "healing" mean for those soldiers who may have volunteered, and then were trained, to defend "us" and attack "them"? What horrors did they see? Did they commit? One invades another country and in the process of killing others, loses a dear buddy...one calls in an airstrike on an enemy village, killing everyone, and then discovers it was a friendly village...one puts one's life on the line for a year and is defeated and returns home in shame...one fights in a bloody civil war and then lives next door to one's former enemy. These are pernicious contradictions. Soldiers have been coming home from war since the beginning of civilization and have had to face the confusion, the ambivalence, the quiet, and the memories disturbing their days in "peacetime." Society has helped soldiers on the winning side recover by labeling them heroes and honoring their great effort, and not asking them about the horrendous mistakes and terror they experienced. Soldiers from the losing side have been ignored, punished, and shamed (Shay, 1994). It is not a coincidence that the modern emergence of post-traumatic stress disorder occurred among soldiers coming back from a war they did not win. Defeat laid bare the bones of the disorder.

ABSENCE

Of the many types of experiences veterans have after an armed conflict, one of the most important is absence. Now absence is not loss exactly, for loss is something valuable that has gone away and is not retrievable. Loss leads to sadness, perhaps depression. Neither is absence nothingness, for one expects nothing of nothingness; nothingness has never been. In fact, many veterans desire nothingness, sleep, death. No, absence is something valuable that is not here, but should be, like when you are absent from school, or you have an absent expression on your face. Veterans are haunted by absence, by shadows of things not present but which cannot be buried or laid to rest. This disquieting absence is implied in a number of expressions: "the thousand yard stare"..."the hollow men"..."the black hole of trauma." It is memory that refuses its status as memory; that seeks to rise up, to come alive again; that calls out to be found; that is missing.

Thus many civilians expect a war testimony to be a story of loss or courage, when instead a real war story is a story of absence and fear. The highest authority on the war story is novelist–veteran Tim O'Brien, whose books, *Going After Cacciato* (1978), *The Things They Carried* (1990), and *In the Lake of the Woods* (1994), are meditations and exhortations on the missing. In *Going After Cacciato*, Cacciato, a grunt in Vietnam, simply decides to leave his unit and walk out of Vietnam. "He's gone! He's walking home." His unit decides to follow him, and follow him they do, through Southeast Asia, India, Europe, and finally Paris, along the way finding traces, but never catching him. In O'Brien's novels, the main characters are told, over and over again, "Give up, you know he is dead!" The search continues, the person is never found. O'Brien reminds us of the essential incompleteness and arbitrariness of the war memory:

> [I]n any war story, but especially a true one, it's difficult to separate what happened from what seemed to happen. What seems to happen becomes its own happening and has to be told that way. The angles of vision are skewed. When a booby trap explodes, you close your eyes and duck and float outside yourself. When a guy dies, you look away and then look back for a moment and then look away again. The pictures get jumbled; you tend to miss a lot. And then afterward, when you go to tell about it, there is always that surreal seemingness which makes the story seem untrue, but which in fact represents the hard and exact truth as it seemed. (O'Brien, 1990, p. 78)

The entrance into war is a confrontation with meaninglessness and chaos: in an ambush hundreds of bullets are thrashing through the air, some will hit, most will miss, but whose bodies are hit cannot be predicted from any combination of measurements, most certainly that of the value of their lives. In those moments, all semblance of reason or destiny evaporate:

> A true war story is never moral. It does not instruct, nor encourage virtue, nor suggest models of proper human behavior, nor restrain men from doing the things men have always done. If a story seems moral, do not believe it. If at the end of a war story you feel uplifted or if you feel that some small bit of rectitude has been salvaged from the larger waste, then

you have been made the victim of a very old and terrible lie. There is no rectitude whatsoever. There is no virtue. As a first rule of thumb, therefore, you can tell a true war story by its absolute and uncompromising allegiance to obscenity and evil. (O'Brien, 1990, p. 76)

Through these tough words, O'Brien reminds us that history is the telling of the tale from within the continuities of political and national narratives, involving the defense of the homeland, the war on terror, a nation's destiny, the noble crusade. These narratives are used to provide meaning and value to the war and to its soldiers. From the viewpoint of the soldier in the battle, however, these narratives have no relevance, leaving the participants in a world of chaos, disorganization, and fragmentation. What begins with songs and marches and flags ends with retching and terror and the fight for survival, feelings so unrepresentable that they appear to be from another dimension. The veteran spends the rest of his or her life traveling along another plane, intersecting here and there with ours, passing in and out of presence, in and out of absence.

That these ideas are not merely a novelist's fancies is supported by numerous tales of disappearances during wartime. Perhaps the most interesting is "The Vanished Battalion," those men of the Royal Norfolk Regiment who fought the Turks at the beginning of World War I near Gallipoli. During the battle, the entire battalion disappeared and their bodies were not found. They were presumed dead until two soldiers who were eyewitnesses each independently reported under oath that they had witnessed "the Norfolks march into a strange cloud that engulfed them, then lifted and drifted away, leaving nobody behind." This soon became legend, which more than a few came to believe, until years later when their remains were finally discovered in a valley near the battle. They had been slaughtered by the Turks. Nevertheless, this legend somehow spoke to a truth about war that resonated with many veterans.

VIETNAM VETERANS

This type of absence is like being haunted by presences unseen, out of reach, from the past, the undead. We have learned much about this haunting by the generation of soldiers who fought in the Vietnam War.

Over three million men and women served during that decade of conflict (1965–1975), which ended with 57,000 dead, 153,000 wounded, and 150,000 with psychological disabilities. Of importance in this conflict was that it was a war on foreign soil and that in the end we retreated and left the region, which soon was overtaken by the enemy. Unpopular at home, subject of intense public protest, the war created an uncertain and at times hostile homecoming for many veterans, who sometimes chose to hide their own participation in the war. The experience of the Absent, of the Missing, became concretized in an interesting way: in 1976, shortly after the final withdrawal, accusations were made that the US government had intentionally left behind a number of the Missing in Action, or MIA (that is, those whose bodies had not been recovered and were therefore either dead, imprisoned, or possibly defected). A large and widely supported movement developed that proclaimed, "We Shall Never Forget," and sponsored many attempts to recover the bodies and/or find the missing soldiers from the war, of which there are still 1,742 listed. The well-known POW-MIA flag, consisting of a black silhouette of a man and a guard tower, still flies on many government and private buildings to this day. The assumption behind the flag is that the whereabouts of every soldier should be known, indeed that in the end all uncertainty should be eradicated.

There have of course been MIAs in every war: officially there are still 74,384 Americans missing from World War II, and 8,051 from the Korean War. The missing in action during World War I are staggering. In the Theipval Memorial to the Missing of the Somme (a large battle), there are 72,090 British names for men whose bodies were never found and for whom there are no graves. At the Menin Gate in Belgium, a similar memorial exists for 54,896 Allied soldiers who died in the Battle of Ypres. And the Douaumont Ossuary contains the unidentified remains of 130,000 French and German soldiers missing in action from the Battle of Verdun. Shortly after the war, Britain and France constructed "Tombs of the Unknown Soldier," beginning a tradition many other nations have since followed.

The persistence of interest in the MIA issue from the Vietnam War is fueled in part by this sense that something or someone is missing or absent, but should not be. The intensity of distress over the approximately 1,700 MIAs from Vietnam seems out of proportion when compared to the much higher numbers of missing in other wars. In fact, on average, the percentage of MIAs to deaths in Vietnam (4%) is significantly lower than for Korea (15%) and World War II (19%). The anger about MIAs in Vietnam was linked to the accusation that the US government intentionally left these men behind because they did not care, and that the government was in collusion with the government of Vietnam to cover up the fact that there were still soldiers alive and being kept prisoner. This blaming the government for the MIA is unusual. In World War II, for example, the entire Allied Army of over 400,000 men was forced to evacuate back to England by the superior German advance. "The Miracle at Dunkirk" refers to the massive rescue effort that saved an amazing 338,226 British and French soldiers, who were picked up over 6 days and transferred across the Channel. However, almost 50,000 soldiers were left behind and captured or killed. There was little public anger or movement calling for the identification of those soldiers; they were presumed dead, and honored as heroes. There was no miracle for the families of those men.

In the end, it is the uncertainty over the missing that eats at the veteran's soul. Until the uncertainty can be resolved, the person is not yet dead or gone, and therefore one cannot mourn (Shay, 1994). One waits for them to come through the door someday. This is the limbo within which our veterans live; it is they who have been left behind, they who are missing in action, they who are still prisoners of war. If we are to look for the truly missing, they are here, all around us.

CHALLENGES FOR APPLIED THEATER AND DRAMA THERAPY

One of the most central functions of applied theater and drama therapy performances with special populations has been testimony, that is, the performance allows for unheard voices to speak, untold stories to be told, traumatic events to be documented (DeRose, 1996; Thompson, 2006). In so doing, theater/performance disrupts both the unintentional and motivated marginalization of distressing information in society, providing the audience with an education about experiences they have not had, or freeing the audience to speak up and/or act upon experiences they have had. The narratives allowed for returning combat soldiers from war are highly constrained by political, social, and familial barriers. The soldier must make reference to risk, but only so much risk; must in the end support the reigning explanation for the war; should evoke patriotism; should include a moment of courage, etc. The veteran receives immediate feedback if he moves outside of these boundaries and, more likely, anticipating them, never wanders into disturbing territory.

These constraints to the soldier's story appear to be exactly those conditions noted by O'Brien as constituting an untrue war story. This poses a dilemma, because what kind of theater portrays narratives that are incomplete, lack coherence, and privilege randomness over meaning? What kind of therapeutic theater will be able to embrace an "absolute and uncompromising allegiance to obscenity and evil?" If theater cannot instruct, encourage virtue, or suggest models of proper human behavior, if it cannot uplift our spirits, then perhaps it cannot be theater, for are not these the very things that we seek in theater? If by definition a trauma narrative cannot be fully understood because it is unrepresentable, then are we not placing our clients in a situation of certain defeat, for after their performance will they not sense that the audience did not fully comprehend? How can the signs of trauma— the open mouth, the silent scream, the pain with no message—be effectively dramatized without importing some familiar story structure recognizable to the audience? Primo Levi, the quintessential testimonial writer of the Holocaust, confided that despite his many books he had never been able to provide enough detail to communicate what happened, "for my Holocaust lies hovering between the words, drips from the punctuation marks, staining everything, while remaining invisible to all others" (Thomson, 2004). Perhaps being partially successful is sufficient. The audience gains by seeing the effort made by the victims to communicate their experience, and the actors appreciate the audience's efforts to understand. Everyone knows that at the end of the performance, the traumatic act itself will remain untouched, inviolable. What may have changed is the meaning of survival (Sajnani, 2009; M. Solomon & Siegel, 2003).

The aim, then, appears to somehow be able to *perform* incomprehensibility, rather than trying to *be* comprehensible; to show absence through mime, gesture, tone, and stillness, rather than only to tell the story through word. The challenge will be to bring forth what has been written upon the body by the traumatic act into the realm of the social fabric, woven as it is in story and word. Theater, like poetry, gives room for gaps, empty spaces that give rise to the shadows unseen in conversation and prose. Surely the avant garde theater (absurd, dada, minimalist) may offer some means by which these aims can be accomplished on stage. By disrupting the usual forms of continuity on stage, perhaps the sense of the thing will be communicated. On the other hand, abandoning attempts at representation altogether may lead to recreating the traumatic event and enacting it again on audience members, so that they too can get a feel for what it was like. Here we arrive at the boundary between theater and real life, in the regions of Antonin Artaud, guerrilla theater, political rally, and religious rites (such as the Mass).

THE LIMITS TO TESTIMONY

We say we want to hear the victims' testimonials and we encourage them to express themselves. We say that therapeutic theater allows victims to share their burden, but I question whether that is possible. What is more likely is that therapeutic theater creates palatable symbols of the victim's burden that the audience members imagine (or pretend to share). There are limits placed on testimony and limits to what the audience is willing to bear, as in the following example.

I am reminded of a man who was still on active duty, who came to see me for a consultation prior to being redeployed to Iraq for his second tour. He carried with him an enormous photo album. He sat down and looked at me with that hollow stare I know so well. I asked him if he had talked to friends or his family about what he had experienced in Iraq, and he shook his head in the negative, "but it's all in here." He gave me the album. As I looked at the dozens, no hundreds, of photos of mutilated, burnt, beheaded, disemboweled bodies of American soldiers, Iraqi men, women, and children; pieces of separated body parts; and children run over by armored vehicles, I became nauseated, frightened, horrified. I could not finish it. I resented him for bringing it. These images trouble me still. The album cannot be shown to anyone. He needs to find an acceptable euphemism for it, such as "Yes, we sustained many casualties" or "You are right, urban warfare is very challenging." The photo album must be locked away; what he actually experienced must remain hidden in him. Any theater that portrayed what happened to him would be banned, or more likely, never attended.

The root word for both veteran and veterinarian is the same: *veter*, which means "beast of burden." The combat soldier will carry the extra load to the end of his days. In the end, therapeutic theater may be unable or unwilling to alter the fundamental condition of isolation in the survivor of trauma. This may not be a criticism, only a statement of fact, about a limiting condition of theater.

PRODUCTION OF *THE LAST MIA*

From 1988 to 1994, I ran the Specialized PTSD Inpatient Unit at the Veterans Hospital in West Haven, Connecticut, where 27 cohorts of 8 to 15 veterans were treated in a four-month program. They received intensive individual, group, family, and creative arts therapies (James & Johnson, 1996; Johnson, Feldman, Southwick, & Charney, 1994; Johnson, Feldman, Lubin, & Southwick, 1995, 1997). As part of their experience, they were in weekly process-oriented drama therapy groups, and also developed and performed an original play about their experiences in the war or after the war, which was performed both in the hospital and at times outside the hospital to various audiences. A total of 26 plays were produced. Plays continue to be produced in an outpatient setting (Abbott, 2007).

The play I will discuss in this chapter specifically engaged the theme of Absence, stimulated by Tim O'Brien's novels. The premise of the play was that the last MIA was found and was being returned home, eliminating the need for the POW-MIA flag to be flown. That is, the play begins with the impossible act of completion. Following the theme of O'Brien's work, at that moment Joe, a veteran, husband, and father, disappears, forcing his friends to go after him. Past and present, memory and reality, are intermixed as the wish to "finally be done" is frustrated again. The intent of the project was to explore the conflict between our patients' desires to reach closure and the truthfulness of absence. Though the play was a highly valuable experience, we were unable to overcome the challenge we gave ourselves: in the end, the project remained a play, constrained by the theatrical conventions we desired to subvert. The need to smooth out the inconsistencies in the narratives and to maintain the veterans in sympathetic roles remained a powerful influence on the process.

Procedure

Following long-standing methods of applied theater and drama therapy, the cast of the play, consisting of eight veterans participating in the program, plus three staff members, engaged in 2-hour rehearsals twice a week for 8 weeks, then 3 rehearsals a week for 4 weeks, and then 4 rehearsals a week for 3 weeks. The final play was 75 minutes long and was performed at the ending ceremony of the program, with staff, veterans, and their families as audience. The play was performed two times. The initial rehearsals consisted of open-ended improvisations about relationships that the veterans found important in their lives. We used a model called the Relationship Lab (James & Johnson, 1996), that rapidly identifies situations that hold particular energy or interest for the group members. At week 8, the cast and director had several discussions about all the scenes created and ideas about the major theme or message of their potential play. On the basis of these discussions, the director organized an integrated play with coherence and continuity, consisting of the scenes selected by the veterans. These were then re-worked for coherence and consistency (Bailey, 2009; Emunah & Johnson, 1983; Snow, 2009). Then, in the spirit of the project, elements of scenes were removed or disrupted in order to replicate the sense of fragmentation and absence we wished to portray.

Synopsis

The play occurs perhaps 10 years in the future on a morning when the government announces that the remains of the last MIA from Vietnam have been found and are being returned. The implication is that finally there is no more need to delay mourning the end of the Vietnam War and that a state of "completion" has been achieved. The veteran Joe should be driving his two children, Kenny (age 14) and Ellie (age 8), to school, but when they look for him, he is not in the house. His wife, Cathy, becomes concerned, sends the children to school, and then calls her husband's work to see if he went in early. They have not seen him. Becoming more concerned, she calls a friend of her husband, Bill, who has not heard from him, but who agrees to go to the local bar to see if her husband has "lost it again" and is drinking. Bill finds out that the veteran was just at the bar and has left, leaving a valued cigarette lighter he had while in Nam. Bill knows how important the lighter is and calls another friend, Bob, to meet him at the state park where Joe often goes to be by himself. There they find his cap. They now fear he may be intent on hurting himself and so go to the local Vet Center to find the veteran's counselor, Ed. Ed at first downplays their concern, but when confronted with the lighter and hat, agrees that there is a problem. He agrees to call the sheriff, who says he will meet everyone back at Cathy's house.

At the house, the veterans press the Sheriff to begin looking for Joe. They accuse him of not understanding, and he tells them of a nephew he lost in the war. Cathy has found a letter in Joe's room that he wrote to his mother from Vietnam. The Sheriff then leaves to begin a search of the woods. At this point, Bob and the bartender each tell a story from their combat experience, and Ed reads Joe's letter.

Finally, the Sheriff calls to say that he has not been able to find anything, and that he is calling off the search to wait for Joe to reappear. Everyone becomes very upset by this, and the four veterans, Bill, Bob, Ed, and the bartender, decide to go themselves to the woods to find him. They find a piece of his clothing. They enter the woods and it becomes unclear whether the scene is in the present or the past in Vietnam, as Bill narrates his own combat story.

The scene shifts back to the house. Suddenly, Joe's son Kenny runs into the living room shooting a toy machine gun, and all four veterans hit the floor in fear. The Sheriff arrives and informs them that the husband has been seen in neighboring counties, though these are in opposite directions from one another. The sheriff and bartender leave, reassuring Cathy that her husband will come back soon. Kenny speaks about not remembering what his father looks like. Cathy speaks about feeling numb, and Ellie, while building a house of cards, tells a story about a dinosaur being rescued. Strangely, they talk about Joe in the past tense, as if he has been gone a long time. It is not clear whether the scene is occurring months later, or whether Joe was one of the MIAs from Vietnam and had never returned.

Footsteps are heard, the door at the back of the stage opens, footsteps in the room are heard, though no one can be seen. Ellie stands up and sees someone, whom she goes to. She whispers, "Daddy!" and places her hand on her cheek as if he kissed her there. The outside door to the house now opens and the footsteps fade away. The radio announcement about the last MIA being found plays again, as the audience is left with the ambiguity about when and why Joe was missing.

Narratives

Throughout the play, each character tells a story about a loss or absence. The stories from the veterans were their own real combat experiences, told in their own way; those of the non-veteran characters were created from what the veterans reported their loved ones had told them. I will now examine more carefully these narrative fragments as a means of revealing aspects of the combat veteran's experience.

Joe's Letter

Dear Mom, how is everybody back home? I hope you are okay. We have been out here chasing Cong for 11 days now. I haven't washed or changed my clothes. I really don't feel that great. I got my first really bad shot seven days ago. We were in a hut for the night when we got hit by our own artillery. Three of our guys got blown to pieces, right next to me. My buddy Tom is gone. Mom, I want to say something now before something happens to me. I think you are the greatest mom. I appreciate everything you have done for me. I know I've caused you a lot of heartaches and I'm sorry for every one of them. But in the event something does happen to me, I want you to know how I really feel. I'm really scared. I know I'm far away but I think it's the right thing to do to fight them here rather than in our backyard. So mom, goodbye. Tell everybody I love them. Love, Your son, Joe.

This letter, an actual letter sent home by one of the cast members, is a letter from a scared soldier afraid he will die, wanting to express his feelings of appreciation, remorse, and love for his mother and his family. This is not a trauma narrative. It expresses feelings, it is understandable, the events and the views are congruent, it is poignant, it is what should be done. Many veterans had similar experiences, outside and around their traumatic experiences, times when they were scared and wanted to be home and not to die. This letter is not filled with absence, but presence, presence of emotion, truth, and reason. The soldier even is able to sustain connection to the political rationale of the war—to stop communism—and evidences his choice to be there. He is frightened, but not helpless. This soldier has courage.

Ed's Narrative

I know what it's like to be too late. We were on our first op out of Phu Bai, out four days, when we were asked to cover an LZ on top of this mountain. After a day everything seemed secure so we were called back, we left a mortar platoon on top. Everybody was laughing at us because we had to walk down the mountain instead of being taken out by chopper. We got halfway down the mountain, still joking about having to hump it, when the first radio message came in: "Come back, we're being hit!" Everybody was real tired, everybody had a 50-pound rucksack on and I had a radio weighing another 25 pounds, but we turned around and started scrambling back up the hill. I had to ditch the radio as it was just too heavy, when the last message came through, "Please, hurry!" It took us awhile to get up there, and when we got to the top, we were too late: there were 20 guys, only 18 and 19 years old, with their brains blown out. The VC had made sure they were dead, shot both the dead and the wounded through their heads....we were late all right.

This narrative is that of a soldier, who takes things as they come, and is angry when things do not go right. Note the use of army jargon: VC, LZ, op, hump it. Each act is explained: they need to cover the hill, they took time to get back up the hill due to the weight of their rucksacks, the soldiers' brains were blown out because the VC wanted to make sure everyone was dead. The point of the story is a soldier's point: being late has serious consequences. This makes sense. And like a true soldier's tale, it is not sad or meaningless, but angry, and one senses that this soldier will come away from this experience dedicated to doing even better the next time.

Bill's Story

We were sent out to find the patrol, six of them, who hadn't returned. They should have been back long before. The captain waited, then told us to go after them and find them. We did, near checkpoint Bravo, all dead, well, all dead but one unaccounted for. Five of the six, dead. Maybe the sixth one got away, hid, is still alive! Carefully we explored the perimeter, moving out, until I spotted him, sitting wide-eyed against a tree 100 yards away. He was alive! I yelled, "Don't shoot, I'm an American!" He didn't move though. When we approached we saw that he too was dead, shot through the upper chest. His hand was clutching a live grenade, the pin had been pulled out, his stiff fingers holding the trigger in place. He had been ready to take a few of them with him when they approached, but they shot him before he could let go. I can only imagine those last final moments. He was ready for them. I carefully pried his fingers off the grenade, put the pin back in and laid it on the ground. We carried him back. We had found the last one. The last one had been found.

In this narrative, physically finding the last one appears to be almost as important as having him be alive. The narrative ends with a sense of completeness: all are found, the pin is put back into the grenade, the man is carried back. This characteristic indicates that this story is not a trauma story, rather it is a reassuring war story, sad though it be. The mission is accomplished, and courage is shown. Bill can feel settled. This type of story can be lived with.

Bob's Narrative

Waiting and waiting. Seems like all we ever do is wait....last time I saw him he was crawling off into the treeline. We had got hit bad, and I was lying on the ground, my face smashed into the mud, my arm bleeding. He had been hit in the leg. He crawled over to me, there were still some random shots being fired over our heads, and he said that he'd get us out of there. I couldn't see the others and didn't know if I was the only one left alive. Then he crawled off and I never saw him again. He told me to wait. About four hours later a chopper landed near us and we got pulled out. I think he did it. He got us out. He had been taken to a different hospital. That was it. Never saw him again. Every year I call the State Department and ask if they have any information about him. He's not on the Wall. I fear the worst. I'm not going to quit trying. I really want to see that man again. He got us out.

Note, in this narrative there is no attribution of courage or heroism, though clearly the acts described fulfill these criteria. The story is chopped up. Each sentence is unto itself. Though continuity is implied, it is not explicit. Bob does not know about the others in his squad. He never sees "him" again. "He" cannot be found. No feelings are expressed. The story seems to boil down to one idea—*he got us out*—but the reader is left not entirely sure that this is true, and left with the ambiguity about "his" location. Trauma dislocates experience so much (produces skew, angles) so that one perception simply passes through on its way somewhere else. **For Bob**, finding "him" is the equivalent to filling in the gaps. And Bob is not at rest in this effort, for he remains in a perpetual state of "active waiting" for this arrival.

Bartender's Story

I still can't believe it. Our convoy got ambushed. The lead truck blew up right in front of us. I mean, it blew up and was gone. Big cloud of smoke and fire. Road mine. No shots, though. No snipers. Just silence, weird. Then Jimmy, he was driving the truck in front of me, pulls his truck over to the side of the road, stops the truck, and gets out. Weird, he looks just, well, matter-of-fact. Then he puts his weapon down on the ground, I mean he puts his weapon down on the ground, I can't believe it, and walks straight off into the woods. Everybody just looks at him, don't get out because it's too dangerous, just looks at him walking off. He doesn't come back. After awhile, we start up again and drive to base. They sent a team out later to look for him but never found him. I don't know if he went to take a piss, wanted to get killed, or defected to the other side. Whatever it is, don't make sense. He's listed as MIA. I can't believe it.

This narrative illustrates much of O'Brien's criteria for a true war story: it makes no sense. It just happened: Jimmy gets out of his truck, puts his weapon down, and walks into the woods. The context is ignored: one of their trucks just got blown up; they are in an armed conflict in Vietnam. The story is credible because the chances of Jimmy defecting, wanting to be killed, or needing to piss are just about equally unlikely, and worse, indeterminate. The evident fascination of Jimmy's buddies as he acts in this manner reveals some nascent understanding that such behavior in that circumstance might not be unreasonable, though it most certainly does not make sense. It just is what it is. Weird.

Ellie's Story

This is Bruce, my dinosaur. Bruce and his mommy went into the forest, I don't know why, I think Bruce was trying to help his mommy find help, help in the forest. But it got dark, real dark, so Bruce told mommy to stay there by a tree and he went away to find help. Mommy was lost. Bruce was lost. They couldn't find each other, ever.

Ellie's story is a child's story, and through its symbolism of the animal as guide, the fear of abandonment, the anchoring provided by the tree, and the surrounding darkness, her anxieties are processed and communicated to her mother. Where the trace of the traumatic schema can be found perhaps, is in the ending, where *"They could not find each other, ever"* skirts the usual ending of the child's story, with return, repair, and all things being made right. Ellie knows of absence.

Cathy's Story

This whole thing is crazy. Joe's going to walk in the door like nothing happened. Tomorrow morning, when we all get up, he'll be there eating his cereal, take the kids to school, and that will be it. I don't know, I've shut myself off from all this. It's funny, Kenny brought home a picture the other day he had drawn in school. It showed a man in a suit with a briefcase, just standing there. "That's Dad," he said, "the hologram man." I asked him what he meant. Kenny says, "Look, you can put your hand right through him…you can see him from all sides!" Made me wonder how Kenny would draw me. I had the craziest idea: he'd draw me as a snow-woman, a snow-woman with sweat pouring down my face. That's kinda how I feel all the time.

The wife's narrative illustrates the effects of being close to a traumatized veteran: the emotional cutting-off, the sense of being frozen, the anticipation, the constant threat at the edges. Cathy hopes for the resumption of normalcy, though she is aware that this has been an illusion. It is an illusion that must be kept up, however, in order to continue living. She lives with a hologram; she is a snow-woman, sweating. She is telling us about vicarious traumatization; there are few benefits.

Kenny's Narrative

I can't remember what Dad's face looks like. I can't see his face. It's been so long. I look in the album with all his pictures from Vietnam. He looks so young. It's different. I can't remember. The image of his face keeps floating away. I wish I knew him.

In the play, this narrative in addition to others raises the question in the audience's mind whether Joe had in fact returned from Vietnam. To make sense of this statement, one could conclude that Joe died in Vietnam while his wife and two young children were back home, and that Kenny's only memories of his father are from looking at the album his mother constructed out of photos sent home. This would be the non-trauma narrative. Or, if this were the narrative of a child of a Vietnam veteran who had been home for many years and later in life had two children, who drove Kenny to school every day, then this would be a narrative of absence. His father, a man with no face, a hologram man, whom "*you can put your hand right through,*" that shell of a father one sees in the morning but who is not really there. An impenetrable distance. Kenny is on his own.

The Effect of the Performance

The veterans reported that they found performing the play to be helpful to them in thinking more about their experiences, in being witnessed by family and friends in the audience, in underscoring the importance of their therapeutic work in the program, and in feeling more comfortable being open about their identities as Vietnam veterans. They did not believe that the audience had any better understanding of what happened in the war, and they felt no particular relief from their memories of the war.

The audience members, who consisted of family, friends, and staff members, appreciated the play greatly, and said that they felt respect for the veterans, as soldiers and as actors. Many audience members said they understood that the play pointed out that the veterans could never feel closure from the war. No one, however, said that they felt there was no closure. For non-participants, the war is over. Most audience members were confused by the contradictory elements portrayed in the play, such as the ambiguity over what time period the play took place in, whether Joe had left on purpose or not, and why only Ellie could see her father at the end.

Obviously, one performance in a veterans' hospital treatment program has a minimal effect on the world, but does it have any effect at all? Does it help in any small way toward repairing or preventing or healing? Viewed in the positive, the performance was part of a large collective effort in America to process the Vietnam War and to heal the veterans and its people from the emotional toll that the war exacted. In addition, the play attempted to communicate that lack of closure is an inevitable component of the veterans' experience, and to reassure both family members and staff members that this fact is not due to their own failure or the program's limitations. Viewed in the negative, the performance may have served as a form of containment or even suppression of what really happened. The narratives were improvised from real experiences, but very condensed and smoothed out, to be able to be presented on stage. The performance was not intended to ask questions about society's responsibilities for the war; the performance avoided divisive issues regarding the rightness of the war or the veteran's acts of perpetration while in the war, and instead maintained a largely sympathetic context for the characters in the play. The performance did not intend to stimulate social action to change conditions that might lead to another armed conflict. This activity primarily helped to consolidate the values and perceived validity of the therapeutic program, even while disrupting the standard romantic narratives often presented for this purpose.

PERFORMING ABSENCE

Performance of traumatic experience intrinsically involves the incomplete, the absent, the missing, and, for the performance to be credible, these gaps must disrupt the aesthetic principles of harmony, continuity, and tragedy, for traumatic experience interferes with catharsis and mourning.

Theater is itself a space that calls forth the absent. Like all art forms, theater lies across the boundary of the seen and unseen, the symbol being a bridge that allows the imaginal and liminal worlds to reveal themselves. Theater makes the absent present, whereas trauma makes the present absent. Trauma in fact may be viewed as the anti-thesis to theater or art: trauma sucks the present into the unseen, as in the concept of the "black hole." Characters on the stage are "larger than life," while trauma victims feel that some essential part of them has been removed or stolen. Although theater takes us to the point of catharsis of emotion, trauma leads us to emotional numbing and the cold stare into elsewhere. Theater develops, it moves us; trauma repeats, it freezes us.

Applied theater and drama therapy productions with traumatized populations therefore are confronted with a dilemma: whether to adequately show the truth of the traumatic experience, or to tell a story that fits in with expected pathways of recovery. Each of these storylines maintains coherence, makes a point, and comes to closure; and each makes for an engaging evening of theater. For an authentic performance of trauma, however, the production will have to come to the edge of theater, and break down, stop, or repeat itself in a tortuous loop. Just as the trauma victim in a flashback cannot differentiate the event from a memory of the event, a "true act" in the theater will lead to a moment where the audience cannot tell if the actors are acting or being real, where the promise made by theater that "all is pretend" is betrayed, and their fear is triggered.

I remember vividly in one of my early productions at the Yale Psychiatric Institute (YPI), we placed one of the patient-actors in a real straightjacket, tied just as if he had required one. The other actors sat in a circle around him, lightly pounding the floor, whispering, "Free!" The actor then attempted to get out of the restraint, which took him approximately 10 minutes. The audience, made up of other patients as well as staff, saw that the restraint was real, but also assumed that the young actor was agile enough to get out eventually, this being our "promise" that his restraint was not real. This was good theater, because everyone understood the message, entitled, "The Struggle for Freedom," an iconic American narrative. Yet, suddenly, a male patient in his early 30s who suffered from schizophrenia and was psychotic much of the time, stood up and, with great passion and fear, cried out, "Free that man!" He said it with so much alarm that a wave of fright sped through the audience as the boundaries of theater and life wobbled for everyone. The man stepped forward onto the stage and an aide gently came to him and guided him out of the room, as he continued to shout, "You cannot do that to him! Free him!"

This event was later characterized as a breakdown of boundaries caused by his psychosis, and the scene was criticized for being too intense for some of the patients. However, many audience members had become intensely aware in that moment of their own passivity: of being bystanders to the albeit pretend suffering of the patient-actor, and though they had been held back by the as-if agreement of theater, the psychotic man had actually tapped into what can only be described as an authentic response. In fact, his response may have been the appropriate response! Had all members of the audience joined in with him, crying out, "Free that man," or had even come onto the stage and collectively removed him from the restraint, what a terrific action that would have been! Would it have been theater? That is not clear, and could not be clear. Certainly their role as audience members would have been radically altered. It is as if this breaking of the theatrical convention reveals the truth of a traumatic act. What conditions must be employed to invite the audience to think and act beyond the permissions assumed in the traditional theatrical encounter?

Other artists have explored disrupting the boundary between art and life. Augusto Boal's Invisible Theatre experiments with this boundary by having a scripted scene enacted in a public setting as if it were happening for real, hoping to activate passers-by into joining the discussion about racism, sexual harassment, and other issues (Boal, 1992). This work raises the question of whether there is a difference between performing an opinion (as Boal's actors do) and giving an opinion (as the passers-by do) and, if so, hiding that difference from the audience. Here the fundamental honesty of the theater to reveal itself as theater seems to have been breached, for the purpose of audience engagement.

The Rat Piece

The following example is an extreme one, in which the artist engaged in an act of real perpetration during a performance, which thereby nullified itself as a performance, in the hopes of activating the audience members. In 1976, the artist Kim Jones produced an exhibition called *The Rat Piece*, in which he appeared smeared with mud, carrying a wooden cage. Three live rats were held in this cage. He then sprayed the rats with lighter fluid and set them on fire, and periodically sprayed them again, as they died, screaming and running around frantically. When they were dead, he buried them in a vat of mud in the exhibit hall. The attendees reacted with varying degrees of horror.

Afterward, Jones was charged with cruelty to animals and paid a small fine. The exhibit director was fired. Some pointed out that everyone hates rats; if it is fine to poison them at home, why not at an art exhibition? Jones's only comment was that no one tried to intervene on behalf of the rats, that the artistic convention at the exhibition prevented the audience members from taking action, despite their horror and disapproval. Kim Jones, it turns out, is a Vietnam veteran. He and his buddies often killed and tortured rats that they caught in the jungle. But his exhibit was perhaps more importantly symbolizing the napalm American forces had sprayed on the Vietnamese and the passivity of the American public as bystanders to the war or, for that matter, the passivity of the public to any war. By breaking with the conditions of the aesthetic to restrain from harm, Jones challenged his audience to break out from their role as audience. Like my patient at the YPI, perhaps breaking out of this role might have been the right thing to do.

Martin Harries, in his commentary on *The Rat Piece*, notes, "Not to intervene is what it is to be an audience: Audiences do not intervene, or when they do intervene, the members of this group become something other than an audience....The success of the performance relies on the failure of the audience, its failure to intervene...(and the performance) demonstrated the domination of audience conventions" (Harries, 2007, pp. 162–163). However, this constriction lasted only as long as the performance; after the performance people felt free to express their outrage, and action was taken: Jones was arrested. Clearly, killing animals as both an act of perpetration and artistic symbolism, much like the spectacle of bullfighting or animal sacrifice in religious rites, raises important questions about the boundary region between theater and trauma.

In our production of *The Last MIA*, these themes pervade the show: each character is confronted with the choice to act or to wait. Each story within the play repeats this theme of waiting or acting. In most cases, the action when it came was in vain. The rat died anyway. And this is also the dilemma for the audience, who choose—just like Jones's audience—to sit back and watch the suffering of the veterans, filled with sympathy but restrained by theatrical conventions as well as by the notion that this suffering is history. Though the events being described are historical, the veterans' suffering is not; their suffering is real and present, and the audience members include their families, whose care and hurt are also real and present. Could one of the veterans' own daughters in the audience have run up to them on stage and call out, "Daddy!" as Ellie does to the non-existent Joe? Could one of the veterans' wives have cried out, "I miss you!"? Would she have been gently ushered out of the theater? We cannot say; they waited until after the performance to say these things.

The moment societal or artistic or Geneva conventions break down is when the truth of a situation is tested; when social change begins or martial law is imposed. In the case of Vietnam, some people did, like my patient at the YPI, stand up and shout, "No, stop the war!" and were taken away. Others have at times refused to participate in the expected, disrupting the calm either for good or evil. The trauma story begins when someone breaks through this veil, and calls out, or just walks away, like Cacciato, or the man in the bartender's story who simply walks off into the woods, or Joe, who simply is no longer there. When, at the end of the play, Joe passes through the house, as a shade, only his daughter Ellie can see him, for she is not yet bound by society's demands. As in *The Emperor's New Clothes*, only the young can see, though that is not actually true, for in that story everyone can see that the emperor is naked, only the child is able to tell the truth, embarrassing as it is.

We the audience do see, do know, whether it be Rwanda, or Darfur, or Nazi Germany, or Cambodia, or Vietnam, or Joe; we just choose to remain in the audience and complain later, our capacity to respond nullified by so many repetitions. In this way, we too turn presence into absence, truth into fiction, by our pretending. Audiences of trauma testimonies are placed in the same situation: they must sit back and watch someone else's suffering and not intervene, no matter how uncomfortable they are (Sajnani, 2009). Unlike children's theater, where the children cry out to the main characters, "Watch out! The wolf is hiding there!" adult audiences merely stare. As a result, there is a tendency for the testimonies to fit into the expected contours of the trauma story.

There have been some remarkable exceptions to this practice. The revolution that led to the independence of Belgium was sparked by a performance of Daniel Auber's *La Muette de Portici* on the evening of August 25, 1830, at the Brussels Opera House. During the song "*Amour sacre de la patrie*," sung by Adolphe Nourrit, the audience became so excited it poured out into the streets and moved directly to occupy government buildings, beginning the revolution. More recently, the independence of Estonia was declared via the indirect route of a "Song Festival" held on September 11, 1988, at the Tallinn Song Festival Arena, where 300,000 Estonians began singing "Song of Estonia." Under the guise of this performance, the entire nation was galvanized into action. At the right time, with the right song, the levers of change can be shifted.

The fact of trauma means that there was no rescue and that no one intervened to prevent it. The mother looked the other way when the father slipped into the child's bedroom; the neighbors closed their shades when the police came for the Jews next door; no one in the apartment building remembers hearing the screams from the hallway. No one was watching and if anyone was, that person would deny he/she could have done anything. There is no audience to trauma, and if this be true, can there be a theater of trauma (Langer, 1993)?

OTHERNESS IN THE TRAUMA TESTIMONY

The traumatic process disrupts the continuities and flow of the text, removing pieces seemingly at random, repeating phrases over again, inserting sections out of order, or leaving large gaps that cannot be bridged. The result is a text that seems to have been corrupted and thus may not be credible. Trauma narrative seems to be a text that has not been edited; for the purpose of the editor is to check for and eliminate these disruptions in continuity, to untangle the jumble and fill in the gaps, so that comprehensibility is maintained. The trauma narrative is more like a painting with graffiti on it; the work has been spoiled, ruined, intruded upon, by someone other than the author. It is an unpermitted writing-over of the victim's experience.

Is it possible that the cuts and gaps within the trauma narrative are best understood as signs of the perpetrator, rather than the fears of the victim? The victim's testimony has been defaced by the author of the original violent act, who like a censor blacks out what he or she wishes. If so, then a radical de-centering of authorship has occurred in the trauma narrative, for the victim can no longer be considered its sole author. This has resonance with the nature of the trauma itself, which is the result of the agency of the perpetrator, not the victim. The victim may be better understood as a reporter attempting to communicate the horrendous act of another. The victim falls into silence and incomprehension, as if he or she were not there, emanating "that surreal seemingness which makes the story seem untrue." The victim was not the author of the event.

This analysis may explain why a true trauma narrative or theater piece calls out for the intervention by an Other, who must arise to expose and then stop the perpetrator. When the trauma testimonial remains within the established boundaries of aesthetic convention, where the gaps and discontinuities have been smoothed out and filled in, the active presence of the perpetrator remains hidden. Without his presence, there need be no call to action. But when the edge has been reached, the Other must arise to expose the perpetrator and to stop him—the man who cries out "free him," the woman who puts out the flames on the rat, the child who calls out for her daddy, and the young men who rush out of the theater to occupy a government building.

In the theater, there is only one source of this Other—the audience. Thus true trauma testimony will push the audience to the edge of its status as bystander, and call for it to transform into an authentic witness to the traumatic event, to stand up and show that they have finally seen what happened. These will be moments of intense discomfort, for the aesthetic conventions will be broken, and the continuity of the theatrical presentation disrupted. Writing such actions into the script or using confederates in the audience will not produce these moments. The intrusion into the narrative must be spontaneous and come from without. The actor's script has been set, the traumatic event has occurred, and what remains uncertain is the question, What will the audience do? The aim, then, of applied theater in trauma is to confront the audience with that question, for it will not be the actors or the victims who will right the wrongs and prevent the evils of this world; it will be us.

Therapeutic and social action theater productions must consider taking theatrical conventions to their edge: in the show-and-tell of the trauma story, the deep discrepancy between the "show" and the "tell" should be revealed by spontaneous acts of courage by actors and audience members, who become compelled to question their roles, and demand that things change. What will compel them is fear, fear that arises when the perpetrator is revealed behind the screen of absence in the trauma narrative. Perhaps then applied theater can affect the causes of traumatic events such as wars, child abuse, rape, or violence. On the other hand, fear may paralyze them, drive them away. We will be left with acts of courage and no audience. Our dilemma remains: Without some confrontation with the unbearable absence—the hidden perpetrator—in the trauma testimony, applied theater may have only illusions of healing and repair to offer. We leave the theater solaced by the victims' resilience and satisfied with our attention to these issues, as the conditions and people that gave rise to the horrors swirl around us, unabated.

REFERENCES

Abbott, R. (2007). *No unwounded soldiers* [Film]. Abbott Media.

Bailey, S. (2009). Performance in drama therapy. In D. Johnson & R. Emunah (Eds.), *Current approaches in drama therapy* (2nd ed., pp. 374–392). Springfield, IL: Charles C Thomas.

Boal, A. (1992). *Games for actors and non-actors.* New York: Routledge Press.

DeRose, D. (1996). *Vietnam War literature.* New York: Scarecrow Press.

Emunah, R., & Johnson, D. (1983). The impact of theatrical performance on the self-images of psychiatric patients. *Arts in Psychotherapy, 10,* 233–240.

Harries, M. (2007). Regarding the pain of rats: Kim Jones's Rat Piece. *Drama Review, 51,* 160–165.

James, M., & Johnson, D. (1996). Drama therapy for the treatment of affective expression in post-traumatic stress disorder. In D. Nathanson (Ed.), *Knowing feeling: Affect, script, and psychotherapy* (pp. 303–326). New York: Norton.

Johnson, D. (2003). Deterioration of innocence and neutrality in international conflict. Book review of *Sharing the front line and the back hills: International protectors and providers: Peacekeepers, humanitarian aid workers, and the media in the midst of crisis,* by Yael Danieli. *Contemporary Psychology: APA Review of Books, 48,* 405–407.

Johnson, D., Feldman, S., Lubin, H., & Southwick, S. (1995). The use of ritual and ceremony in the treatment of post-traumatic stress disorder. *Journal of Traumatic Stress, 8,* 283–299.

Johnson, D., Feldman, S., Southwick, S., & Charney, D. (1994). The concept of the second generation program in the treatment of post-traumatic stress disorder among Vietnam veterans. *Journal of Traumatic Stress, 7,* 217–236.

Langer, L. (1993). *Holocaust testimonies: The ruins of memory.* New Haven, CT: Yale University Press.

O'Brien, T. (1978). *Going after Cacciato.* New York: Dell.

O'Brien, T. (1990). *The things they carried.* Boston: Houghton-Mifflin.

O'Brien, T. (1994). *In the Lake of the Woods.* Boston: Houghton-Mifflin.

Rosen, D. (2005). *Armies of the young: Child soldiers in war and terrorism.* New Brunswick, NJ: Rutgers University Press.

Sajnani, N. (2009). *Permeable boundaries: Towards a critical, collaborative performance pedagogy.* Unpublished doctoral dissertation, Concordia University, Montreal, Canada.

Shay, J. (1994). *Achilles in Vietnam: Combat trauma and the undoing of character.* New York: Atheneum.

Snow, S. (2009). Ritual/theatre/therapy. In D. Johnson & R. Emunah (Eds.), *Current approaches in drama therapy* (2nd ed., pp. 117–144). Springfield, IL: Charles C Thomas.

Solomon, M., & Siegel, D. (Eds.). *Healing trauma: Attachment, mind, body, and brain.* New York: W.W. Norton.

Solomon, Z. (1993). *Combat stress reaction: The enduring toll of war.* New York: Plenum.

Thompson, J. (2006). *Digging up stories: Applied theatre, performance, and war.* Manchester, UK: Manchester University Press.

Thomson, I. (2004). *Primo Levi: A life.* New York: Picador.

4 The "H" in "HIV" Stands for "Human": Action Approaches to an Ongoing Global Crisis

MARIO COSSA

Author's Profile

I first became interested in Sociodrama and Drama Therapy/ Psychodrama in 1984, when I was working with the Children's Performing Arts Center in Keene, New Hampshire, as Artistic Director and Theater Educator. While creating a show with local teens dealing with substance use and abuse, it became evident that we were doing much more than "putting on a show," and my interest was piqued in the ways drama could be used as a tool for personal growth with young people. Returning to graduate school at Antioch, I developed the ACTING OUT program, which combined expressive therapy with issue-oriented, audience-interactive, improvisational theater. The more I learned about HIV, the more opportunities I had to meet and work with those infected with and affected by it, the more my commitment grew to use drama to inform and motivate young people about HIV/AIDS. In later years, when my work in psychodrama with trauma survivors took me to South Africa, my awareness of the depth and breadth of this pandemic was expanded even more.

Mario Cossa, MA, RDT/MY, TEP, is one of the leading psychodramatist-drama therapists. He has Master's degrees in Education and in Counseling Psychology. The program he developed as a student—ACTING OUT—received a contract from the New Hampshire State Department of Education to provide school-based programs and teacher trainings focused on HIV/AIDS Education. In 2009, he received the ASGPP's Neil Passariello Award, re-located in the Bay Area, and, together with Regina Moreno, founded the Bay Area Moreno Institute in Berkeley, California.

INTRODUCTION

The year was 1981, and I was working at the front desk of a gay resort hotel in Vermont when mumblings about a new "gay cancer" started filtering though the sounds of the disco. It wasn't long before it had a name: GRID, gay-related immune deficiency. By 1983, the letters had been changed to the more inclusive AIDS, acquired immune deficiency syndrome, and a causative factor had purportedly been identified: HIV, the human immunodeficiency virus (About.org, 2009). As I recall, that identification was beset with controversy over whether the French or the Americans had actually discovered "It" first. Whoever found "It," we were hearing that HIV/AIDS was starting to appear in other places around the world, although the major outbreaks were still focused in the cities. We thought we were fairly safe in rural New England. That safety was momentary.

HIV/AIDS quickly transitioned from an epidemic focused in a few spots in the world into a pandemic, becoming part of everyone's reality as a fatal, albeit preventable disease. It sparked massive efforts in prevention education, beset with controversies about abstinence-only versus safer-sex approaches, and care for those infected, complicated by fear and misinformation. A quilt was created to celebrate and remember those who had succumbed to the infection and a Broadway show was created to celebrate those living with it.

The face of this pandemic has changed several times along the way. It is no longer the disease that "just affects gay men and Haitians." The fate of those infected has changed as well. Being diagnosed HIV-positive is no longer tantamount to a death sentence. HIV, however, has not disappeared, and its effects on those infected are in no way insignificant. In keeping with the focus of this book, I am approaching the pandemic from the perspective of Collective Trauma. According to reports from the Centers for Disease Control (CDC) (Dunham, 2008):

- 1.1 million Americans currently are living infected with HIV;
- In 2006, there were 56,300 new infections in the USA, more than were previously estimated;
- In the USA, HIV/AIDS disproportionately affects Blacks of both sexes as well as gay and bisexual men; and
- 75% of all AIDS deaths worldwide in 2007 were in sub-Saharan Africa, where 22 million people are infected.

The current climate, within which HIV/AIDS prevention/education and treatment occurs, is beset with: burnout and compassion fatigue among human service providers; new challenges in motivating behavior change to prevent a treatable rather than invariably fatal illness; new realities in providing treatment and support to those infected with and affected by HIV; and ongoing political, social, economic, and cultural impediments to effective prevention and care throughout the world in countless communities that have been severely impacted, if not ravaged, by HIV/AIDS (Surdoval, 2009).

In October 2008, I received an e-mail from a colleague with whom I had conducted workshops for sero-discordant couples some years before. She attached a report containing current HIV/AIDS data and the comment:

> I read this and shake my head. After so many years of HIV prevention work, nothing really changed did it?…This is a 100% preventable disease. Now that it's moved from a fatal condition to a chronic one, I suppose it's not surprising how lax behaviors have become. When I think of the hours I spent trying to figure out creative ways of promoting exciting, safer sex, I just wonder if my time wouldn't have been better spent elsewhere. (M. Caulfield, personal communication, 2009)

The frustration she expressed in her e-mail has been echoed by many people I know who have worked in the field and, over the years, have had to deal with government strictures against safer-sex-based programs, decreases in available funding, and out-and-out lack of interest. The need for dedicated HIV/AIDS workers has not decreased and we need to find ways to support and motivate both those workers we have as well as encouraging new individuals into the field.

The needs of those infected and affected by HIV are also no less pressing today. The disparities in available treatment and care between various cultures within various countries as well as between developed and developing nations reflect deeper social issues and concerns.

This chapter explores the ways in which sociodrama, sociometry, and related action methods can be tools for combating compassion fatigue in human service workers, developing effective prevention education, working with infected and affected individuals, and combating political and social impediments to progress. It is hoped that the suggestions provided stimulate the readers' warm-up and generate additional ideas and opportunities for imbuing the work with spontaneity and, thereby, increasing its efficiency and effectiveness.

COMBATING COMPASSION FATIGUE

Compassion fatigue is a term originally coined to describe a phenomenon that occurs with therapists and social service providers who work with survivors of trauma (Figley, 1995). It relates to: the ways in which the work restimulates the worker's own trauma history; the vicarious traumatization (McCann & Pearlman, 1990) that occurs when one witnesses or hears about another's trauma; the stresses of working within agencies and organizations that are, themselves, dysfunctional; and the lack of appropriate support and supervision for the worker (Courtois, 1993). Compassion fatigue is a contributing factor to what we call, in common parlance, burnout.

With slight adjustments in terminology, these listed causative factors certainly apply to HIV/AIDS workers. Many, if not all, have been deeply and personally affected by the ravages of the epidemic over more than two decades. Hearing the stories of infected and affected individuals is part of the job description. In responding to an e-mail explaining this chapter and asking for permission to quote her, and neither having heard the term before nor read my description of it, the colleague, quoted earlier, wrote:

> Forget about compassionate fatigue, I think the longer you worked in this field you are more likely to have some form of PTSD. I was watching [a TV program] several months ago and there was a piece on AIDS orphans. It reduced me to mush as I recalled the times holding kids as they were screaming that their Moms were dying (which they ultimately did) as well as Moms whose children were dying. (M. Caulfield, personal communication, 2009)

In our experience, the difference between those workers who more successfully cope with the stresses of the first two causative factors listed above and those who quickly reach burnout is generally found within the final two factors. Despite positive intentions and heroic efforts on the part of many, the organizations and agencies that work in the field are hard put not to get caught in the dysfunctional systems that provide funds and monitor outcomes. With workers (to paraphrase Alice's White Queen) "running as fast as they can just to stay in the same place," there is seldom time or resources for adequate support and supervision.

I recently adapted a sociometric and sociodramatic approach that I found helpful in supporting trauma workers in a number of countries for use in training HIV/AIDS workers and to help revitalize and re-motivate their efforts. This training begins with clarifications of norms and the creation of a safe and confidential space within which participants can share how they have personally been affected by their work in the field. With larger groups, a paired sharing may precede a sharing with the entire group.

Circle Sociometry can be one way in which the large-group sharing is conducted. Group members stand in a circle and, one by one, step into the circle as they make a statement that is true for them, for example: "I have been working in this field since the 1980s" or "I get frustrated when clients miss scheduled appointments" or "It breaks my heart each time I attend the funeral of someone with whom I have worked." If the statement is true for other members of the group, they step into the circle as well, and look around to notice the commonality of feelings and thoughts. This process continues, giving each member a chance to offer something to which the group can respond. Throughout the warm-up phase of the training, members develop a sense of common experience and purpose, and celebrate the fact that the real expertise comes from the wisdom of the group and not solely from the facilitator.

The participants then engage in an action *locogram* in which four sites in the room, marked with scarves, chairs, and so on, represent the impact they have experienced on their work and lives from each of the four compassion fatigue causative factors: restimulation, vicarious traumatization, the stresses of working within dysfunctional agencies, and the lack of appropriate support and supervision. A fifth site is established to represent stress factors not stated, which are also relevant to any group member's experience.

Participants are instructed to move between the sites and notice the degree to which they are affected by each. They might rate it on a scale of 1 to 10 to explore relative impact between the items. After they have explored each site, they are invited to go stand at the site that they rated the highest. Members within each cluster are given the opportunity to share thoughts and feelings and then each cluster reports to the full group the essence of what was shared in the clusters. For example:

> We mostly gave fives and sixes to the ways this work reminds us of the people we have lost to this disease, as well as to the impact of hearing other people's stories. We're over here standing between the other two factors because we gave a nine to the dysfunction of the system in which we work. We also felt that when we and our coworkers have time to support each other, we do it well, but most of the time we are so busy so we rated it a nine as well.

After a training I conducted in South Africa with 35 trauma workers, one participant commented that after years of attending trainings, this was the first time she had ever been invited to share her feelings with other workers. Training evaluations also reflected that the opportunity to share their experiences and frustrations was valued highly by many participants.

Sharing frustrations without taking steps to address the causes, however, does little to provide long-term relief for the participants. Therefore, the experience then moves into a sociodrama in which participants work to create, as characters in the drama, a panel of experts on self-care and support. Characters can be modelled on actual or imagined people who demonstrate appropriate self-care. As the drama begins, a set number of individuals step into the roles of the consulting panel. Others are encouraged by the director to rotate into these roles as the action continues.

Participants at each of the causative factor sites then create a character that is the prototype of someone negatively affected in the extreme by that contributing factor. The consulting panel moves from site to site and offers or elicits strategies for dealing with the issues presented by the characters under stress. It might sound something like this:

Vicarious Traumatized Character (VTC): Sometimes by the end of the day I don't have the energy to make dinner when I get home, so I grab a burger en route and then feel bad about eating like crap.

Panelist: What could you do to decompress before you drive home, to allow you to leave the stress at the office?

VTC: I suppose I could go sit by the pond in the park next to the office and watch the swans for a few minutes before getting into the car.

The director helps to facilitate the conversation between the characters as well as instructs the participants to move between roles and, at times, from active participant to witness. The drama concludes with sharing, focused on which elements of the drama especially moved the participants or provided significant insight.

The training concludes with participants, individually, or in groups—perhaps made up of those with similar issues, or who work at the same agency—developing personal and organizational aftercare strategies. This stage of the training provides participants the opportunity to start developing concrete plans for identifying and changing those elements that contribute to the compassion fatigue over which they have some control.

STRATEGIES FOR PREVENTION EDUCATION

Although HIV infection is now a treatable condition, about 14,000 Americans died from AIDS in 2006 (Dunham, 2008). Additionally, those who survive face a lifetime of medication and health monitoring. Richard Wolitski, Acting Chief of the CDC's HIV/AIDS prevention division, has said: "We're not going to be able to treat our way out of this epidemic. We need to have strong prevention programs so we can prevent these infections from occurring in the first place" (Dunham, 2008, p. 2).

Research conducted in 1996 and reported in the *Journal of the American Medical Association* (Resnick et al., 1997) pinpointed four primary factors that contribute to effective youth HIV/AIDS prevention programs, that is, programs that actually contribute to behavior change for participants. These factors are: utilizing action approaches to teaching (involving the participants, not lecturing to them); reaching youth before risky behaviors become a way of life; utilizing peer education, when possible; and providing the opportunity to practice healthy behavior options. The first and last factors are related to the kinds of action strategies being discussed in this chapter.

Sociodrama can not only provide information about the realities of HIV infection, but can also motivate behavior change by giving participants an experience of the tension and anxiety that surround being diagnosed as HIV-positive and the life changes that follow this diagnosis. The following description is taken from the core activity that I presented at the Neil Pasiorello Invitational Workshop at the 2009 American Society for Group Psychotherapy and Psychodrama Annual Meeting in St. Louis, Missouri.

The director describes four principal characters who will be used in sequentially played scenes: a high-school-age girl; a male in his late 20s; a woman in her 40s; and a gay male in his 50s. Although they will never meet in the drama, their stories will be played out side by side, alternating among them at various steps along the way. Some details of the characters' stories are presented to help warm the participants up to selecting a specific character through whose eyes they will experience the drama.

The high-school-age girl is presented as having recently been in a relationship with a college-age guy. From the start, she experienced a lot of pressure to be sexually active, to which she finally succumbed. She attended a number of "wild" parties with her boyfriend over the course of several months. On or after these occasions, they engaged in unprotected sex. She was using the pill. He soon lost interest and broke up with her.

The male in his 20s is presented as having been involved with intravenous drugs a few years earlier. With support from family and friends, he turned his life around and became clean and sober. He is now thinking about enlisting in the armed forces and knows they will do an HIV test.

The woman in her 40s is presented as recently divorced after finding out that her husband had been having sex with prostitutes while on business trips over the past few years. She is beginning to get over the shock and strain of the divorce and is starting to re-enter the dating scene.

The gay male in his 50s is presented as having been in a monogamous relationship with an older man for many years. About a year and a half previously, his partner died suddenly from a heart attack. He moved from a rural to urban area and back into the gay club scene. He began having sex again, mostly with younger men, and not always "playing safe."

These basic role descriptions, printed on index cards, are placed on chairs spread apart in the room. Participants move between them and finally pick "their character." Starting with the provided information, the sub-groups then agree upon further details to flesh out their characters. They give their characters names, ages, ethnic and racial backgrounds, etc., and decide how they will present these characters to the rest of the groups. They might use a group soliloquy, in which they stand in a cluster, alternately voicing each character's thoughts and feelings. They might take turns sitting in the "character's chair" and each giving pieces of the character's life details as they speak from the role and continue their warm-up to their character.

This soliloquy for the high school character and following dialog quotations are reconstructions of what was generated in the workshop:

> My name is Amy, and school used to be the most important thing in my life until I met Joe. I couldn't believe that a college guy could actually be in love with me. All my friends were so envious. I would have done anything for Joe, and I guess I did. After he dumped me I started hearing rumors that he had given other girls the same treatment. I feel like such a fool. I'm glad I was on the pill. At least I don't have to worry about being pregnant.

Four brief scenes are then presented, side by side, in which the characters talk with friends about why they should be tested and why they might be resistant to getting tested. One member of the subgroup will generally play the character and another the friend as the rest of the sub-group members join the remaining participants as audience. The director facilitates and shapes each scene so that it ends with a decision to be tested. In the case of the young man, it included the following:

Character: I know the military is a good choice for me. At least I can learn a trade or something. And I've been clean and sober long enough that I should pass the physical.

Friend: Yeah, but you know they'll give you an HIV test. You haven't been tested before, have you?

Character: No, man, I was too scared of what the results might be.
Friend: Well, you could just wait until they test you, but that would be one hell of a way to find out.

When these scenes are concluded the character groups then step forward, one group at a time, to participate in a "testing ritual," facilitated by the director in the role of an AIDS Service Organization worker. The participants are asked to open their mouths and imagine the swabbing that occurs to provide the material for the oral test that gives results in twenty minutes. At this point, they are each given a stapled-shut piece of paper with the "results" of their test. They will not be able to open the slips of paper for another 20 minutes, but they are told that one person in each subgroup has been handed a slip which says "HIV-Positive."

Once each group has undergone this procedure, they return to their clusters, arranged in a circle around the room. Two people from each cluster participate in a sociodramatic vignette in which questions are asked, taken from the interview that generally occurs while individuals await the result of their test. One of the participants from each cluster speaks the soliloquy of their character's internal reaction to hearing the question, and the other answers the question with what the character might state aloud. Questions include:

- How many partners have you had in the past year?
- Have your partners been men, women, both?
- Have you had unprotected oral sex —passive, receptive?
- Have you had unprotected vaginal sex?
- Have you had unprotected anal sex?
- Have you shared needles for injecting any substances?

In the case of the gay character, a segment of his scene was as follows:

AIDS Worker: How many partners have you had in the past year?
Inner Voice: How am I gonna answer this question? I don't even know. Those times at the baths I lost count. God, I feel like such a fool.
Character: Oh, I don't know, maybe six or seven.

Members of each cluster then open their pieces of paper and those with the negative test result create a group soliloquy about how it feels to receive the negative test result. This is followed by the soliloquy of the person who has received the positive diagnosis.

The soliloquy of the HIV-positive, middle-aged woman included the following: "No, this can't be happening to me. I didn't do anything wrong. How was I to know what he was doing? It isn't fair! It just isn't fair!"

The activity may end at this point or additional sociodramatic scenes may be developed in which the positive individuals disclose their diagnosis to significant friends and family members, seek support and information, confront their fears, etc. Future projection scenes showing the character's possible life at various points in the future can also be employed. Scenes can be created that predate the high-risk behavior in which the characters practice making different choices.

Participants then move out of role to process the experience. Depending on the nature of the presentation and the participant group, they might then discuss how the activity can be modified for a setting in which they will be working, or further practice social skills for making healthy choices.

In the early 1990s I used this type of activity, using sealed pieces of paper to represent test results, with a high school audience of over three hundred people, with four audience members receiving the "positive diagnosis." The tension was palpable as participants opened their "results," and those whose slips indicated "HIV-negative" reported a tremendous sense of relief. Those who received the "HIV-positive" diagnosis displayed a range of intense, real, and typical feelings upon opening their slips, even though they knew they were participating in a drama. One member tried to hide his slip of paper, another began to cry. These participants then joined the actors who had facilitated the experience in a number of powerful scenes about disclosing their results and trying to make plans for the future.

In all settings, it is important to "de-role" the people playing characters (Cossa, 2006), especially those who have received an HIV-positive diagnosis. Intense roles can often linger with the actors and cause anxiety or distress for them or for those who witnessed them in these roles. Characters may consciously step out of the role, remove it like a garment, or make a statement about how they are different from the character they played, as part of this de-roling process.

WORKING WITH INFECTED AND AFFECTED INDIVIDUALS

The rate of new HIV infection is once again on the rise, even among populations in which significant prevention efforts in earlier years had begun to decrease the incidence of infection (Dunham, 2008). Medical and social service personnel working with infected individuals and their loved ones can utilize action methods, especially in group settings.

Staying Healthy

For individuals living with HIV (and their partners, housemates, and support networks), focusing on maintaining a "healthy" lifestyle becomes crucial. There are many ways that sociodrama and its cousin psychodrama, coupled with other action approaches, can contribute to the process that aims to support those whose immune systems are compromised.

The LIFE (Learning Immune Function Enhancement) Program of the non-profit organization, Shanti, in San Francisco, uses a number of action methods in working with its clients infected with HIV. The information that follows is provided by one of their staff members (J. Olesen, personal communication, 2009).

The LIFE Program is a health counseling program that integrates HIV prevention, treatment, and adherence interventions. The Program presents 18 psychosocial co-factors known to influence risk behavior, immune functioning, and/or adherence to medication schedules and other health routines, and each is explored through didactic and experiential learning. The co-factors are divided into three categories:

1. Medical and body care: status of primary health care and relationship with physician; exposure to infections, including re-exposure to HIV; nutrition and eating patterns; breathing patterns; sleep; physical exercise; adherence to health routines; and toxin intake (including drugs and alcohol).
2. Psychological: unresolved grief and loss; self-assertiveness; survival stress; crisis coping; grief and depression; and beliefs regarding HIV disease progression.

3. Social and interpersonal: altruism, spirituality, and volunteerism; risk behavior; life purpose and goals; and trusted social support via self-disclosure and active listening.

LIFE participants complete online questionnaires in order to self-evaluate their cofactor performance and in workshop sessions are then asked to place themselves on action spectrograms representing individual cofactors. One end of a given spectrum represents completely health-enhancing behavior and the other represents health-risking behavior. For example: Where do I rate myself on the Depression–Elation continuum? On a continuum of physical exercise? On sleeping patterns?

Psychodramatic role training is used to sharpen self-advocacy, increase listening and self-disclosure skills, and improve patient–provider relationships. Participants are encouraged to take, play, and create new roles that will serve them in managing their sometimes complicated health care.

Increasing individual participant performance in the health cofactor of Trusted Support is achieved by noting the sociometry of the workshop group as a whole, recognizing the social desires of each individual and acknowledging the isolating nature of AIDS itself.

Whether in the LIFE Program, or in other programs around the world, common wisdom of human service workers in many fields is congruent with the theory expressed by the role analysts in the Australian and New Zealand psychodrama community (Clayton, 1994) and articulated in the concept of *Prescriptive Roles* in the *Therapeutic Spiral Model*™ for psychodrama with survivors of trauma (Hudgins, 2002). That is: the work is more effective and less likely to re-traumatize the clients when healthy roles from which individuals have learned to operate are established and reinforced before moving on to their current challenges.

Laying this positive foundation may be done via a sociodrama in which a scene is developed of a debate between healthy-functioning roles, in which each articulates the importance it serves in enhancing immune function. For example: "I am Joe's Thoughtful-and-Nutritious-Eater Role, and when he allows me to help him make his food choices, his body responds with greater vitality and less stress."

A more psychodramatic approach would ask individuals to have a dialogue with the selected roles, offer appreciation, articulate aspects that are often undervalued, or discuss strategies for enhancing the relationship between self and optimal health even more. This can then lead to participants' utilizing the well-developed roles to support underdeveloped or emerging roles. For example, the Healthy-Eater role described previously might consult with the Stress-Manager Role and say something like:

> Don't you think it's time we worked together? I finally get Joe's diet under control and then, as soon as other stresses come along, you allow him to fall back on old habits like smoking as a way to calm down. Let's look for healthier stress management strategies. How about yoga? Joe's done well with that in the past.

Relationships with healthy people assist individuals in making more healthy choices, and sociometric activities and explorations of the social and cultural atom (J. L. Moreno, 1993) can help assess the strength and breadth of a client's social network. Action methods can also be used to enhance specific relationships within these networks, for example, with one's partner.

Enhancing Communication Within Sero-Discordant Couples

Role reversal, one of the basic tools of psychodrama, can be employed in working with sero-discordant or "magnetic" couples: couples in which one member is HIV-positive and the other HIV-negative. Having one person repeat back to the other what he/she heard his/her partner say is a common tool in communication skills building. With role reversal, however, Person A does not just repeat back what Person B has said, but reverses roles and becomes Person B, allowing him/herself to feel the other's feelings, take on the other's perspective, and communicate it.

When utilizing role reversal in a couple's session, it is important that it not degenerate into a contest of who can do it best, or become an attempt to show the partner how foolish he or she sounds. Ann Hale, noted sociometrist, has developed a process that she calls Double Bond Role Reversal, in which when Person A takes on the role of Person B, Person B acts as a coach to Person A until s/he "gets it right" (Hale, 1985). After each member of the couple has had the opportunity to experience the other's role and position as authentically as possible, not only do both people feel heard, they have had a chance to sense the feelings of their partner and develop a true empathic bond as well as a better understanding.

In working with a group of couples, one can begin with a "fishbowl" activity. All the HIV-positive members sit in the middle, surrounded by their HIV-negative partners, who comprise an outer circle of silent witnesses. Members of the inner circle have a conversation among themselves about their experience of being the HIV-positive member of the couple, with whatever thoughts and feelings that entails. For example: "I always feel he is hovering over me to make sure I don't forget to take my meds" or "I feel so guilty some times that I am the one who brought this plague into the relationship."

Then the HIV-negative members become the communicating inner circle with their partners in the role of silent witness. They may voice thoughts such as "She is so cavalier about being infected, while I am devastated just by the idea of possibly losing her." This activity allows members of each circle to feel supported by the other members of their circle as well as allowing each subgroup to gain a new understanding of the other subgroups' perspectives. This process can be taken one step further, into a group role-reversal. The HIV-negative subgroup speaks to each other from the roles of their HIV-positive partners, and vice-versa, providing another level of empathy and understanding.

Challenging though the work may be, for those of us who have spent most of our lives within the United States or other "developed" countries, it is difficult to comprehend the difference in scale of economic resources available to individuals and communities in developing nations. Add to that systems of political, social, and cultural norms and traditions that are significantly different from those in "the West" and the result is a context that is so multi-faceted it is hard to know where to begin. The remainder of this chapter is focused on using action approaches in facing the particular challenges of working in a developing nation, such as South Africa.

WORKING IN DEVELOPING NATIONS

One cannot effectively address the HIV/AIDS epidemic in South Africa without placing it within the context of decades of Apartheid and the struggles to end that oppressive system in order to create a democracy.

The ongoing birth pangs of that democracy, and all the cultural variables of diverse tribal communities that exist within the country, account for ongoing stress. There are interwoven layers of complexity to be unraveled, and the scale of the epidemic is immense.

In 2003, it was estimated that 20 to 30% percent of adults in South Africa were HIV-infected (Avert.org, 2009). The need for medical intervention was huge and immediate, and yet the government was reluctant to become involved with the large-scale treatment programs then becoming available due to international pressures on the drug companies to make medications available to "third world" countries. Even after treatment began, only 33% of those needing treatment were receiving it by the end of 2006 (Avert.org, 2009).

Combating Impediments to Treatment and Prevention Efforts

On March 17, 2009, the AP News' lead story on the AT&T Business Internet Service home page (Simpson, 2009) carried the headline: "Pope Benedict XVI says condoms will not solve Africa's AIDS problem, could make it worse." Pope Benedict was referring to the entire African continent. With such a significant public health threat besetting this country, political, social, and religious leaders still struggle to come together to find a common ground from which to launch a united effort to educate and develop effective prevention programs. The fact that the incidence of HIV infection in South Africa seems to be stabilizing in recent years only means that about as many people are dying each year as are becoming newly infected (Simpson, 2009).

In his book *Sociodrama and Collective Trauma*, Kellerman (2007) states: "Major traumatic events…transcend the realms of individual suffering and enter the universal and collective sphere.…There can be no complete healing for anyone as long as the collective sources of trauma remain unaddressed" (p. 9).

Clearly, the AIDS epidemic is but one social trauma to impact the South African people. Amid facts and figures, there is also a wealth of misinformation and myth about HIV, its prevention, and its cure (Alers, 2009). Tremendous resources and efforts are currently being brought to bear in South Africa. Sociodrama and sociometry could be used to help direct these efforts and ameliorate many of the challenges to an effective response. Dr. Kellerman (2007) describes models for working with large groups of stakeholders joined together in their connection to a collective trauma. The interested reader is referred to his work.

Supporting Infected Individuals and Those Who Serve Them

Over the course of several years, culminating in 2005, I had the opportunity to work with staff of a non-profit organization near Johannesburg, South Africa, called *Acting Thru Ukubuyiselwa* (ATU). *Ukubuyiselwa* is a Zulu word that means "to get back what belongs to you, including your dignity." ATU specializes in utilizing action methods (including psychodrama, drama therapy, and music and art therapy) with trauma survivors for their empowerment, healing, self-awareness, and self-esteem building.

During my last visit there, we developed a proposal for a project to work with HIV-positive South Africans on PTSD-related issues, such as lack of self-esteem and social isolation. These factors contribute to non-participation in available health programs and/or poor compliance with established health care regimens (V. Alers, personal communication, 2009). Despite the fact that a number of programs focused on HIV/AIDS have been developed to serve South Africans, some of the core personal and cultural issues are not being addressed (V. Alers, personal communication, 2009). Funding is currently being sought anew for this project, which utilizes sociometric awareness in design and a combination of sociodramatic, psychodramatic, and related action approaches in implementation.

The primary focus of the *Taking Action Against AIDS Project* is to train teams of South African community leaders and counselors in state-of-the-art, expressive group therapy/counseling strategies; establish action counseling groups to provide crucial support to Persons Living with AIDS (PLWAs); and create community support networks for persons infected with and affected by HIV/AIDS and their caregivers.

Action methods have proven to be effective modalities for treatment for adults and youth at risk because they specifically address issues of self-growth, containment, safety, and conscious transformation within a therapeutic group setting (Kellerman & Hudgins, 2002). The central psychodramatic model employed by the project is the *Therapeutic Spiral*

Model™ (TSM), proven to be cross-cultural in its applications (Hudgins, 2002) and modified to suit the diverse cultures within South Africa. Further, these methodologies address the issues brought to light by research in the neurobiology of trauma, namely, that trauma memories seem to become "stuck" in various areas of the midbrain and right brain and are not adequately accessed by traditional "talk" therapy methods (Soloman & Siegal, 2003).

It is important that PLWAs be provided counseling support over an extended period, and not only at the pre- and post-status testing period. A failure to provide this service, which is sorely lacking in the most disadvantaged areas of South Africa, perpetuates secondary victimization through domestic violence, stigma, isolation, and rejection (V. Alers, personal communication, 2009).

Receiving an HIV-positive diagnosis is a traumatic event that results in dramatic lifestyle change as well as a change in the PLWA's attitude toward life (V. Alers, personal communication, 2009). The extent of the negative impact on people affected by HIV (family, colleagues, friends, therapists, and medical professionals) also cannot be overestimated. Trauma counseling provides positive outcomes for the recipients and also for their loved ones and, by extension, their communities. With adequate support and appropriate tie-in to social and educational networks, PLWAs can contribute to a better understanding within their communities about the effects of the past on the present. All the stakeholders can work cooperatively to develop strategies to overcome stigma and intolerance. In this manner, the sustainability of ongoing participation in both medical and counseling regimens can be improved.

Project Objectives of the Taking Action Against AIDS Project

The long-term objectives of this project are to facilitate the process of self-actualization, self-acceptance, and positive self-esteem in persons living with HIV/AIDS through the provision of cost-effective, relevant psychological support and to connect with community education efforts to reduce the stigma of HIV/AIDS. The approach works to counter the isolation felt by infected and affected individuals and the people who serve them. It further focuses on training local providers, who already have connections within the communities, rather than bringing in outside providers.

Specific project objectives include:

- training teams of local counselors in the utilization of effective, action-oriented, expressive-arts group therapy strategies;
- creating counseling groups for serving PLWAs and those affected by their illness, with each group serving 8 to 12 individuals for a minimum of eight sessions; and
- supporting the creation of ongoing, peer support groups for PLWAs in various localities.

Project Activities

The therapeutic approach utilized, developed, and adapted from TSM is ideally suited to the multi-cultural South African communities, in which traditional narrative therapy is neither cost-effective nor possible. It is also more in keeping with tribal traditions of music, drama, and art as intrinsic parts of the healing process (V. Alers, personal communication, 2009).

In developing the support groups for PLWAs, at various sites, care will be taken to incorporate a sociometric selection process for establishing membership. As much as possible, sessions are to be conducted in the mother tongue of the participants, recognizing that South Africa has eleven "official languages." As participants' social atoms are expanded, group leaders would also work to develop richer cultural atoms by interfacing with local programs, clinics, health providers, and hospitals as much as possible.

The initial groups are to be trained by core staff connected with ATU. Subsequent sessions would then be offered by the newly trained and experienced community leaders/counselors, with support and supervision by ATU staff. By the end of the project period, these groups should be ongoing and self-sustaining. In her 2007 video series Zerka Moreno states, "[J. L.] Moreno always said if you want to introduce this in a different culture, you have to create indigenous leaders who can...go out into the world and make a difference" (p. 42).

To continue connecting the smaller groups into larger circles of life enhancement, participants would be guided to set up ongoing peer networks within the communities. These will provide interpersonal support for the PLWAs as well as begin to establish community education programs. Care will also be taken to interconnect these networks with networks for the caregivers. The caregiver networks will provide regular supervision and support for self-care for the providers as an antidote to compassion fatigue.

Moreno's vision, which demands we maintain a global awareness in our efforts (J. L. Moreno, 1993), is well served by the methodology itself, which lends a "multiplier effect" to the project. Since it is an experiential model, participants' understanding of the techniques and principles of the model increase with self-experience. These participants are thereby "trained" to serve as peer educators for others who may not have yet been recruited. Professionals and community leaders will be able to use this model not only in their work with those infected by HIV, but also when they present other community workshops or when developing a wide variety of support groups in the community.

IN CONCLUSION

As an expressive therapist, I often work with metaphor in exploring the "story beneath the story" that a participant may be reaching to discover. In many ways the HIV pandemic is a powerful metaphor for the struggles of our current age. HIV has reached nearly every corner of the world. It attacks the immune system, the body's innate ability to remain healthy, and, although it is no longer killing everyone who contracts the disease, it prevents many from enjoying full health. It demands constant attention and monitoring, and even for those who seem to be doing all right, there is insufficient distance from which to adequately evaluate the long-term effects. This struggle for individual health mirrors our society's struggle for social health.

In my experience, action methods can make a significant contribution to personal and social healing. I fully believe that the expressive therapies and their sibling social and educational forms have the power to transform the world, one person, one group, one community at a time. Moreno said: "a truly therapeutic procedure can have no less as its objective than the whole of mankind" (1993). In a world beset with trauma, yet where hope still survives, we can utilize sociodrama, psychodrama, sociometry, and related action methods to:

■ heal the healers who dedicate their lives to the service of others;
■ educate ourselves and each other in how to make choices that are more sane;

■ work with those infected and affected by HIV and other life-altering conditions; and

■ combat the political, social, cultural, and personal impediments to progress.

This, I believe, is the invitation of the current millennium. It is time for us to respond.

REFERENCES

About.org. (2009). *The history of HIV/AIDS*. Retrieved October 26, 2009, from http://aids.about.com/od/newlydiagnosed/a/hiv+melive/htm

Avert.org. (2009). *History of HIV and AIDS in Africa*. Retrieved October 26, 2009, from www.avert.org/history-aids-africa.htm

Clayton, G. M. (1994). *Effective group leadership*. Caulfield, Victoria: ICA Press.

Cossa, M. (2006). *Rebels with a cause: Working with adolescents using action techniques*. London: Jessica Kingsley Press.

Courtois, C. (1993). Vicarious traumatization of the therapist. *NCP Clinical Newsletter, 3*(2), 2–9.

Dunham, W. (2008). *CDC says 1.1 million Americans infected with HIV*. Yahoo! News.

Figley, C. R. (Ed.). (1995). *Compassion fatigue: Coping with secondary traumatic stress disorder in those who treat the traumatized*. New York: Brunner Mazel.

Hale, A. (1985). *Conducting clinical sociometric explorations*. Roanoke, VA: Royal Publishing Co.

Hudgins, M. K. (2002). *Treating PTSD in action: The therapeutic spiral*. New York: Springer Publishing Company.

Kellerman, P. F. (2007). *Sociodrama and collective trauma*. London: Jessica Kingsley Press.

Kellermann, P. F., & Hudgins, M. K. (Eds.). (2002). *Psychodrama with trauma survivors: Acting out your pain*. London: Jessica Kingsley Press.

McCann, L., & Peralman, L. (1990). Vicarious traumatization: A framework for understanding the psychological effects of working with victims. *Journal of Traumatic Stress 3*, 131–149.

Moreno, J. L. (1993). *Who shall survive? Foundations of sociometry, group psychotherapy and sociodrama* (Student Ed.). McLean, VA: ASGPP.

Resnick, M. D., Bearman, P. S., Blum, R. W., Bauman, K. E., Harris, K. M., Jones, J., et al. (1997). Protecting adolescents from harm: Findings from the National Longitudinal Study on Adolescent Health. *Journal of the American Medical Association, 278*, 823–832.

Simpson, V. L. (2009). *Pope Benedict says condoms will not solve Africa's AIDS problem, could make it worse*. Associated Press–AT&T Business Internet Service, 3/17/09.

Solomon, M., & Siegel, D. (Eds.). (2003). *Healing trauma: Attachment, mind, body, and brain*. New York/London: W.W. Norton.

Look Behind You: Using Anti-Oppression Models to Inform a Protagonist's Psychodrama

LETICIA NIETO

Author's Profile

I first encountered J. L. Moreno's sociodrama and psychodrama in the library, as a young person in Mexico. After completing my studies in the United States, as a professor and professional, my interest in psychodrama, sociodrama, and other expressive therapies became a cornerstone of my work because these approaches flowed naturally into the orientation towards personal and social transformation. They informed my early work with incarcerated youth and college students—especially in the residence halls—dealing with addiction, foster youth, and members of marginalized communities, including displaced, migrant, and immigrant communities. I have benefited from guidance and training from individuals in the United States such as Ann Hale, John Mosher, Brigid Mosher, and Jonathan Fox. Also, I gained greatly from colleagues and trainers in Mexico, including María Elena Sánchez Azuara, and Rafael Pérez Silva. Reflecting on more than two decades of work developing anti-oppression and social justice models and consulting for community empowerment, I see that sociodramatic and psychodramatic methods, expressive arts techniques, and Playback Theater have been key to my most successful contributions to anti-oppression education. As a professor teaching in a graduate program in counseling psychology, I bring these influ-

ences into my work with students about to enter the field of psychotherapy.

Leticia Nieto, PsyD, is known for her work with marginalized groups. Working as a pioneer in the area of racism and oppression, she is known for her innovative methods, which represent the latest techniques and research combined in an original and comprehensive body of work. She works and teaches both in the United States and in Mexico, as a full professor at St. Martin's University, where she received the Outstanding Faculty of the Year Award for her work in the Masters in Counseling Psychology Program. She is also a faculty member at the Escuela Europea de Psicodrama en Mexico, as well as the International Trauma Treatment Program. She is a member of the International Playback Theatre Network, as well as the American Association of Marriage and Family Therapists.

INTRODUCTION

Jacob L. Moreno inspires me as a psychodramatist and as an anti-oppression educator. Moreno's early work with refugees and with sex workers in Vienna demonstrates his concern with the stigmatized and persecuted (Marineau, 1989). Haworth (1998) emphasizes that "Moreno developed psychodrama along with sociometry, sociodrama and group psychotherapy as ways of addressing social as well as personal issues" (p. 16). I embrace that vision. Here I describe an example of psycho- and socio-dramatic work informed by analysis of the social forces resulting from a person's social group memberships. My objective is to show Morenian approaches used in an integrated way that addresses social and personal issues.

There is broad agreement about areas of social membership that are overvalued and those that are marginalized. Looking for an integrated structure for the groups impacted by such social conditioning, one finds helpful volumes moving from focus on a single particular group to those bringing together several. For instance, the anthology *Race, Class and Gender* (Andersen & Collins, 2001) gives good coverage of key concepts named in its title. Adams, Bell, and Griffin (1997), in *Teaching for Diversity and Social Justice*, along with Adams et al.'s (2000) *Readings for Diversity and Social Justice*, offer material for a curriculum on racism, anti-Semitism, sexism, heterosexism, ableism, and classism. Sue and Sue (2003) break down the central section of their widely used text into counseling African Americans, American Indians and Alaskan Natives, Asian Americans, Hispanic/Latino Americans, individuals of multi-racial descent, sexual minorities, elderly clients, women, and individuals with disabilities. The extent of their survey signals the complexity of considerations for practitioners.

I adopt Pamela Hays' comprehensive model presented in *Addressing Cultural Complexities in Practice: A Framework for Clinicians and Counselors* (2001). Her AD(d)RESSING structure draws from guidelines of U.S. and Canadian professional organizations designed to "focus practitioners['] attention on those groups that have traditionally been neglected" (p. 4). Her language and use of categorization may not be familiar to the reader who finds new territory in unpacking the multi-dimensional social influences on identity. For the work of anti-oppression, this structure is helpful both to the client groups and to the director of active groups. By discussing together age, disability, religion, ethnicity, socioeconomic status, sexual orientation, indigenous heritage, national origin, and gender, she reminds us to first remain alert to the full range of memberships our clients may have, and second to consider the influence on individuals with a number of intersecting memberships from this list. AD(d)RESSING is a mnemonic device for these social categories. This framework provides concrete, sociodramatic information for the director's role choices in anti-oppression work.

ANTI-OPPRESSION MODELS

What follows is an example of psychodramatic work that identifies and supports those parts of the protagonist identified with socially marginalized groups. I describe the model I use to illuminate social memberships that are either marginalized or granted privilege in the United States today. I also provide an overview of the map of skill sets I assembled to guide clinicians in negotiating these memberships. I will use these maps to explore a clinical example illustrating psychodrama that addresses social transformation.

Each of us lives with a number of group memberships. Some reflect our choices: we may choose to be vegetarians, opera fans, gardeners; we are not likely to face discrimination because of these memberships.

In contrast, we live with another, more fraught, set of group memberships that have profound implications. Socially ascribed memberships in certain groups based on gender, ethnicity, social class, and other identifications become triggers for us to experience either marginalization or advantage. Some groups in our society are overvalued and, as a result, other groups are devalued.

In my anti-oppression education work, I consistently use "Rank" to mean the system of differential privileges and disadvantages our social system imposes on individuals based on their social group memberships (Nieto & Boyer, 2006a). Individuals experience different access and freedom of movement depending, in part, on the social categories ascribed to them. In dominant, favored, or overvalued memberships, people receive unearned benefits along with a socialization that reinforces their Rank and normalizes their advantage. The roles people live out as members of socially overvalued groups can be called Agent group roles, the "beneficiaries" in the system of oppression. Members of subordinate, unfavored, and devalued groups receive unjust restrictions, along with a socialization that reinforces social marginalization and normalizes disenfranchisement. The roles of members of socially devalued groups can be called Target group roles (Hardiman & Jackson, 1997).

For each AD(d)RESSING category there is an Agent and a Target group. In the age category, Agent group members are adults of age 18 to 64. Target group members are children, adolescents, and elders. In the disability category, Agent group members are physically, mentally, emotionally, sensorially, and/or developmentally "able" persons. Target group members are persons with disabilities. In the religious culture category, Agent group members are cultural Christians, agnostics, and atheists. Within the Target group are Jews, Muslims, Hindus, and members of all other non-Christian religions. In the ethnicity category, Agent group members are "White" Euro-Americans. Target group members are people of color. In the social class category, Agent group members are middle and owning class/rich (Yeskel & Leondar-Wright, 1997). Target group members are poor and working class. In the sexual orientation category, Agent group members are heterosexuals. Target group members are lesbians, gay men, bisexuals, and questioning individuals. (In brief, to understand why I include people questioning their sexual orientation as members of the Target group, consider what social forces would cause a person to not know their sexual orientation; it would likely be the socialized messages of heterosexual supremacy.) In the indigenous heritage category, Agent group members are non-Native people. Target group members are people with indigenous heritage. In the national origin category, Agent group members are U.S.-born individuals. Target group members are immigrants and refugees. In the gender category, Agent group members are biological males. Target group members are female, intersex, and transgender people.

Socialization enforces differential implications in early life (Andersen & Collins, 2001). Family, the workplace and economic system, the state, and cultural institutions that transfer ideas, such as schools, peer groups, popular culture, and the media, are all contexts where we learn conventional social constructs. Membership in society involves exposure to environments and institutions that socialize us, in part, by causing us to internalize dominant norms. As a result, the tendency to overvalue everything related with the Agent groups (adults, able-bodied persons, heterosexuals, non-immigrants, White people, and so on) takes shape and expresses itself in a detached, thoughtless way, below consciousness.

In *Blink*, Malcolm Gladwell (2005) explores the implications of the IAT, the Implicit Association Test (IAT Corp., 2009). In a fraction of a second's time, one responds to words and images associated with particular social memberships, such as ethnicity, and registers either a positive and overvaluing, or negative and devaluing reaction without being aware of it. His work leads to a discussion of how systems of socialization shape our perceptions so that each of us continually makes "implicit associations." This dynamic is part of the Rank system. Having learned these things non-verbally or indirectly adds to the difficulty of unpacking these perceptions. Psychodrama, sociodrama, and other action methods are especially well suited to the investigation of roles and unconscious messages. Rafael Pérez Silva (2007, p. 88) observes that psychodrama addresses both blocked energy and socialization; "*La intervención con el psicodrama favorece la liberación de la vitalidad, y recuperar la vitalidad significa recuperar también la capacidad de expresar las emociones, sentimientos y afectos que habían sido bloqueados en el proceso de socialización.*" [Psychodramatic intervention favors the liberation of vitality, and to recover vitality also means to recover the capacity to express those emotions, feelings, and affects once blocked through the process of socialization.]

Differential valuing leads to differential conditioning, which includes ignorance of inequalities as well as internalized versions of those inequalities. For example, a woman may live in relative ignorance of sexism and learn to overvalue men and things associated with men. A man may live in relative ignorance of sexism and male privilege while internalizing unconscious gender supremacy. Through socialization, these largely complementary roles are experienced as natural in the Rank system. The roles include the attitude of male superiority along with the learned tendency in women, intersex, and transgender individuals to unconsciously devalue their group, the gender Target group. This dynamic of devaluation is called internalized sexism (Andersen & Collins, 2001).

Social convention asks us to maintain "in-role" behavior ascribed to social memberships. Someone who acts in ways contrary to the prescribed role associated with their group may invite responses to "keep them in line." Such responses range along a continuum from silent disapproval to direct criticism to legal sanction to violence.

EXERCISE: TRUTH AND REALITY

Rank categories are intrinsically flawed, based on false information, and applied arbitrarily. At the same time, the presence of Rank categories is tangible, a part of everyday life, especially for members of Target groups, where the effects are often devastating. The exercise called "truth and reality" is a metaphoric way to explore an often confounding characteristic of oppression. In the exercise, I ask group members to hold the "truth" in one hand and "reality" in the other, thinking about the Agent and Target categories. I say, "These Rank categories are false, but real." For example, there is an ongoing conversation about how two gender categories prove insufficient to describe the varieties of gender expression (Wilchins, 2004). This discussion is emerging in public consciousness with non-fiction works like *As Nature Made Him* (Colapinto, 2000) or in popular fiction with intersex people as primary characters such as *Middlesex* (Eugenides, 2002). On the "one hand," we hold the "truth" that we cannot make a binary distinction of gender. On the "other hand," we hold the "reality" that the social context is gendered in a binary way. From aspects of our language to the conventional assignment of bathrooms, we are socialized to imagine that gender is limited to males and females.

AGENT SKILL SETS AND TARGET SKILL SETS

I use the term "skill set" to emphasize that people continually increase their skills for responding to social conditions. To counteract a hazard I have noticed with my students of developmental theory, I introduce the skill set concept and lean on a holarchical sensibility when describing developmental sequences. A chart of developmental stages can be conceptualized as a set of ladder steps that we climb only in one direction, always moving up. But, as Wilber (1996) states, "No self is ever simply 'at' a stage…there are all sorts of regressions, spirals, temporary leaps forward, peak experiences, and so on" (p. 148). People do not always use their most sophisticated abilities. A person may have developed the capacity to read complex professional texts. In states of lower energy because of illness, however, he or she might be limited from using that skill and look for a less demanding book; the person may read a magazine; he or she may just watch TV. The more complex the skill, the more resourced a person has to be in order to exercise it. The image of the skills as a chocolate fountain helps illustrate that each skill is a container that must be filled before energy can begin spilling into the next one. One can imagine the use of these skills as expanding from tight and limited to wider and more encompassing. Basic skills never fade, but they can become elements of a repertoire of ever more complex and up-to-date skills if they remain "full" and healthy.

In Agent and Target social group memberships, individuals expand from constricted, socially defined roles toward roles including liberated, spontaneous, and anti-oppressive elements. The skills models are designed to help group members learn to respond with greater spontaneity in spite of oppressive social conditioning (Nieto & Boyer, 2006b). In group work, part of my objective is to guide participants to constructively manage the experience of success and failure in acquiring new skills and to be able to empathize with others in that situation. The skills are described sequentially, but we do not graduate out of one and into the next, never to return. Instead, their use can extend a person's range, much as one would a vocal range. Any of us may expand our vocal range in stages. But after gaining the ability to vocalize in a new part of the scale, we do not use only the newly acquired part; we still sing in the earlier parts of the scale, and at times "reach" for parts that are now brought into range. We are apt to spend more time using our least advanced skills while returning to our basic, rudimentary skills, even after we have gained the ability to access sophisticated ones. I describe separate models of skill sets for the Agent roles and Target roles, to explore the progress of one's response to Rank dynamics and examine their change and development over a lifetime. For a more detailed look at the skill sets and how they function, see *Beyond Inclusion, Beyond Empowerment* (Nieto, Boyer, Goodwin, Johnson, & Smith).

THE AGENT SKILLS MODEL

The Agent skills model includes five skill sets: Indifference, Distancing, Inclusion, Awareness, and Allyship (Nieto & Boyer, 2007).

Indifference

Though the use of "skill" to label this behavior may be surprising, I call the first skill set Indifference, the ability to screen out anything not related to one's Agent membership. Target group members, as well as Target-related values and behaviors, fall below the radar of the Agent group members' perceptions. Indifference skills are a form of unconscious selective perception that requires a minimum expenditure of energy. For example, it is within the accepted socialized role for a heterosexual person, who holds membership in the sexual orientation Agent group, to say, "I don't think we have any gay or lesbian people in our organization."

It is hard to think of actions that are outside of our consciousness as skills or abilities. Part of what I describe as Indifference skills is their unconscious aspect. By analogy, although I once learned to write, I do not have to activate consciousness of how to write to make a grocery list, I simply write. Many skills are internalized once learned, and performed without consciousness, but they remain skills.

Group work with anti-oppression means bringing recognition to things that were learned-of awareness, as a result of social conditioning, both as a result of and as a perpetuation of the system of oppression. Because they were learned unconsciously, it is not easy to notice them.

Peggy McIntosh's (2001) widely read essay illustrates her thoughts after realizing, "I think Whites are carefully taught not to recognize White privilege, as males are taught not to recognize male privilege" (p. 95). As she observes, the not noticing is itself a taught skill.

Distancing

This skill lets the dominant group hold the Target group at arm's length, limiting further experience of and exposure to Target group members. Exercising this ability protects group members from having to process information that could challenge their self-perception, perhaps resulting in fear, guilt, and discomfort. Distancing skills focus on the imagined deficiency and "otherness" of the Target group. Discussions among Agent group members using Distancing skills may include remarks about how much "they" are not like "us." When a person who, because he/she is U.S. born, holds membership in the national origin Agent group says, "I don't want too many foreigners in my country," the person is acting out of a role established by socialization. From a wider perspective, the effort may serve to distance the Agent group from eventual perception of unearned advantage.

Inclusion

Inclusion skills focus on the similarities between Target group members and Agent group members. Expressions emphasize sameness and connection, like "We're all children of God," "We want to transcend differences," or "Treat everyone as an individual." Socialization supports, as appropriate, in-role behavior for a person who holds Agent membership in the ethnicity group because they are White to say "I accept everyone equally; I don't see color." When using Inclusion skills, the Agent group member tends to identify with "tolerance and acceptance" and to highlight overt bigotry as "the" problem. It is fairly easy to think of this as a "skill" because tolerance has become an objective of many diversity initiatives. If we take "tolerance" and "dialogue" as signal words for using the Inclusion skill, it may seem that for some groups, Inclusion is the height of intercultural appreciation. For members of a Target group their coworkers are being taught to "tolerate," it may only be a slightly less hostile form of treatment. They are still "other" and still are not clearly seen.

It takes a while to notice Inclusion skills' limitations. Use of Inclusion skills means not noticing or challenging the differential valuing ingrained in the Rank system. Members of Agent groups benefit from the—institutionalized and internalized—consistent overvaluing status quo of the Rank system. When using Inclusion, an individual is not yet exercising the skill of Awareness, keeping in focus the facts of inequality, or maintaining in consciousness one's own unearned privilege.

Awareness

Using Awareness skills means opening perception to the reality of the Rank system and beginning to realize how much it favors the Agent group. Agent group members will have developed Indifference, Distancing, and Inclusion to support the emergence of this skill. When using Awareness skills, a person becomes conscious of and grapples with the workings of oppression and privilege. A person using these skills may feel immobilized and disoriented by emotions such as guilt and shame. Part of the challenge is that members of the Agent group are not trained to view their own part in a conflict involving a Target group. The person using Awareness skills steps into a role unsupported by socialization. The role taken by a person, not of Native American ancestry, practicing their Awareness skills in the area of indigenous heritage, might sound like, "I realize I've gained from unearned benefit; I've done nothing to deserve that, and the cost to Native American people continues every day. I have to come to terms with the idea that I can't fully imagine what the experience is like for someone in that group."

Allyship

Members of Agent groups can learn to manage the discomforts of Awareness and nurture the capacity to listen to Target group members, trusting their description of experiences of oppression. Allyship can be understood as Awareness plus action. Agent group members learn to notice the Rank system operating within themselves and others, and actively engage with anti-oppression struggles.

An individual who is biologically male, with membership in the gender Agent group, may say to another gender Agent, "We have to do something to draw attention to unequal pay for women and bring change to that problem." This illustrates the use of Allyship skills by extending Awareness of the Rank system with the ability to critique and act against injustice at its base. As greater spontaneity and liberation from conventional socialization are accessed, Allyship becomes possible.

THE TARGET SKILLS MODEL

The Target skills model includes five skill sets: Survival, Confusion, Empowerment, Strategy, and Re-Centering (Nieto & Boyer, 2006b). Those aware of the Racial/Cultural Identity Development Model (Sue & Sue, 2003) have the opportunity to gather further insights by considering the correlations.

Survival

Survival skills form the basic initial skill set absorbed by Target group members. The Rank system's key dynamic is overvaluing the Agent group. So, Target group members' role in the Rank system is satisfying Agent group norms, adopting behaviors that allow them to become as much as possible like the Agent group. Alternatively, Target group members often shape-shift into stereotypical behaviors expected by the Agent group. For girls and women, this can mean meeting the requirements of socially expected "feminine" behavior: to have unattainable weight, the right tone of voice and, especially, the right attitude towards men. Using Survival skills, they internalize the tendency to do whatever is necessary to make men comfortable.

With this repetitive role-play, Target group members learn to submerge their own, authentic personalities when the Agent group's comfort demands it. A vivid example of Survival skills is a gay man who has not "come out" to himself. We can describe this as meeting the expectations of the Agent group by denying a central part of his being.

Survival skills forbid the individual thinking critically about Rank dynamics. Using these skills, members of a Target group may say there is "no such thing" as sexism, racism, or classism—whatever form of oppression is operating against their group. Target group members using Survival skills may even criticize themselves or other members of their group. "Oppressive beliefs are internalized by victims as well as benefactors" (Adams et al., 1997, p. 5). This is the internalized oppression process.

Confusion

The second skill set for Target group members I call Confusion, another word not usually associated with a learned ability. However, I discuss it as a skill within the Rank system to illuminate its functionality. Under favorable conditions, when Survival skills are sufficiently developed, Target group members may gradually notice the unearned privilege enjoyed by others and begin to become aware of Rank dynamics. They may, on occasion, perceive they are expected to conform to subtle and not-so-subtle inequalities.

The ability to be confused becomes self-protective. With the exercise of the Confusion skills, the Target group member can bear partial noticing of oppression, while still not having the language to make sense of it or ways to express it. This mixture of knowing and not-knowing makes Confusion an apt label for the skill. Someone using Confusion skills may still be constantly adapting to Agent norms, but will also begin to notice, for example, that the leadership at work is White while the workers are Latino and Asian, or that the men in the organization earn more than the women. For example, a professional woman with a graduate education working at a college came upon a paper left in the photocopier and unexpectedly saw the list of employees and their salaries. The numbers revealed a clear discrepancy in pay. Even women with superior education and experience had lower salaries. Her response, "This can't be true; it must be a typo" demonstrates the Confusion skill.

Empowerment

Empowerment skills can only be developed when the Target group member has access to a homogeneous group devoted to their specific Target group, that is, in an "Empowered Target-only" space. This is a place where people sharing a common socially devalued membership get together to talk about what they face, how it feels, and what do to. Examples are a women's group, a Black students' alliance, a Lesbian, Gay, Bisexual, Transgendered, Intersex, and Questioning center, or a labor union. The Empowered Target-only space can be the context for sharpening that perception and practicing a new voice. Compelling need and ability to express the experience of oppression is a defining characteristic of Empowerment skills. Target group members suddenly want to talk about nothing else. Continued focus on describing and critiquing Agent group norms anchors recognition of the Rank system, once it has come into view. Expressing the pain of oppression, and amplifying the sense of voice—getting loud and angry—reinforces the new clarity and establishes a contrast with the quiet denial of oppression. A person who is deaf, breaking out of in-role Target conditioning and crafting a liberated role using Empowerment skills, may express the message, "We will use only sign at this event."

Strategy

As Target group members begin to evaluate what works and what does not, they may make more conscious choices about when to bring up issues in the context of their interaction with the Agent group, when to walk away, when to concentrate on other matters. They develop Strategy skills, choosing their battles and discerning the most effective action. Using Strategy skills, one can make informed decisions about when to work with other Target group members, when to make demands of social institutions, when to confront individual Agent group members, and when not to act. Target group members using Strategy skills align themselves with the best values and norms of the Target group and spend less time reacting to the Agent group and Agent expectations. This allocation is highly liberatory.

A Jewish person may choose to speak privately with a person who knowingly, or unknowingly, scheduled an event on a Jewish holiday. Rather than remaining silent, using Survival or Confusion skills, or confronting publicly, characteristic of using Empowerment skills, the people using Strategy skills have the role-flexibility to choose their moment and to expend their energy in an effective—and safer—way.

Re-Centering

Re-Centering skills enable Target group members to access their own optimal, liberating norms and values and become free of dehumanizing ones. They turn away from overvaluing Agent-centric norms. In this rapid overview of Target skill sets, the reader may notice that the skills have been centered on the Agent group. There is a set of skills to "Survive" Agent advantages and "Confusion" about Agent norms. Individuals become "Empowered" facing oppression, and become "Strategic" about coping with Agent supremacy. In contrast, Re-Centering is the skill of living with a different center, without Agent-normed references. In this model, the first three Agent skill sets (Indifference, Distancing, and Inclusion) and the first two Target skill sets (Survival and Confusion) display the limited responses of a conserved, dehumanizing Agent or Target role that is based on a person's social group membership. There also is an opportunity to craft emergent and spontaneous roles by using the last two Agent skill sets (Awareness and Allyship) and the last three Target skill sets (Empowerment, Strategy, and Re-Centering).

In a role created by their use of Re-Centering skills, Target group members appear to an observer as simply living. But though it looks simple, it takes tremendous energy to live with equilibrium, compassion, and groundedness in the face of oppression. An adolescent who is using Re-Centering skills may expand their role to include wisdom, personal power, and equanimity. Organizing with other members of the same Target group, this adolescent may guide the group to selectively include only a few adults in a decision-making process and gradually learn to function independently.

GROUNDWORK: A PSYCHODRAMATIC WARM-UP USING THE RANK MODEL

The group engages in inquiry using the AD(d)RESSING chart and Target and Agent skills. The group's familiarity with the models as well as their common interest in developing new skill sets forms the groundwork needed to allow the participants to disclose elements of their socialization.

A warm-up informed by sociometry and the AD(d)RESSING elements is created in the group space. Designating nine lines across the room creates a "map" of memberships. Each line represents a different category: age, disability, religious culture, ethnicity, sexual orientation, social class, indigenous heritage, national origin, and gender. As participants step onto each line, they are asked to evaluate whether they have been ascribed Target or Agent membership that category. If members of the Agent group, they step to the right. If members of the Target group, they step to the left. The director asks participants to speak one phrase from the voice of each specific social membership in order to explore it.

For example, on the "age line" of the map, a participant may step onto the line and, determining that he/she is over the age of 18 and under the age of 64, discovers that his/her age-group assignment is as a member of the age Agent group, a beneficiary of ageism. The director then invites the participant to step to the right, and inhabit fully what it means to be a member of the group called "Adults," speaking one line from that voice. Through the psychodramatic technique of soliloquy (Marineau, 1989), the protagonist can be invited to list unearned advantages that come with that membership.

The participant might say, "I didn't realize how little I have to think about advantages I'm offered simply by being over 18 years old." Using the interview, the exploration continues with questions like "Where did you learn what it means to be an adult?" or "What are the positive and negative aspects of this role?" or "What part of the role feels like it is contaminated with adult supremacy?" After initial exploration, the director may work in this way through all of the nine memberships. Over time each participant can explore the membership map as it applies to him/her and witness how it applies to other group members. In each category she/he will have different role baggage. The director can also observe which of the AD(d)RESSING channels are and are not activated with an emotional charge in that moment.

Even in this simple inquiry, someone with Agent Rank may practice skills that go beyond their current skills development by beginning to examine how privilege informs his/her worldview and experience. A member of the Target group may begin to voice, in a protected space, "I've experienced injustice in this area."

Traveling the map is a concretization of the participant's social membership profile, letting them experience it in the space in an embodied way. If auxiliaries are used to hold each of the AD(d)RESSING roles, the participant can witness his/her social profile. As the activation continues, the participant may be asked to address one category with more depth, as a possible starting point for a psychodrama.

In my experience as a director, this kind of work demands that the director check carefully with the protagonist when an auxiliary repeats her lines, asking, "Is that right?" for example, and to reverse roles again to improve the auxiliary's representation, if necessary. Since the protagonist may be discovering a new language as the work deepens; informing and shaping the auxiliary's tone and feeling when speaking is important.

EXAMPLE OF PSYCHODRAMATIC WORK: GINA

The following section will illustrate how the anti-oppression models support marginalized aspects of the protagonist's Target memberships, create awareness of unfair advantage in her Agent memberships, and can help to access more resourced skills. The descriptions that follow represent a composite. However, in order to keep the description authentic, key elements of the narrative have a factual basis in one participant's story and appear in an altered form to protect privacy.

Gina, the protagonist in these sessions, is a creative, intelligent, charismatic, and accomplished person. As a person in her 30s, who does not live with disabilities, raised Catholic, a member of the middle class, she carries Agent memberships in the categories of age, disability, religion, and social class. At the same time, as a Pacific Islander with indigenous ancestry, as a bisexual, immigrant woman, she carries Target memberships in the categories of ethnicity, sexual orientation, indigenous heritage, national origin, and gender. As director, I remained aware that all of these Agent and Target group memberships are elements of her socialization, even though they are not each specifically referenced in the discussion below.

Gina's Work on Gender and Her Maternal Ancestors

Gina chooses to engage on the gender channel of her map of memberships. The director asks her to speak from the voice related to gender Target group membership. Gina says, with some energy, that she is "sick and tired of being dismissed." The director asks who is dismissing her. Gina replies that she is talking to men from her workplace. Through role reversal, Gina explores the feeling of being dismissed and having her knowledge discounted. Having Gina reverse roles with the men from her workplace, the director asks the auxiliary serving as Gina to say, "I'm sick and tired of being dismissed." Gina, in the role of the men at work, says, "I don't know what you're talking about."

Using the skill sets model, we can assess that Gina is using Empowerment skills. She has become disturbed by the status quo of her experience as a gender Target group member and is voicing her anger. In this exchange, the men's message stemming from Agent group socialization evidences Indifference skills in failing to register oppressive dynamics.

The work deepens as the anger stemming from Gina's experiences in the workplace is exposed. The emerging responses include feeling that her professional standing and input is less noticed and valued than that of her male counterparts. Among her reactions is a feeling of being unsure what to do. She is a physically slight woman and one of her questions is, "Should I get bigger, get louder, get nastier, get rougher?"

Another aspect of her experience includes being objectified and scrutinized in a sexualized manner, sometimes blatantly, but most of the time, covertly. She remembers these actions vividly, but her reactions waver between "Should I complain and insist on it all stopping?" and responses like "If that's how it is here, I should just work it. You're looking at my breasts—I'll wear something tighter tomorrow! Then I'll get the budget for the program I want to run!"

Her impulse to accommodate the men's reactions some of the time and, at other times, to look for ways to live with dehumanizing stereotypes in order to achieve her goals, reflects Survival skills. In order to keep her job, she feels that she needs to accept the situation. Her anger is mixed with uncertainty about whether to say aloud that the experience is toxic to her; this is evidence of Confusion skills. When she voices anger at the mistreatment, she accesses Empowerment skills.

Gina changes from crying to angry and crying. The director asks Gina to describe what is happening. Gina replies that she was thinking about her mother. At this point, we have a clear direction for a psychodrama, and it is time for another scene. My preference, with an appropriately sized group is to not de-role auxiliaries completely at this point. I would ask them to sit to one side, not on the stage, but not in the audience space.

Gina describes her mother as quiet, complacent, and compliant. She says she was "run over" by males—both the men in the previous generation, her father, uncles, and grandfather, and men in her own generation: brothers and husband. She felt the same way about the next generation, stating that her sons were often "running roughshod" over her. Through role reversal, the director interviews the mother with an eye to eliciting the messages she gave to Gina about what it is to be female. The mother's lesson can be summarized as, "The way to endure is to roll over, keep quiet, and keep to yourself." Gina experienced her mother as having quiet endurance in challenging circumstances. However, Gina did not feel she received guidance to help her own task of finding strength in tough situations.

In the interview, Gina's mother speaks of her own mother. The director asks Gina if she is interested in speaking with her grandmother. Gina responds that she needs to connect with seven generations. Working with the figures of all seven (Gina, her mother, and five maternal figures beyond), the psychodrama moved past personal memory, past her grandmother, to more archetypal female figures. European, Asian, and indigenous qualities emerged. Like a Greek chorus, they invoked conflicting messages about the role of a woman in the world, about beauty, about what a woman should or should not accomplish, how a woman should carry herself, and what she ought to care about.

These figures and their ideas represent a composite of Gina's internalized sense of what it means to be a woman. The director works to understand the gender role socialization embedded in these messages. Even though we entered into the work looking at gender, all nine elements of the AD(d)RESSING framework are active. Using the framework helps keep a focus on the truth that Gina's socialization as a Pacific Islander, embodied in her female ancestors' "voices," includes the history of colonization of the indigenous people by Europeans, as well as gender history, among other forces.

Through role reversals, Gina engages and dialogues with each of seven generations in her maternal line. At the final exchange, Gina tells us this work is completed. The director guides her back through each of the ancestral roles and asks her to offer them a healing word and, if she wishes, a word of understanding. This set of steps brings her back to her mother. At the end of a longer exchange with her mother, Gina speaks in a soliloquy: "I see why you made the choices you made; I realize that you didn't have options that I get to try. I am discovering a huge forgiveness. I see that you preserved the line for me in a secret way that lets me have a different fullness of living."

The director asks the auxiliary representing the men from Gina's workplace to return to the stage and invites Gina to address them. Her statements include: "Your games are so unimportant. This place is only where I work now. You don't matter to the essence of who I am. I can choose my battles. I don't have to stress and strain to prove that I'm twice as good as any of you at what I do. I'm just going to prioritize things in a way that makes sense to me."

As director, I test Gina by repeating the message "I don't know what you're talking about" in the voice of her male co-workers. I watch for signs of further resonance of the complementarity of roles. For example, had she responded to the men with "I'm talking about how you treat me badly and don't show respect! I'm talking about how much I have to put up with!" she would have been using Empowerment skills in response to the Indifference skills of the men. Instead, at the conclusion of the psychodrama, Gina's comments demonstrate that she is practicing Strategy skills.

Gina's Father, Her Adolescent Self, and Issues of National Origin

In another session, the director uses warm-ups that include the map of social memberships based on the AD(d)RESSING categories. Gina is selected to work and enters through the channel of National Origin. As she faces the auxiliary representing her National Origin Target membership, the director invites her to reverse roles. Gina speaks from her voice as an immigrant, saying, "I don't know what I'm doing here. I don't have a choice. I was two years old when we came. I don't belong here. Worse, I don't belong there either. I don't know how to be. I don't know who I am."

The director returns Gina to her original position, facing the auxiliary representing her immigrant experience, and asks her to speak to the part of herself represented by the auxiliary. Gina supports her: "No, you really don't know who you are or how to belong. No wonder! I don't know how to help you. I don't know what to do for you. I just wish you weren't there." The director asks, "You wish your immigrant part just didn't exist?" Gina replies, "Yeah," and the director says, "Tell her." Gina tells her auxiliary immigrant part, "I wish you didn't exist." The director calls for another role reversal with that part. The participant serving as Gina's auxiliary ego repeats, "I wish you didn't exist." Gina, as the immigrant self, responds, "I wish I didn't exist either." The director offers a prompt, "If I didn't exist…" and Gina responds, "If I didn't exist, my father would be so alone." The role of her father is cast and Gina, as her father, is interviewed: "What's your name, sir?

How old are you? I hear you brought your daughter and family to live in the U.S. when she was two? How old were you at that time?" In this part of the work, we gain information about Gina and her family background. Using the interview together with other facts Gina has revealed to the group, we now know that her family of Pacific Islanders comes from an area of the world that endured sequences of colonization including Spanish, Portuguese, and United States military action. The family tree includes indigenous and European members. The AD(d)-RESSING chart categories remind us that she is living in the United States, as a Person of Color, whose National Origin membership is non-United States, and that her experiences are also informed by the other Agent and Target group memberships ascribed to her. The direction of the work remains focused on her struggles with socialization as a Pacific Islander, an immigrant to the United States.

The director asks Gina, speaking as her father, "What went into the decision to come to the U.S.?" He replies, "Well, things were rough, and there were opportunities for my family. A better life." The director returns Gina to her original position and an auxiliary serves as her father. The director asks, "Hearing some of what your father is saying, how old do you feel?" Gina replies, "I feel 13." The director asks, "What happened when you were 13?" Gina answers, "That's when my cousin and uncle came from our country to move in with us."

Working with this situation, we find out that more people from her family were coming over time to live in the house, forcing Gina to give up her bedroom and share with her sister, which she experienced as an annoying imposition. "These people put me out of my room and they don't even speak English." The group easily understands a young teen's reaction when displaced from her room. Using the Target skills model, group members notice that the antagonism towards the family members is shaped by elements of the Survival skill set. Gina looked down on her relatives for characteristics stemming from being immigrants. Gina's work illuminates dynamics behind actions of horizontal oppression, where individuals express disdain for members of the same Target group.

As Gina explores her experience as a 13-year-old more deeply, she reveals another important element. "Dad decided I needed to go 'home' so I would learn once and for all what it means to be from there, and really be part of this family." The director guides Gina and the auxiliary serving as her father through the scenes of the trip. To complete this trip in the psychodrama, the director uses surplus reality (Moreno, Blomkvist, & Rützel, 2000) to help Gina find what she needs. She reveals that at that age she hated her birthplace. Deprecation of one's Target group is characteristic of the Survival skills. She remembered a heightened experience of not fitting in, despite her family's welcome and the acceptance she received from the residents of her home country. Still, the trip made a compelling impression.

Gina registered the trip as an ambiguous experience and a reference point. In work with others in a similar situation, structuring the psychodrama around a ritual of retrieval has been helpful (Mosher, 2000). The director has Gina cast an auxiliary to serve as the split-off part of herself, the 13-year-old Gina who has been living in her home country all this time.

Acting out the return plane trip using surplus reality, Gina travels with her father and the 13-year-old part of herself. They return to the United States. The director asks, "Where is the 13-year-old going to live? Do you have to share a room?" Gina laughs. The director asks, "What is it going to be like having this 13-year-old with you now?...This 13-year-old part of you that stayed in your birthplace. How are you going to make it worthwhile for her to be staying with you now?" Using role reversals, the director guides a dialogue between Gina and her recovered 13-year-old self. The dialogue builds and demonstrates a sense of friendship between Gina and her 13-year-old self, ending with an embrace. To close the scene Gina says, "You have a place you belong; you belong with me." The function of this portion of the psychodrama was to provide Gina an experience of negotiating a re-integration with part of herself that identifies with and values her National Origin group membership and, in a related way, her indigenous heritage group membership. Re-valuing her Target group is part of the foundation for her to exercise Empowerment skills. The director invites Gina to speak to her father again. She says, "Thank you. I didn't think I was ready to go 'home' or that I needed it. But now I feel that I would have been lost if I hadn't gone. Thanks to you I know where I am from and who I am. This helped me know why it matters."

In a final soliloquy, Gina says, "A lot of people and events had to move around for me to come here the first time. Now, again, a lot of things are in play. I end up here and I can say 'I belong.' I come from so many people and so many places—the whole world can be home to me. I'm European and Asian and Pacific Islander and American."

CONCLUDING THOUGHTS

In the years prior to the drama, Gina had built up a successful track record in a sizeable business institution. Following that work, she decided to set up her own business. Her stated goals were to create a context that would permit her to work in her own way and to be able to choose to work with people who could affirm her and her approaches to the profession. These life choices can be seen as thematically in accord with the narrative from the drama involving her maternal ancestors. Also, in the time since the psychodrama, Gina has evolved her business in ways that require her to spend time traveling in other parts of the world. This evolution may also reflect themes from that psychodramatic work.

In this case, we were only able to show application of psychodrama. When more than one participant has the same Target group membership there are opportunities to also apply sociodramatic techniques.

Gina's example shows us how analysis of anti-oppression issues can provide insight into the protagonist's life experience and give the director tools to make informed psychodramatic choices to foster and anchor growth, healing, and liberation.

REFERENCES

Adams, M., Bell, L. A., & Griffin, P. (Eds.). (1997). *Teaching for diversity and social justice: A sourcebook*. New York: Routledge.

Adams, M., Blumenfeld, W. J., Castañeda, R., Hackman, H. W., Peters, M. L., & Zúñiga, X. (Eds.). (2000). *Readings for diversity and social justice*. New York: Routledge.

Andersen, M. L., & Collins, P. H. (Eds.). (2001). *Race, class and gender: An anthology* (4th ed.). Belmont, CA: Wadsworth.

Colapinto, J. (2000). *As nature made him: The boy who was raised as a girl*. New York: Harper-Collins.

Eugenides, J. (2002). *Middlesex*. New York: Farrar Straus Giroux.

Gladwell, M. (2005). *Blink: The power of thinking without thinking*. New York: Little, Brown.

Hardiman, R., & Jackson, B. W. (1997). Conceptual foundations for social justice courses. In M. Adams, L. A. Bell, & P. Griffin (Eds.), *Teaching for diversity and social justice: A sourcebook* (pp. 16–29). New York: Routledge.

Haworth, P. (1998). The historical background of psychodrama. In M. H. Karp (Ed.), *The handbook of psychodrama*. New York: Routledge.

Hays, P. A. (2001). *Addressing cultural complexities in practice: A framework for clinicians and counselors*. Washington, DC: American Psychological Association.

IAT Corp. (2009). *Project Implicit.* Retrieved January 20, 2010, from http://www.project implicit.net/generalinfo.php

Marineau, R. (1989). *Jacob Levy Moreno 1889–1974: Father of psychodrama, sociometry, and group psychotherapy.* New York: Routledge.

McIntosh, P. (2001). White privilege and male privilege: A personal account of coming to see correspondences through work in Women's Studies (1988). In M. L. Andersen & P. H. Collins (Eds.), *Race, class and gender: An anthology* (4th ed., pp. 95–105). Belmont: Wadsworth.

Moreno, Z. T., Blomkvist, L. D., & Rützel, T. (2000). *Psychodrama, surplus reality and the art of healing.* New York: Brunner-Routledge.

Mosher, J. R. (2000). *Cycles of healing: Creating our paths to wholeness.* Seattle, WA: Blue Sky Counselors.

Nieto, L., & Boyer, M. F. (2006a, March). Understanding oppression: Strategies in addressing power and privilege. *Colors NW Magazine, 5,* 30–33.

Nieto, L., & Boyer, M. F. (2006b, October). Understanding oppression: Strategies in addressing power and privilege, second installment, skill sets for Targets. *Colors NW Magazine, 6,* 48–51.

Nieto, L., & Boyer, M. F. (2007, March). Understanding oppression: Strategies in addressing power and privilege, Part 3: Skill sets for Agents. *Colors NW Magazine, 6,* 34–38.

Nieto, L., Boyer, M. F., Goodwin, L., Johnson, G. R., & Smith, L. C. (in press). *Beyond inclusion, beyond empowerment: A developmental strategy to liberate everyone.* Olympia, WA: Cuetzpalin.

Pérez Silva, R. (2007). Un modelo de intervención. In M. E. Sánchez Azuara, A. De Luca, & R. Pérez Silva (Eds.), *Emociones, estrés y espontaneidad.* México: Editorial Itaca.

Sue, D. W., & Sue, D. (Eds.). (2003). *Counseling the culturally diverse* (4th ed.). New York: John Wiley.

Wilber, K. (1996). *A brief history of everything.* Boston, MA: Shambhala Publications.

Wilchins, R. (2004). *Queer theory, gender theory: An instant primer.* Los Angeles, CA: Alyson.

Yeskel, F., & Leondar-Wright, B. (1997). Classism curriculum design. In M. Adams, L. A. Bell, & P. Griffin (Eds.), *Teaching for diversity and social justice: A sourcebook* (pp. 231–260). New York: Routledge.

6

Healing the Wounds of History: Germans and Jews Facing the Legacy of the Holocaust

EVA LEVETON AND ARMAND VOLKAS

Authors' Profiles

Leveton: *Born half-Jewish in Hitler's Germany, this work has personal meaning for me (Leveton, 2000). My Jewish father was one of the many German Jews who could not make up their minds to leave the country they had come to believe was their "Vaterland." When he was finally persuaded to escape through Holland, it was too late. Though he was able to go on to the United States, my mother and I were asked to leave by the Dutch government, which had strict rules against giving asylum to anyone who was not fully Jewish. Sent back to Berlin, to live with my grandparents, my mother and I, unable to obtain visas to emigrate, were left behind to live out World War II in Berlin.*

Eva's Berlin, Memories of a Wartime Childhood (Leveton, 2000) is the story of a family split and wounded by political oppression. My mother's dashed hopes for her life with my father, my own alienation from the German Nazi culture, combined with my ignorance of Jewish traditions, which could not be mentioned for fear of endangering our lives—these were themes that thickened the air without being discussed. Although Berlin was probably one of the most tolerant cities for a Mischling *(mixed race)—my father's back-*

ground was known, my mother was never arrested despite her frequent and public defiance—I also developed deep problems of identity. I was Jewish, but I lived as a German. I was German, but my mother and I were outsiders. Unlike those who wanted to join the Hitler Youth but couldn't (Massaquoi, 1999), I grew up fearing the Nazis I saw all around me. While other children were sent to the country to avoid Berlin's harsh bombing, I remained in the city, my public schooling replaced by a private teacher who had returned from a concentration camp, and adults who tutored me during air raids.

Arriving in this country at the age of 11, I struggled to adjust to a culture that identified me, with my German accent, as the enemy. Until recently, the problems of post-traumatic stress disorder in the civilian population were largely ignored and untreated (Kellerman, 2007). There were no programs for children and parents suffering from the aftermath of a collective trauma, racism, bombing, and hunger. Arriving in a grammar school in San Francisco, I could find no way to make room for myself as a German girl—and I soon decided to "pass" as an American. It was a successful transformation and allowed me a modicum of acceptance and adjustment, but it deprived me of continuity and support and caused great internal conflict and anxiety.

I was rescued by the theater. Although it did not address my problems of identity and past trauma directly, it allowed emotional expression, refuge, and escape. Being an actress in a theater company guarantees a sort of group belonging without demanding the allegiance that most other social contracts demand. The theater became my temporary, expressive family where I could express myself fully in a role, escape for a time, and be free to leave when the play was over.

Individual Jungian therapy and experiential work with Fritz Perls's Gestalt Therapy, psychodrama, and drama therapy helped in the later aspects of integration of my heritage with my American life (Leveton, 2007). Gradually, my interest in psychology led to a degree and to work that allowed me to explore questions of identity in family therapy and to begin to voice the trauma of war and the internalized conflicts of German and Jewish identity. My experience in the theater led me to develop the first psychodrama groups in San Francisco and to conclude that active, experiential work was appropriate for many trauma survivors. I joined the faculty of the Drama Therapy Program at the California Institute of Integral Studies, where I met Armand Volkas, and the opportunity to help others with similar legacies arose. I have been teaching workshops with *oppressed groups and with survivors of the Holocaust and World War II ever since.*

Volkas: *I was born in France to two remarkable people who had, somehow, managed to survive the unspeakable humiliation, degradation, and trauma of the camps with their dignity intact. I absorbed their story through osmosis, through my mother's milk, through their silences, through the flood of stories, sense memories, and affective memories poured onto my plate each evening at the dinner table. I swallowed these stories whole. I can choose to ignore them much of the time, but the images seared into my synapses can never be erased from my mind.*

My parents' stories were marked by a rare combination of courage, heroism, and a determination to hold on to their humanity under extreme circumstances. Born in Lithuania, my father was an activist who partook of and survived clandestine activities since his early 20s. He fought in the International Brigade during the Spanish Civil War against Franco, and later was the only 1 of 12 parachutists to survive behind White Russian enemy lines. As a partisan, he bombed Nazi trains and helped Jews in the ghettos until he was arrested, deported, and forced into slave labor in Auschwitz.

Born in Poland, my mother survived persecution in Paris. Her first husband became a French prisoner of war and she took care of my half-brother during the first years of his life while working as a member of the French underground. After she was discovered and followed by a collaborationist French gendarme, she narrowly escaped arrest by jumping from a two-story window. Knowing that her days of freedom were numbered, she placed my brother with a French family in Normandy and continued her work as a resistance fighter until she was finally arrested, tortured, and deported to Auschwitz. There, she ended up on the infamous "Block 10," where Dr. Josef Mengele and Dr. Clauber performed their sterilization experiments, but thanks to the benevolence of a Czech doctor she evaded surgery.

My parents met in Auschwitz, where both were part of the underground resistance in the camp. My father was forced to work with the confiscated goods of Jews who had been gassed. After seeing my mother from a distance, he managed to smuggle a pair of boots to her. During the evacuation of Auschwitz, they were sent to different camps. After the war, reunited with her first husband and my brother, my mother's first marriage failed. Discovering that his entire family in Lithuania had been murdered by the Nazis, my father came to

France looking for my mother. They found each other in Paris and, together with my brother, began a new life.

I was born in Paris after the War. Wanting to leave Europe's blood-soaked earth, my mother, father, half-brother, and I moved to the United States to start a new life. I came into consciousness in the Southern Californian culture of the 1950s and 1960s. Theater gave me a way to begin to address the existential and identity questions that troubled me. After graduating with a Master of Fine Arts Degree in theater from UCLA, I created a theater piece with other post-war Jews of my generation on the legacy of the Holocaust. Feeling more culturally identified than religious, I created an experimental theater company to explore Jewish culture and values.

In the mid-1970s, sons and daughters of Holocaust survivors in the United States began to discover each other and compare experiences in Children of Survivor support groups. I found these groups helpful at first, but soon realized that they were serving to perpetuate our victimization without finding a way to transform it. I also began to wonder about the Germans of my generation. Were the children of perpetrators struggling with their legacy like I was? I wanted to understand what I called "the perpetrator in all of us." Is it tamable? If so, then how?

In 1989, I invited seven children of Holocaust survivors and seven children of the Third Reich to spend several days exploring their legacy using sociodrama, psychodrama and drama therapy techniques, which evolved into the Healing the Wounds of History (HWH) approach. In that first workshop, I witnessed something profound and transformative take place. Participants who had come to the workshop depressed or enraged left with a new perspective, as well as tools to help them integrate their legacies of collective trauma into a more life-affirming stance. I realized this work was powerful and could help others with their inheritance of collective trauma and that by doing more of it, I could make an impact on the world. I had found my life's work.

Eva Leveton, MS, MFT (ed), has taught family therapy and psychodrama in the United States, Europe, India, and Africa for the past 50 years. The recipient of the Zerka Moreno Award for Distinguished Work in Psychodrama, Sociometry, and Group Psychology, she has written three books—*A Clinician's Guide to Psychodrama; Adolescent Crisis: Approaches in Drama Therapy;* and *Eva's Berlin, Memories of a Wartime Childhood.* She is an associate professor on the faculty of the Drama Therapy Program and the Somatics Program at the California Institute of Integral Studies.

Armand Volkas, MA, MFA, MFT, RDT/BCT, is an associate professor in the Drama Therapy Program of the California Institute of Integral Studies. He is the director and founder of the Living Arts Counseling Center, where Psychodrama and Drama Therapy are taught and he directs a Playback Theater Group. In addition, Volkas teaches regularly in Hawaii as well as France, his place of birth. The development of Volkas' method, Healing the Wounds of History (HWH), forms the theoretical background of this chapter. The processes used in HWH will be described and elaborated in two case examples.

As coleaders of groups affected by historical wounding, Leveton and Volkas focus this chapter on the relationships of first- to third-generation descendants of Jewish survivors of the Holocaust and The Third Reich. Both authors have worked extensively with oppressed groups. In addition to working with Germans and Jews, Leveton has worked with Japanese Americans, Native Americans, Croats and Serbs. Volkas has conducted workshops with groups of Israelis and Palestinians, Armenians and Turks, Japanese and Chinese, and many other groups touched by intercultural conflict and collective trauma. The authors' view is that the processes described in this chapter have a particularly deep connection with the facilitators' personal histories, especially in the transgenerational transmission of the legacy of the Holocaust, with which they are deeply familiar. Therefore those histories are presented here at some length.

THE HWH PROCESS

Healing the Wounds of History (HWH) is a process that was developed to address collective trauma and intercultural conflicts such as the Holocaust (Volkas, 2009). The impact of collective trauma carried in our psyches can often be traced through many generations. Our experience suggests that each group of victims develops a particular story that is absorbed both consciously and unconsciously and strongly affects cultural and national identity. In the families of survivors, the stories may be carried not only by the survivors themselves, but by their children and grandchildren in the form of unexpressed grief (Hoffman, 2004). In addition, the families of survivors often experience isolation, alienation, and inadequacy, both culturally and in terms of their national identity. The history of oppression leads to the identification of polarities, such as that of victims and perpetrators. HWH takes the view that all humans are capable of becoming perpetrators, and that healing the divide means working toward integration by facing the humanity of both groups and helping them both to view each other as human beings, and to take responsibility for past dehumanization and cruelty. In HWH workshops, groups learn to express and to face themes which were often suppressed in their families, to grieve their losses both personally and collectively, and to find meaning in their suffering through acts of creation and of service (Sichrovsky, 1988).

The HWH process uses commemorative material and documentation, the techniques of socio- and psychodrama (Moreno, 1993), as well as drama therapy and Playback Theater to allow group members to experience their personal and collective stories through spontaneous role-playing. Later in the process, the creation of poetry and music can enhance the experience. As the group learns to play and to take part in a collective creative process, the tension between the opposing groups is momentarily eased. As people tell their stories through various active techniques, to be illustrated in the case examples, the taboo against speaking to the "enemy" can be broken. The facilitator, along with the "emotional pioneers"—the bravest participants—become "resistance fighters" against the pervasive emotional legacies of groups in conflict. There are times when the feelings of participants run so high that the facilitator has to help the group recognize the courage required to participate and to develop ways of de-escalating strong emotions. For the facilitator, all of the principles and elements of conflict resolution come into play, including effective listening, an empathetic and non-defensive stance, and an understanding of the art of apology.

The Techniques

In our work with German and Jewish survivors and descendants of survivors of the Holocaust and World War II, a variety of techniques help us build initial trust and confidence to express aspects of the trauma and to transform it. Our workshops vary in length from one day to a week. We will describe the warm-up to the group work here and elaborate the deeper work in the case histories.

To begin the warm-up to this work, participants are invited to bring to the session(s) an object representing a personal aspect of their historical legacy. Before the group's formal beginning, group members place their objects on an altar which has been arranged for them, containing a menorah, a *Wehrmacht* medal, a passport, an altar cloth, and a prayer shawl, as well as some flowers. Objects placed there have included personal and newspaper photographs, articles of clothing, family and concentration camp documents, newspaper articles, relevant books, and many more personal items that set the context for the group's beginning. This activity sets the scene for a workshop that will include the personal, the political, and the spiritual dimensions. Also on the altar is a basket of stones, to be used later on as the objects are named and discussed. In addition, because the groups usually meet at nine in the morning, we provide breakfast: a variety of bagels, cream cheese, fruit, and coffee that allows the group to begin to make sociometric choices (Dayton, 2005) and relate spontaneously and informally.

Because the people who come to these groups are generally without prior knowledge of socio- or psychodramatic techniques, we usually begin by making short statements about our reasons for coming, either in the circle, in pairs, or in small groups.

Now that the group has located itself in its present context, we offer them a variety of exercises that will acquaint them with dramatic techniques culled from psychodrama (Leveton, 1991, 1996, 2000), sociodrama (Dayton, 2005), and drama therapy (Emunah, 1994; Landy, 1986). The simplest of beginnings is often the most effective:

> Let's make a circle. I will begin by taking on a physical position that shows how I'm feeling right now. Then the group will imitate that gesture and we will go on to the person on my right.

This exercise can be repeated by adding a sound, and it can be followed by a spectogram that lines group members up in terms of the ones who feel quite comfortable on one end and those who feel fearful or anxious at the other. Group members then choose the space that most suits their experience and share the particulars of their choices.

Because so many of the issues that arise in these groups deal with problematic relationships to authority—inner and outer—we often begin with a double circle where pairs can be formed between a person in the outer and one from the inner group. We don't access war or Holocaust experiences in the initial warm-ups, which are designed to help the group become acquainted and learn to play together. The instruction is then given for quick role-plays in which one person may play a teenager wanting a car and the other a parent. After each role-play, the outer circle takes one step to the right and new partners are formed. As individuals become more creative, the roles can become more surreal: for example, one person plays ice cream, the other someone on a diet; one person a delinquent, the other a probation officer; and so on.

Following the double circle, we may choose to do more spectograms and locograms (Dayton, 2005), in which group members locate themselves in space according to how they feel in response to a given question from the leaders. In a locogram, the room can be divided into different areas representing different countries of origin or family origin, for example, and people can begin to identify themselves and their past for the group. The groups that result from this exercise may be asked to share a sentence or two about their origins before moving on.

The reader will have noticed that we have not yet spoken about the objects on the altar. That is an activity we leave to the end of the morning, when the group is sufficiently warmed up to begin personal sharing. Photos of homes and relatives lost, prayer shawls, records of concentration camp deaths and survivors, pieces of inherited jewelry, yellowed newspapers detailing persecutions, a medal from the German army—these objects and their stories begin to form deeper sociometric bonds. After the sharing, group members are invited to respond to what they have heard and seen and to tell us whether there is anything that they might like to work on in the afternoon's sociodrama or psychodrama. We have moved from the social roles we shared in the kitchen and generic roles played in the double circle to our personal histories. Now we are ready to encounter the weight of the trauma caused by the legacies of our collective wounds. The development of the deeper aspects of the work will be illustrated by the following two case histories.

Case Example 1: Aaron Blum

Context

Research has demonstrated that the suffering of Holocaust survivors affects a child's identity and self-esteem, interpersonal relationships and their view of the world. Sometimes resilient traits such as adaptability, initiative, and tenacity—the qualities that enabled survivor-parents to survive the Holocaust—are also transmitted (Danieli, 1998; Epstein, 1979; Fogleman, 1998; Kellerman & Hudgins, 2002). Danieli (1998) reports that a kind of "child of survivor(s)" syndrome emerged. Survivor parents tended to be overinvolved in their children's lives, overprotective to the point of suffocation. Their distrust of external environment(s) made it difficult for their children to become autonomous and to trust people outside their family. Separation became associated with the fear of death, and the sons and daughters of the Shoah had difficulty with separation and individuation. They often developed an intense need to act as protectors of their parents.

Yael Danieli (1998), the well-known trauma specialist, describes four adaptational styles of survivors' families—"Victim families," "Fighter families," "Numb families," and families of "Those who made it." These roles illustrate the life-long and intergenerational transmission of Holocaust trauma. These post-war styles of adaptation or roles and quality of adjustment are representative of the Holocaust and post-Holocaust life experience.

These case examples, composites of one Jewish group member and one German (to protect privacy and allow for the description of more of the specific techniques), will illustrate the development of the HWH process, as the deeper issues of the Holocaust's legacy are addressed.

Case Material

When Aaron received an announcement about a 3-day HWH workshop that brought together descendants of Holocaust survivors and the Third Reich, he was both drawn and repelled by the thought of engaging with the sons and daughters of Nazis. However, his strong curiosity and drive to confront his Holocaust legacy overpowered the taboo against facing the descendants of the "monsters" of his childhood nightmares. Scanning the faces of the participants on the first day of the 3-day workshop, however, he was surprised by the realization that, except for the occasional lilt of a foreign accent, he could not distinguish between Germans and Jews. He remained anxious, yet primed to participate.

The beginning progression of playful drama therapy exercises confused Aaron, as he didn't understand what an exercise like Sound Ball—throwing an imaginary ball around a circle while expressing a creative vocal utterance—

had to do with the Holocaust. But he gradually learned to play. With each playful role-play, his resistance began to dissolve.

In the next phase of the workshop, Aaron was paired with a German. They were asked to interview each other and then present one another to the group in a simple act of role reversal. Saying "My name is Hans Doering and my father was a Nazi," felt awkward. Obliged to empathize with his "dreaded enemy," the process began to shake up Aaron's entrenched beliefs about Germans. Hearing Hans' story of his father, who came back from the battle of Stalingrad a broken man and never shared his pain with his son, Aaron was struck by the similarity of his own experience to Hans' experience of anger, shame, and guilt.

In the succeeding exercise, the facilitators asked group members to present the objects they had brought, conveying the essence of their connection to the legacy of the Holocaust. Aaron showed his father's identity papers, issued by the Nazi occupiers of Poland with the word "Jew" clearly marked in German: "*Jude.*" His voice broke as he displayed a photograph of his father's family, saying, "All of these people are dead." The old photo showed 15 people from three generations, all of whom had been exterminated at Auschwitz. In the tense silence that followed, Aaron was surprised by the depth of his grief and rage.

Growing up, Aaron had experienced the Holocaust as a thick, depressive fog that suffused his family's life. Aaron's mother and father, both from Jewish villages outside of Lodz, Poland, had performed slave labor in the infamous factory run by Mordecai Rumkowsky in the Lodz Ghetto before being deported to Auschwitz. His mother, torn from the arms of her own mother on the platform that brought the family to Auschwitz, survived the war with her sisters. His grandmother was gassed. His father's parents and 10 brothers and sisters all perished in concentration camps. After the war, both of Aaron's parents ended up in displaced-persons camps. They met in Cyprus in 1947 on their way Palestine. In the 1950s his family immigrated to Brazil and then came to the United States. Aaron grew up in Brooklyn and moved to the San Francisco Bay area as an adult.

Although his parents were not particularly religious, they had instilled in Aaron a strong Jewish cultural identification. The family spoke Yiddish in the home. Their hatred of Germans was expressed in a boycott of all German products.

Placing the passport and the photo on the altar already full of Holocaust memorabilia, and following the leader's instructions, Aaron picked up a stone from the basket and stated, "I carry the story of my parents' rage and depression."

In another HWH exercise, Aaron stood in front of the group and stated, "My name is Aaron Blum and I am a Jew." When asked by the facilitator what came up for him, Aaron stated he had a feeling of pride in his Jewish identity but that he still felt a danger in saying the word "Jew." He felt like a target. His "broken" parents' inability to feel joy had carried over into his own life. A feeling of contained rage filled him up as he looked at the faces of the German participants gathered in the room.

It became clear that Aaron was an important emotional leader in the group; he was willing to express the underlying, often unexpressed rage the facilitators knew to be present in every encounter between Germans and Jews. He could pave the way for other participants to follow into emotionally taboo territory.

On the second day, after a morning spent bringing Holocaust historical photographs to life through embodied sociodramatic enactments, the facilitators placed two chairs facing each other in the center of the room. One chair represented the collective German stance towards the legacy of World War II and the Holocaust. The other chair symbolized the collective Jewish stance. The facilitators then asked the participants to take turns stepping behind the chair and speaking out loud the collective messages they received from their respective cultures about the German/Jewish relationship. The encounter, which the participants later titled "Angry Voices," produced the following dialogue:

Jew: I want you to feel shame. I want to humiliate you with images and memories. I want you to suffer the past, too.

German: Why persecute me? I wasn't there. I wasn't even born yet.

Jew: My family died at the hands of people like your father and your uncle and your grandfather. They were murderers. And I can never forget, never really forgive any of you.

German: I don't understand why I should be blamed all the time. There were others at fault too. Even your people were at fault.

Jew: You Germans will always hate us.

German: You Jews will always hate us.

German: We suffered too. You don't have a monopoly on loss.

Jew: Your suffering can never compare with ours....I want an apology. I want repentance from Germans.

German: I want to be left alone. I want relief.

Jew: When I meet a German I want them to know right away what happened to my family. I want to make them ashamed, humiliated. They deserve it.

German: The Holocaust could have happened anywhere.

Jew: The Holocaust happened in Germany because Germans have always hated Jews. Even now you're glad to be rid of us.

German: Every time I meet a Jew it's the same thing. They want to know where my parents were, what they did in the war. It's none of your business.

Jew: I have a right to know if your family murdered mine.

This exercise, with the emotionally distanced protection of speaking from the collective instead of the personal role, deepened the process by allowing politically incorrect feelings, usually hidden, to emerge.

To Aaron's surprise, the Germans expressed relief at seeing Aaron show his rage during the exercise. "Feeling and witnessing your rage is less frightening than imagining it," one participant said. The facilitators asked Aaron to share a formative personal story at the root of his pain. The following is the story that emerged from his memory:

> When I was 8 years old my father would sit in the large chair in front of the TV to watch "Combat" (Pirosh, 1962–1967), a weekly series about American soldiers fighting Germans in World War II, popular in the 1960s. When the Americans would win, as they always did, my father would yell, angrily, as if cheering at a Super Bowl game, "*Fabrendt zostau veren, Fabrendt zostau veren.*" When he got into that ecstatic crazy anger, I would get so scared. I knew that "*Fabrendt zostau veren*" meant "You should be burned," in Yiddish, but I didn't really understand the full meaning of the phrase until my father came to visit me just last year. We were on a terrace overlooking the city, looking at a book about the Lodz Ghetto where Polish Jews were gathered and forced to work before being sent to Auschwitz. He pointed at the pictures and told me little vignettes: "I worked at a machine like this; my father worked in a factory like that; my mom cooked in a pot like that." I asked him, for the first time in my life, what specifically happened to his family in the Holocaust. He told me that, one night, German soldiers came pounding on the door, came inside and took his father and brother. That was the last time he saw them. They looked him over but left him there. Later, they took his mother and his little sister, his small little sister of about 5 whom I pictured with wide innocent eyes and a white sun dress. They were "*Fabrendt,*" he said, and started crying. I held my father as he sobbed. That's when I finally understood that "*Fabrendt*" meant burning in the ovens of Auschwitz.

Playback Theatre short forms (Fox, 1994) helped Aaron to re-experience his story, first cathartically, and, finally, to gain the necessary distance from his painful memories. Group members offered embodied aesthetic expressions mirroring Aaron's experience in fluid sculptures and soliloquies, monologues spoken by German and Jewish group members in the character of 8-year-old Aaron, of the Nazis who took his father's 5-year-old sister away, and of his father expressing deep rage at Germans while watching "Combat" on TV. The exercise demanded an act of emotional generosity from the participants, themselves deeply moved and disturbed by the story. Aaron's courage in his self-revelation was matched by the risk-taking and capacity for empathy in the group. The improvisational offerings were so truthful and deeply felt that they made a powerful, aesthetic impact. Aaron felt held by the group.

The Playback enactment evolved into a psychodrama. The German man chosen by Aaron to play his father courageously rose to the occasion in the role. Holding his father in his arms Aaron raged at the Nazis and the regime that had caused his father so much anguish saying, "Damn you all for doing this to my family! I didn't want this inheritance. It's been a fucking burden on my life!" Then, holding his father in his arms, Aaron whispered, "I am so sorry, Papa, for what happened to you but I can't carry it anymore. It's too much. I have carried your pain my whole life. I can't do it anymore."

In a more reflective moment, he realized that he also resented the Germans in the room. Whereas he had inherited the burden of his parents' pain, he felt that Germans had gotten off scot-free. He didn't know how to work through his resentment of this continuing injustice, even though, by now, he also felt great empathy for their experience.

A major goal of the HWH process is to help participants develop the capacity to hold the complexity of two such disparate emotions as rage and empathy. The sharing that followed the psychodrama revealed the common experiences of Germans and Jews growing up under the shadow of the Holocaust. In the group, Germans, who had survived witnessing and holding the rage of Jews, realized that they could also claim the right to their own authentic feelings. The Jewish participants felt the compassion of their German counterparts and felt the potential healing aspects of being truly seen by their former "enemy."

The final day of the workshop culminated in the projection of a future Holocaust commemoration. The directive was as follows: "Imagine it is 500 years from now, and the Holocaust has passed into history. Both German and Jewish cultures have created a commemoration ritual for the events of this time. Using art, movement, music, theatre, and elements you find in nature, we want you to spend the next hour creating a ritual that incorporates the story of the Holocaust and attempts to create meaning out of the horrific details of this time." The German and Jewish participants collaborated in using this exercise to integrate the feelings that had been opened up in their three days together.

In the closing moments of the workshop, Aaron returned the stone to the altar that had been created at the beginning and said, "I place this stone in honor of my parents and in honor of the resilience of the human spirit....including my own resilience in the face of a heavy burden." Picking up the passport and the photo he had brought with him three days earlier, he closed with these words: "I take with me a resolve to continue my search for healing."

Aaron came to several more HWH gatherings between Germans and Jews, including one in Berlin that focused on creating the rituals of a Holocaust Commemoration Day in Germany. He decided to take a year off to spend time in Germany and Poland, culminating in a pilgrimage to Israel, where he studied Jewish mysticism for a time. Realizing HWH's goal of completing the process with meaningful action, Aaron then studied bibliodrama and became a practitioner of and trainer in Non-Violent Communication.

Case Example 2: Fritz Balzer

Context

Research supports the experience of HWH in demonstrating that the children of the Third Reich are also beset by problems inherent in their legacy. Caught in a cycle of guilt, shame, and rage, their families were seldom capable of open communication about their roles in the past. Unguarded moments in pubs or in the company of other former soldiers sometimes provided surprising facts about the fathers' histories, and mothers were often experienced as trying to normalize the experience without addressing negative aspects, especially in the decades following the war. Many of the fathers committed suicide in an attempt to escape the guilt that haunted them for the crimes they had committed. Other fathers came back from prisoner-of-war camps in Russia, angry, and trying to find comfort in reinstating the institution of the strict, brutal Prussian father. Yet other families, unrepentant, secretly idealized the time of the Third Reich (Bar-On, 1989).

The generation of Germans who came of age in the sixties raged against their parents, shaming them for the moral choices they had made under Hitler (Sichrovsky, 1988). In the continuing cycle of shame and guilt, they, in turn, became the teachers for the next generation, who poured their shame and guilt on the Third Generation; and so it continues, as denial and disinterest, on the one hand, struggle against rage and blame, on the other.

Many children and grandchildren of the Third Reich describe the trauma of being bombarded with facts about the Holocaust over and over again, without discussion or emotional support for what they were witnessing. Having watched the film *Night and Fog*, a well-known graphic documentary about the Holocaust, seeing the piles of mangled Jewish bodies being bulldozed into pits, without discussion of the film, the students were expected to return to their classes, ready for their next subject. Many recall the horrible experience—repeated several times during their school years—as they explain their reluctance to engage with the topic.

Case Material

Fritz is the son of a World War II German military officer and a mother, who, having a close Jewish girlfriend, expressed regrets about her fear of opposing Hitler's atrocities. After a completely non-politicized youth spent resenting the bombardment with Holocaust images he experienced in school in the fifties, Fritz met a Jewish man who related his experience in Auschwitz so movingly that Fritz decided to devote a part of his life to Holocaust Studies and to do what he could as a German who would try to make amends with awareness of what happened. He became an activist, protesting the Vietnam War and participating in the student activism that reached many parts of Europe and the United States in the late 1960s.

Fritz has been involved with the HWH work with Germans and Jews almost since its beginnings, when he was referred to Armand Volkas as a teacher of improvisation. Only interested in theater work, Fritz was surprised to find that HWH connected him to his German roots and the Holocaust.

In Fritz's first HWH workshop, he encountered a group of Germans who had not lived in post-war Germany as he had, a fact important to Fritz, who felt that the Germans' overt efforts at political correctness had masked deeper, negative feelings that needed to be confronted if change were to occur. At the same time, on getting acquainted with the Jews in the group, he realized that he was very familiar with them, both from playing in a String Quartet with Jewish members, and from visiting the children of his mother's Jewish girlfriend, with whom he had found many surprising commonalities. Two scenes stand out from that workshop in Fritz's memory. In one, a Jewish participant played an authoritative Nazi general, with what turned out to be a humorous twist. The participant had bought some old uniforms in Germany and was wearing one that was a combination of an East German border guard and a German navy uniform, which, of course, a Nazi would never have worn. For Fritz, the incongruity was delightful and enabled him and the others not only to confront him but to use role reversal to play his part.

In the second scene, the Germans created a scene to demonstrate "what it means to be a German" for the group. Fritz chose to enact the Thirty Years War as a way to explore the many years of shame and guilt that German citizens had caused as well as endured. The emotionality of the enactment—yelling, shouting, pounding as the Germans beat the Roman Catholics—freed him to gain distance from his struggles with Holocaust stories. Reluctantly, he came to understand and empathize with the young warriors' enthusiasm and the pain and humiliation of their many defeats. In confronting the endless devastation, the many nationalities being stepped on as the different principalities of what was to become Germany fought on and on, the phrase, "We won't ever let this happen again" was repeated by the survivors. Fritz felt connected to the feelings he sensed in his grandparents after the war, though they had not spoken about it. "Germans start their own history with Bismarck," he said. "How else could they face the amount of devastation they caused over such a long period of time?"

The workshop ended with improvised music—Fritz had brought his cello—and a song commemorating the building of a bridge in a forest as a metaphor for the joining of opposites and the possibilities of peace.

Another outstanding event for Fritz was an HWH Playback performance for the 50-year commemoration of World War II, dealing with the liberation of Auschwitz. His mother attended as Fritz told the story of her favorite brother, his uncle, a navy man, who died at the end of the war, having just returned for duty to protect refugees fleeing from the Russians. He was buried with a booklet of his poems in his coat. This public honoring of a German in Berkeley, without challenge, without opposition, enabled both Fritz and his mother to take another step in integrating their difficult history.

After these events, Fritz knew that what he wanted was to take this work to political and social action. He formed the Institute for Studies of Models of Reconciliation, which led to several conferences exploring what could be done to help both perpetrators and victims gain a new stance for positive acts of reconciliation. He felt that those burdened with the fate of the post-World War II world bear the responsibility to make a positive contribution to peace. During frequent returns to Germany, he helped to explore models of reconciliation used in South America, Vietnam, and My Lai, and among survivors of the Khmer Rouge regime in Cambodia. He founded a newsletter and taught classes at New College in San Francisco. His efforts to find ways of turning the cruelties of the past into positive action for the future continue.

Immersing himself in Jewish history and culture, Fritz married a Jewish woman, learned the basics of the Jewish religion, and attended services at temple. Presently, he conducts Shabbat at home on Friday nights and, because he can't ignore his German origins, feels an internal division that is sometimes hard to bear.

In his latest HWH workshop, Fritz decided to work on this division. In his social atom, his most intense relationships were with his Jewish wife and with his mother, whom he divided into the role of the "conscious mother" who urged him to work hard and look forward in life, and that of an "unconscious mother" who leaned on him, urging him to be a better person than she herself had been. She had not talked about her participation in the war. Now that Fritz, as an adult, brought up the subject, she let him know that she had failed to protest the Holocaust and was looking to him to help right that wrong by speaking up about German guilt and responsibility. Fritz then cast a group member in the role of his Jewish wife, who took a very different position. She told him to forget the Holocaust. "Just convert to Judaism," she said, "and pay attention to raising and supporting your family." His grown daughter, also played by a group member, agreed, but for different reasons. She was embarrassed by her father's reiteration of Holocaust scenes. If he would only stop telling the same stories, she said, he would not embarrass her in front of her peers. In the role of Fritz's sister, a scientist, another group member criticized his position as immature, irrational, and unscientific. "Stories alone," she said, "are just a form of childish behavior. The study of the Holocaust should be conducted using the advantages of scientific objectivity."

Our protagonist's problem was the reconciliation of all the contradictory themes that formed a part of his daily life. During the enactment, one of the leaders asked him to stand in the middle of the two women who wanted opposite things from him—his mother and his wife—arms extended to each woman pulling him in opposite directions: the "unconscious mother" saying, "Remember the Nazis and the Holocaust, never stop speaking about our responsibility" and, at the same time, his wife pulling from the other side, repeating, "Enough about the Nazis and the Holocaust, just convert to Judaism and support the family, okay?" After a few repetitions, the leader asked the protagonist to bring the struggle to a close, if only temporarily. In a surprising and utterly convincing move, the tall German man bent down to embrace both his mother and his wife. He had become aware, he later said, that for him, the love he experienced for both of them helped him sustain his effort to live in both worlds.

The group's feedback supported his courage and his "feelingful" way of handling his relationships. A number of group members echoed his feelings and the problem of speaking out versus keeping silent was once again a central part of the sharing.

CONCLUSIONS

In this chapter, the writers have sought to understand how nations and cultures emotionally and spiritually integrate a heritage of perpetration, victimization, and ongoing collective trauma. Jewish victimization is a historical reality and deals an emotional trump card in the German-Jewish encounter. Many Jews are not willing to give up this claim of ultimate suffering for the sake of reconciliation. That moral stance and the fear of Jewish wrath about the Holocaust keep many post-war Germans emotionally stuck and locked in an alternating cycle of shame, denial, and guilt, triggering an existential rage at the world. Second- and third-generation Germans, who, through no fault of their own, were born into a legacy of perpetration, have trouble finding an appropriate channel to express the grief about their inheritance, as well as their resentment.

We have endeavored to understand how collective trauma is passed from generation to generation in an effort to transform its damaging effects on the individual and society. Implied in this historical wounding is a well of unexpressed and unresolved collective grief that, if not processed in one generation, is passed on to the next. Considering the state of the world, it is our belief that it is critical to find innovative ways to address the impact that this trauma has on the personal and collective psyche and discover ways to end the cycle of re-traumatization.

HWH programs take many forms: workshops, seminars, retreats, poetry readings, performances, art installations, and public commemorations. In addition to therapeutic processes that incorporate drama, psychodrama, sociodrama, art, poetry, and music as means of exploration and expression, each participant of HWH conceptualizes and implements an artistic, educational, or service project in the community on such issues as the ethical and moral development of children, overcoming racism, and the teaching of Holocaust history. In this way, participants concretely transform grief, shame, and anger into creative and constructive action. Sociodrama, Psychodrama, drama therapy, and Playback Theater, with all of their transformative potential, are, we believe, powerful tools for working toward this goal.

REFERENCES

Bar-On, D. (1989). *Legacy of silence: Encounters with children of the Third Reich*. Cambridge, MA: Harvard University Press.

Clayton, G. M. (1994). *Effective group leadership*. Caulfield, Victoria: ICA Press.

Danieli, Y. (1998). *International handbook of multi-generational legacies of trauma*. New York: Plenum.

Dayton, T. (2005). *The living stage. A step-by-step guide to psychodrama, sociodrama, sociometry, and experimental group therapy*. Deerfield Beach, FL: Health Communications.

Emunah, R. (1994). *Acting for real, drama therapy, process, technique, and performance*. New York: Brunner/Mazel.

Epstein, H. (1979). *Children of the Holocaust: Conversations with sons and daughters of survivors*. New York: G. Putman's Sons.

Fogelman, E. (1998). In J. Kestenberg & C. Kahn (Eds.), *Children surviving persecution: An international study of trauma and healing*. Westport, CT: Praeger.

Fox, J. (1994). *Acts of service: Spontaneity, commitment, tradition in the non-scripted theatre*. New Paltz, NY: Tusitala Publishing.

Hoffman, L. (2004). *After such knowledge: Memory, history, and the legacy of the Holocaust*. New York: Public Affairs TM, a member of the Perseus Book Group,

Hudgins, M. K. (2002). *Treating PTSD in action: The therapeutic spiral*. New York: Springer Publishing Company.

Kellerman, P. F. (2007). *Sociodrama and collective trauma*. London: Jessica Kingsley Press.

Kellermann, P. F., & Hudgins, M. K. (Eds.). (2002) *Psychodrama with trauma survivors: Acting out your pain*. London: Jessica Kingsley Press.

Landy, R. (1986*) Drama therapy, concepts and practice*. Springfield, IL: Charles C Thomas.

Leveton, E. (1996). Is it therapy or what?: An exploration of boundary issues between teacher and students of psychodrama and drama therapy. In A. Gersie (Ed.), *Dramatic approaches to brief therapy*. London: Jessica Kingsley.

Leveton, E. (2000). *Eva's Berlin: Memories of a wartime childhood*. San Anselmo, CA: Thumbprint Press.

Leveton, E. (2001). *A clinician's guide to psychodrama.* New York: Springer Publishing Company.

Leveton, E. (2005). Escaping the blame frame, experiential techniques with couples. *Journal of Group Psychotherapy, Psychodrama & Sociometry, 58,* 55–69.

Massaquoi, H. J. (1999). *Destined to witness.* New York: William Morrow.

McCann, L., & Peralman, L. (1990). Vicarious traumatization: A framework for understanding the psychological effects of working with victims. *Journal of Traumatic Stress, 3,* 131–149.

Moreno, J. L. (1993). *Who shall survive? Foundations of sociometry, group psychotherapy and sociodrama* (student ed.). McLean, VA: ASGPP.

Pirosh, R. (1962–1967). *Combat.* New York: ABC Films: Selmur Productions.

Sichrovsky, P. (1988). *Born guilty: Children of Nazi families.* New York: Basic Books.

Volkas, A. (2009). Healing the wounds of history: Drama therapy in collective trauma and intercultural conflict resolution. In D. R. Johnson & R. Emunah (Eds.), *Current approaches in drama therapy.* Springfield, IL: Charles C Thomas.

International Applications

PART
II

7

The Performance of Body, Space, and Place: Creating Indigenous Performance

THOMAS RICCIO

Author's Profile

I was trained as a theater artist in the Western tradition and first exposed to drama therapy while a student in NYU's Performance Studies program. I first worked with indigenous performance and Sociodrama as director of Tuma Theatre, an Alaska Native performance group at the University of Alaska–Fairbanks. My work with Alaska Native people revealed how indigenous populations were socially and culturally traumatized. Unlike Western theater, performance expression was not only a traditional medium of affirmation and entertainment, it was venue in which personal and cultural remediation could occur. Since then, I have conducted cross-cultural research, workshops, and performances in a wide variety of cultural and social settings, working in cultures as diverse as the !Xuu and Khwe Bushmen, the Sakha of central Siberia, the Zulu of South Africa, and the Miao of China. I am currently developing a series of performance immersions that apply ritual and shamanic techniques in a cross-cultural context, bringing together my interest in the areas of mythology, media, experimental theater, ritual, shamanism, robotics, and indigenous performance, to respond to the issues relevant to our globalizing culture.

Thomas Riccio, MFA, is one of the most adventurous of our authors—his work has taken him from a career in the theater to working with indigenous groups all over the world. He continues to be active in teaching theater, where he received the International Distinction Prize in Playwrighting from the Alexander Onassis Foundation, as well as working with indigenous groups. Unlike our other authors, he also has experience in the media. Recent activity includes the publication of *Performing Africa: Remixing Tradition, Theatre and Culture* (Riccio, 2007) and work as Narrative Engineer for Hanson Robotics, Inc., for whom he co-authored several robot personalities featured at the Cooper-Hewitt Museum and at Chicago's Museum of Science and Industry. He is the writer-director of *So There* and *Orange Oranges* (2008) and *Some People* (2009), performance works produced by Project X. He is director of Story Lab, a post-disciplinary initiative based in Dallas, and is an artist-in-residence for Lul Theatre, Addis Ababa, Ethiopia.

INTRODUCTION

Performance for indigenous people puts the everyday into the context and perspective of the continuum of living on earth. Performance (in the form of ritual, ceremony, and social expressions) gave humans their early understanding, interaction, and sense of some control. It gave humans a power by which to apprehend, consider, and create a place in the part of the earth they inhabited, comprehending the everyday mysteries that surrounded them, enabling survival and sustainability. Indigenous performance relied on culling elements from the surrounding world—bird calls, animal movements, the sounds of a certain wind, the pursuit of a hunted animal, and the feelings evoked by a spirit, for example. The sights, sounds, and rhythms of a particular place on the earth were momentarily held and celebrated. Indigenous performance danced, sang and drummed their part of the earth into being. This type of performance came about through a complex, spontaneous intuition, a trial-and-error interaction and process. When humans performed, it was as much for themselves as it was for the spirits, ancestors, elements, and animals. Place was not limited to geography and the material world, but a reflection of a gathered community, a manifestation of a totality, a system, concomitantly tactile and abstract, subject and object, witness, and participant. Place was animated. It was the whole that gave order and significance, and it healed (Kawagley, 1995; Riccio, 2003).

Indigenous performance was as primary and necessary to existence as thinking, it was another kind of thinking, the collective's way of stepping out and viewing itself. Performance was a haptic, heuristic, and psychophysical way of community thinking, making visible and tangible, for a brief moment, the invisible and ephemeral. It was a way to see and feel the deeper structures of reality: myth, archetype, and ritual. Thinking and being through performance was a practical and tactile means of facilitating reflection, adaptation, survival, and evolution.

Modern, non-indigenous performance, however, has lost connection with its origins, power, and potential—the connection to the origins of its culture. Moreno (in Fox, 1987) posited that such cultural conserves underlay all creative activity and determine all creative expression. What activated the cultural conserve in Moreno's view was the spontaneous/ creative process, which was at the matrix and the initial stage of any cultural expression. All forms of spontaneity are linked to creativity. All forms of the cultural conserve are linked to spontaneity. They exist together. When connection to one's cultural conserve is lost the spontaneous/creative is severely limited with the vitality of the expression diminished.

My work with indigenous and mixed cultural populations is based on this awareness and premise. I believe performance is a process of practical and immediate interaction and, through application, a means by which to help an individual, community and the world become whole again. The Indigenous performance to which I refer differs in form and function from the Western dramaturgical model in that it is participatory and, by its nature and necessity, interactive. Such performance demands interaction and participation for its efficacy in the use of all the elements of a community—human, animal, spiritual, geographical, and environmental. In this context movements, objects and linguistic expressions along with music—singing, drumming, rattling, or chanting—are endowed and charged texts which, when applied dissolve the boundaries between elements to create community. The templates and practices of indigenous performance, long neglected, marginalized or exoticized, can contribute to an evolving global consciousness. Coded within the form and function of such performance is the need to gather, reaffirm, heal, and demonstrate the responsibility and interaction of the individual to their total human and non-human community. Such active creation is both expression and celebration of participation and wholeness of a particular place.

(Re)CREATING INDIGENOUS PERFORMANCE

The performance traditions of indigenous people provided me with a profound insight into the fundamental functions of human performance, which, in turn, helped me develop a growing body of working methodologies for my work in indigenous cultural settings. These settings included the Zulu and !Xuu and Khwe Bushmen of South Africa, tribes in Zambia and Kenya, the Greenland Inuit, Sri Lankan Tamils, Burkina Faso, Tanzania, Sakha (central Siberia), and tribal groups in Korea. My work with non-indigenous groups has included groups in Finland, Russia, Italy, England, Sweden, Denmark, and the United States.

In every group—indigenous and non-indigenous—the methodology was refined to suit the particular group. There was no set methodology. Indigenous traditions everywhere are threatened by prevailing cultures. I worked with traces of the traditions that preceded me and applied and adjusted them according to practical need. The work was shaped by its local, social and cultural setting, the personalities, and external circumstances. Paying attention to the many-layered past and the present in terms of interpersonal, emotional, psychological, and physical sensitivities led to new agreements which enabled the groups to work together combining the old and the new. In the old world, for example, a tribe may have assigned the power to make decisions along hierarchical lines, with clear authority residing in the chief, then in the tribal council or elders, then in the men of the tribe and very little overt authority for the women. Newer experiences in combination with the general South African culture, for example, through interaction with government agencies, anthropologists, school teachers, doctors and nurses at the local hospital may have led—among many other things—to the women's claiming more power, to the chief having to share his authority with the authorities in the surrounding towns and state. Working out the consequences of such changes demands negotiation and flexibility, patience, devotion, heightened sensitivity, integrative intelligence, and the ability to read an environment, as well as the capacity to trust self and others in an environment new to the "outsider." The work resembles, in some ways, the work of the traditional hunter-gatherer.

The process of creating performance with indigenous people has no set formula. This is as it should be. Personalities, changing support structures and outside circumstances, such as old conflicts with the wider culture or with other tribes, require constant adjustment, accommodation, and negotiation in order to create indigenous performance. The work is a constant initiation, and requires a leader that can learn, improvise, and deal with surprises. The social, political, economic, psychological, and cultural tumult (if not trauma), which generally surrounded my work with indigenous people (and to a lesser extent culturally mixed populations), gave me a great sense of responsibility. Indigenous cultures are small, fragile, threatened, and much abused.

BODY IN SPACE

The action of locating and articulating a human body in space lies at the core of the methodology. By creating a performance place, be it a circle, stage, film, or other communal gathering point, a meeting place for the community is actualized. The performance place is both literal and metaphoric, serving to organize many formerly disparate spaces, objects, and actions into a meaning system. For example, initial work with the Alaska Native group, Tuma Theatre, was focused on identifying a performance vocabulary based on traditional ceremonial expressions. Concomitant with the establishment of a performance vocabulary was the exploration of traditional masks, drumming, dance, song, and historical presentations.

The re-imagining of the "*kashim*," the traditional performance space, completed the process of extrapolating meaningful codes from the traditional context. The *kashim* held significance in that audiences sat on four sides with a center floor entrance (for performers). Additionally, a canopy of feathers above, representing the universe, was attached with sinew to the wrist of the drummers and moved with the rhythm of the drumming. The *kashim* was not just a performing space; it was mnemonic for the Yup'ik Eskimo worldview, whereby humans were part of a circle, without beginning, end or hierarchy, located between heaven and earth. Traditionally, all entered through the center hole (the earth) and crawled forward, animal-like. The circle of humans was echoed by circles of stars above (as represented by a canopy of feathers in a concentric circle). The entire *kashim* was experienced as pulsating with the rhythm of the drums and the rhythm of the universe: they were experienced as one and the same.

The work of Tuma Theatre drew on the traditional vocabulary, codes, objects, and spacial presentation as containers or transfer points which (re)created a new-old place. It was a means by which the present could connect and coexist with the past. My concept of "place" evolved from my work with indigenous people such as the Yup'ik Eskimos. This concept is, at its core, the systemization of words, codes and signs (gestures, rhythms, objects) to create a deeper sense of self by way of a relational understanding of a totality. "Place" or "*kashim*" is defined by relationships, whereas "space," in my conceptualization, does not depend on a relational understanding of the self and/in the world. We all occupy many and overlapping "spaces" in our lives; "places" are different and more rare.

In brief, a performance place functions simultaneously as a catalyst, metaphor, and mnemonic for a society and its culture. In creating the place, participants take stock and reflect about their context, their values, and their particular perspective. In essence, it serves as an illuminating portrait, a working microcosm of one's world—how it is ordered and functions—identifying and affirming an individual's relationship and place within their worldview. The performance place is also a dynamic and evolving entity, one that responds and reflects, and, out of necessity, changes according to the social/cultural worldview. However ephemeral and transformable, a performance place remains a systematized arrangement of people, gestures, words, objects, time, and space, which provides the particular culture with a powerful tool enabling growth, adaptation, and ultimately, survival.

BODY

At the core of the methodology is the action of locating and articulating a human body in relation to space. The objective of such articulated action is to situate the body relationally in a space and by so doing create a place—the systemization of layered spaces. By creating a performance place, be it a circle, stage, film, or other communal gathering point, an assembly site is actualized. The performance place is both literal and metaphoric, serving to organize many formerly disparate spaces, objects, and actions into a meaning system. A performance place is a site of agency, simultaneously catalyst, metaphor and mnemonic and ultimately a dynamic, microcosmic, and tactile diagram of how societies and cultures are expressed and formulated. Humans do this instinctually, for this is how the species enhances a body's ability to reflect, take stock, and survive.

The body is the sensory receptor through which we perceive and interact with the world. Space(s) is that which surrounds us—the environment, climate, objects, other bodies, energies, feelings, spirits, unintelligible and uninterrupted codes, signs, social and cultural conventions, and symbols. Space(s) consists of elements without inherent connected meaning. Place is both a noun and verb in that it is the act of signification of spatial elements, a systematization to create an integrated meaning system from multiple spaces. Sense of place comes from being able to read and connect to patterns, codes, and bodily relationships so as to create a greater sense of being, purpose, and perspective.

Performance (e.g., ritual, ceremony, drama) is, in essence, a microcosmic paradigm of how a body lives, comprehends, and organizes a variety of overlapping spaces and defines place. For many performance traditions the corporeal body is the unifying power of recreation (Riley, 1997) with its ability to hold together different worlds (i.e., spaces) and embody all times (all ancestors) and all constructs (e.g., heaven, earth, myth, gender, culture). In performance, the articulating body is able to unify, equalize, harmonize, and control the cosmos and put this world back to rights (Riley, 1997). In the Taoist tradition, which is at the origins of the Chinese theatrical tradition, performance "is intended to cause the gods to manifest themselves in the festival, the community assembly. The liturgy thus aims at integration and order, and moreover to 'pass' all being to a higher level in one vast movement, so that the whole world may obtain a natural, spontaneous order of the heavens and be at one with the cosmological system" (Schipper, 1993, p. 66).

Antonio Damasio (1994) articulates how a sense of body (visual, auditory, somatosensory, and so on) is primary, in neurobiological terms, to understanding environment, thinking, and in turn, to conceptualize space and place. The human body teaches us where and how the world is constructed. Our interactions with other bodies, animals, objects, environments, and the sensations they evoke, are what we call the world.

Human life begins and ends with the human body. Human life is defined, and would be inconceivable, if it were not for the corporeal, sensual, and aware body in relationship with an environment, the spaces around us. We breathe in and breathe out the world; we sit to rest and gain perspective; we walk and map our world, we see the sky and comprehend proportion and distance; the sun warms us and we are delighted; the clouds drift by and we travel for a moment with them; an eagle takes wing and we feel soaring flight in our body; a squirrel chatters and the sound vibrates our bones and tissue; it grows dark and the cold passes through us and our feelings become more reflective; our emotions, thoughts and biology shifts; our imagination creates fear to compensate for our diminished sense of space; and then our imagination, emotions and biology shifts again with the warmth of a spectacular dawn.

But the body and the space around us are without inherent meaning or system. It is the felt, habituated and codified, set relationally between body and space, that creates meaning, and it is the systemization of this meaning that creates place. It is place that gives us a sense of belonging, continuity, and identity. It is place that aspires, enables, and functions for the survival of the body in multiple and overlapping spaces. Place is the ether of human society and culture. Place is a construct devised to function as a comfort, for it is a vehicle-vessel-device charged with emotion, value, memory, and significance. Place is what is familiar and known. Place is a system of meaning—a reflexive, interrelated grouping of otherwise disparate elements—creating a pattern of relationships designed to best enable consistency, functionality, and ultimately survival.

For indigenous cultures, spirit and material worlds were one and the same, one reflecting and revealing each other. Yup'ik Eskimo elder Harold Napoleon articulates a worldview, an inspirational template for my work, whereby spirit, body, and material spaces reflexively reveal the material, and spiritual, ancestral, mythic, and ritual ways of being in the world. Yuuyaraq is the Yup'ik word for the "the way of the human being," simultaneously a place and way of being.

> When the Yup'ik walked out into the tundra or launched their kayaks into the river of the Bering Sea, they entered into the spiritual realm. They

lived in deference to this spiritual universe, of which they were, perhaps, the weakest members. Yuuyaraq outlined for the Yup'ik the way of living in this spiritual universe. It was the law by which they lived. (Napoleon, 1996)

The past ways of being in and with the world are gone but not forgotten, but that does not mean they are forgotten and that their wisdom cannot be mined and reinvented in response to the new, emerging, indigenous world many are in the throes of making—a new indigenous system of place. Body + Space = Place. The work I do is about locating the body in a space and defining relationships in order to make, negotiate, and re-imagine a (new) place.

THE CIRCLE

From prehistoric cave drawings onwards the circle, and its abstracted metaphor the cycle, has served as an expression of humanity's desire to identify and participate in wholeness, to grasp the essence of being, to be integrated with harmony, perfection, patterns, and cycles of the natural, material, metaphorical and metaphysical worlds. The circle is the symbolic representation of the cycles of life and death, ecology, cultures, and history that surround and move through us all. The cycle is a recombinant energy, one that returns and permutates itself with the power of life being manifest through eternal cyclical movement (Riley, 1997). Defined by Van Gennep and Victor Turner (Van Gennep, 1984, Turner, 1987) it is a transitional or liminal place of separation where spaces can be transformed and adjusted, and re-integrated into the individual's life and community at large. The circle also meant to establish a way of viewing the world, a perspective, and in turn a structure from which all subsequent work flows. Some of our beginning exercises established working methods, habits, and, significantly, the practice of side coaching.

Exercise: The Mountain

In this exercise, the participants are asked to imagine themselves as the mountain. Every aspect of their bodies represents a different part of the mountain—the head its peak, the blood the rivers and streams that nourish it, and so on. In this meditation, participants take on the mountain's powerful aspects—its calm, its rootedness. These qualities can be used as the participants are guided to now note distracting thoughts and feelings, which they can calmly note, and let pass, as storm clouds do, over the mountain. The goal of this exercise is to empower the participants so that they can become free to choose among their thoughts and feelings rather than passively feeling at a loss.

Beginning in a circle and stillness became an operating motif—circle, cycle, return—and is an organic evolution of the circle motif prevalent in every indigenous culture where I have worked. The circle is central: from the Ohuokhai circle dance that is central to the Sakha people of central Siberia, to the healing circles of the !Xuu Bushmen, to the *kashim*, the traditional community house of the Yup'ik Eskimo. It is not just a circle; it is a mnemonic of a way of being in and of the world (Eliade, 1961). For every indigenous group I have worked with, the circle was a place of revelation, truth and safety.

RHYTHM

My experience with a variety of indigenous and non-indigenous groups has demonstrated the importance of re-establishing an awareness of rhythm in a performer's body and in their life. Rhythm also awakens and invigorates another kind of perception of attunement or synchronization between bodily rhythms and the rhythms of the things themselves, their tones and textures (Abram, 1996), what I term "rhythm reality."

The initiation of rhythm awareness leads to the re-establishment of personal and then cultural rhythm awareness, and it is from this foundation that subsequent work flows. Initial exercises bring awareness to the basic rhythms of life; the heartbeat and breath. Often semi-meditative, these exploratory exercises establish the basic biological self and one's basic rhythm. Such explorations also remind the performer of a simple and basic truth: that the self is the origin and medium of performance. The body expresses the internal-external-eternal self. By apprehending the internal self one can better express the social, cultural, spiritual and potentially eternal sense of self.

Exercise: Diaphragm Breathing

The heartbeat is an immediate and tactile building block in my work from which to reiterate, reaffirm, and re-imagine, self, space and place.

This exercise leads the participants from relaxed, normal breathing, to an awareness of the normal breath, to extending that awareness to the rising upper abdomen, as they breathe in through the mouth and out through the nose. Further instruction encourages deeper, fuller breathing to invigorate the lower body. Next, participants are asked to fill their lungs and to hold the breath a long as possible, exhaling completely with a sound. It is important to return to normal breathing often, as greater lung capacity is developed by holding the breath first for two heartbeats, then an increasing number, increasing the capacity for stillness as well as awareness of the heart's rhythm.

A further extension of this exercise is to ask participants to express the rhythm of their heartbeats into various parts of their bodies—for example, into their fingers, hands, head, and feet.

As the rhythm is used more and more successfully, the participant can express it in alternating, different body parts, returning to stillness whenever the rhythm is lost and awareness needs to be reestablished. Once the exercise has taken hold ask the performers to improvisationally create a dance-like movement based on their heartbeat rhythms. They can go on to dance with each other and add sounds to the movement. Costumes and masks can be added as the dances develop.

The use of sticks to externalize the beat can serve to re-introduce traditional rhythms, and subsequent development of dance signing, chant and performance, to the group. Such sticks should be no longer than the length between the wrist and elbow. Using the stick, drumbeats can begin with the heartbeat and go on to the discovery and sharing of personal (breathing, walking, running) and traditional rhythms and dances, to rhythms they discover in their environment. As these rhythms are shared, a group rhythm can be developed, which provides a reference for all subsequent work, becoming a simple and effective way to enable each group's somatic interaction with its cultural roots.

Every indigenous culture I have worked with has, at its musical core, simple rhythmic beat(s); many cultures have several. I call these primary beats. These beats often provide the basis of dance and performance movement. Dances with ancestors, with animals, and with spirits evolve from cultural rhythms as they are created and recreated by the group. With Tuma Theatre (Alaska Native) the exercise was very instructive, indicating the types of birds, the shifts in weather, and seasonal rhythms typical of the tundra.

As sounds are explored, the exercise can be extended by asking for the sounds of each season, as a group. The group can lie on the floor, gradually sounding together until a group sound for each season is developed. Sound can be further explored by asking performers to pick one short culturally specific phrase they would like to work with either individually as a group. They begin by closing their eyes and repeating the phrase for several minutes—in the same way each time—using the same inflection and rhythm. Then the group sounds the phrase, individually, together, dividing the phrase in choral repetition.

While working with the Sakha National Theatre, the performers suggested several Sakha phrases and chose one, "Nihau Oujugay," a popular expression that means "very, very good." The performers sat in a large circle, with eyes closed. The Sakha, who have powerful throat-singing traditions, extended the exercise into an opera of songs, with performers instinctually working together and playing off of one another. The exercise lasted over an hour and seemed to keep expanding.

This exercise also promotes discipline, self-control, and trust in the participants' own bodily authority—something often lost in our habitually shallow breathing, and, in indigenous people from authoritarian cultures such as South Africa and Russia, from the discouragement of individual awareness.

Exercises to develop the performers' movement in space involve their using rhythm to explore different moods and patterns. For example, they are asked to, "Move with strength...with fear...with love... power...confusion, spiritual conviction." Movements leading with various body parts are added. "Move from your chest, from your heart, from your eyes." In all of the movements, performers are asked to remain aware of each other, and to repeat movements that resonate.

If appropriate, performers are asked to observe three different walks of people from daily life and through their body, present their unique rhythms to the group. The theme of walking, like the theme of the circle, becomes an oft repeated and elaborated motif, evolving in increments that will be used in performance and deepening group confidence. To develop the performance, these exercises will be augmented and elaborated with vocal exploration, musical work, imagination building, storytelling, skills sharing, physical training, and ensemble building, most of which are readily available in books that describe role-playing and improvisational techniques. For the purpose of working with indigenous people, we will explore the exercises of gifting and skills exchange.

GIFTING AND SKILLS EXCHANGE

When working within the context of another culture (indigenous or not), there must be an assessment of pre-existing performance languages. Fundamental to many indigenous cultures is the notion of gifting (Hyde, 1983), which is consistent—in my view—with living with an earth that has given everything to humans. In many of the cultures I have experienced, the proper response is for humans, in turn, to give of themselves and/or their goods to keep the world in balance. For the Inupiat Eskimo, wealth was marked by how much a person was able to give away, a tradition of the Kiviq, the Eagle-Wolf Messenger Feast, which is celebrated to this day in Barrow, Alaska. Essentially, the story goes, the Eagle Mother gave humans the drum and rhythm, the wolves taught humans how to dance and live on the land, and the best way to repay them—because humans benefit greatly and are part of the cycle—is to exchange gifts. Gift exchange is simultaneously a material, communal, and spiritual act, intended to make the Eagle Mother happy, give thanks to the wolves, and give gifts to one another (Riccio, 2003).

In order to become acquainted with a particular culture, I ask the group to simply have a "show-and-tell"—with each giving something they know to the group. The two-week workshop I conducted In Zambia included performers that were Western trained and urban, many of whom were earning a living performing community theater plays sponsored by international NGOs. Such plays might dramatize, for example, HIV/AIDS prevention, hygiene, political corruption, and/or FGM (Female Genital Mutilation) for an audience of rural villagers. In working with several ethnic groups in Zambia, many of which had a history of inter-tribal and ethic conflict, gift and skill exchange was a necessary starting point. The Zambia workshop also included traditional performers who had no theater experience, but were tradition bearers, such as mask dancers, drummers, and storytellers from a variety of ethnic groups.

The 2-week workshop I conducted in Lusaka, as a prelude to a 6-week performance development period, included nearly 40 participants, some of them traditional "enemies" from 32 ethnic groups throughout the country. The objective of our work was to demonstrate how all of the diverse ethnic groups comprised the nation of Zambia. The Western trained, urban actors had little or no exposure to traditional performance of any sort, while the others had experience only in their own performance traditions or those of surrounding groups. For this project, skills exchanges of dances, stories, and personal histories were imperative. In the context of ethnic divisions, which constitute a root problem in much of sub-Sahara Africa, such a diversity of traditions performing together on a national tour proved to be a vivid demonstration of national unity, healing, and understanding.

Moving the Zambian group from the exploration of personal rhythms into cultural rhythms was easily achieved for group members with strong ethnic performance traditions. This practical skills exchange created an expressive and expanding vocabulary for the group at large. However, it is important to note that in terms of working methods and spirit within the group, this practice amplified the process of community and place building as it re-awakened traditional gifting values. Those performers from urban areas, many of whom were deficient in their own traditional performance expressions, offered acting exercises. Interestingly, as the Western trained actors, who initially looked down on the rural participants, became involved in the exchange, they developed a healthy respect for the cultural knowledge held by others. Skill sharing proved to be a great equalizer as the gifting created social bonding much like it does in traditional communities (Hyde, 1983). Also, within the context of skills and gift exchange, inherited ethnic issues (some groups were traditional "enemies") were identified and openly discussed.

From this spirit of openness, the group resolved that ethnic strife had held Zambia back and, as artists, they now saw themselves as leaders who had an opportunity to contribute to the healing of ethnic differences by demonstrating that they were all Zambians. As the performance developed, that theme was evolved and linked to a traditional legend, which showed how they were created as one people and led astray by greed, fear, and pettiness. As a gesture of camaraderie those who were "traditional enemies" taught each other their traditional dances and portrayed the tribe of their former enemy in a performance that resulted in a nationwide tour. The performance, which toured throughout the nation (oftentimes to thousands of spectators gathered in fields and marketplaces), evoked the intended response from performers, audiences, and press alike, all of whom saw the process as demonstrating a new, enlightened perception of self and nationhood.

After nearly 30 year's experience of working in the field of performance training and creation in a wide variety of cultural contexts, I draw on what I know and intuit, adjusting or creating new exercises that serve the group's needs and objectives. It should be stressed that throughout the entire process, the work is discussed and reflected upon openly, its rationale outlined, and exercises explained and assessed in order to further share and make the work transparent. An essential goal of my process is to empower participants to understand and, if they so choose, continue and elaborate on the work in their own way.

SPACE

All the work previously discussed can be considered as prelude. Having internalized the circle, the body in space, rhythm and gifting, the work can now begin to focus on projecting self—into imaginative, cultural, and creative spaces. Discussion, free play and improvisation, as well other exercises are applied. Below are examples (selected from hundreds of options) to indicate how the work might evolve, keeping in mind that it is always shaped by particular circumstances and objectives. All have been applied in a variety of cultural and social settings and have proved resonant and adaptive.

Spot Journey Exercise

Participants are asked to identify a spot on the opposite wall or side of the room, to concentrate on the spot and then to move toward the spot as slowly and quietly as possible. They must move toward their spot as if it is the most important thing in the world, a metaphor that brings patience, and endurance into awareness. Having arrived as close as possible to their spot, participants are to stand facing it with eyes closed, breathing in through their nose and out through their mouth. Once three or four performers arrive at their spots ask them to turn (with eyes still closed) and then open their eyes and find another spot. The performers are then asked to add vocalization to their movements, beginning with low breathing sounds and increasing to express their feelings as they approach their spot. Having reached it, they are to "sing" or vocalize in celebration of achieving their goal/objective.

After they have arrived and sung, the performers are asked to close their eyes and continue singing as more and more participants reach their goal, gradually tuning in to each other and unifying the song. Next, the participants open their eyes to find, instead of a spot, another participant on the other side of the room. As they move slowly toward that person, they are asked to develop a vocalization that responds to how they feel about that person and their own journey. As participants find their partners, they continue to sing together. Suggestions such as "singing" a song of arrival, journey, destination, or hope can help focus the singing.

This exercise can be extended if the group has accomplished the previous steps. The participants can be asked to join the whole group, where they can, still with their eyes closed continue to vocalize evolving a collective song of destiny, hope, or arrival. The use of words and identifiable language should be avoided because of its tendency to take the performer out of the instinctual mode and into an intellectual and self-censoring mode.

Three Movements Exercise

The group is divided into pairs of partners. Each participant is asked to develop three movements, anything they consider interesting and expressive, and teach it to their partner. Then partners are asked to create three movements each for a total of six movements. Generally a short period of time is allowed for showing these movements—three minutes at the most—to the larger group. Generally the movements presented are very telling, indicating pre-occupations and often yielding culturally or socially specific gestures. The facilitator gives no comment or judgment. After all partner groupings have shown their six movements, they are asked to suggest a scenario organically. The movements may repeat and can be in whatever order best serves the scenario, which does not need to make narrative sense. Each of the partners must do each of the pair's six movements at least once in the course of the scenario. Sound, even dialogue, may be added for a third round of development. The scenarios are presented before the larger group.

This exercise can be elaborated. Participants—no longer in pairs—can be asked to develop three more movements, but this time one movement must be cultural, one personal, and one spiritual. The participants then present the movements to the group.

(The movements requested may vary according to need, context, and objectives.) In this variation of the exercise the performer presents the movements to the group. The process of the three movements in this variation of the exercise provides the raw material by which to begin developing the group's unique Ritual Preparation (noted below). However, it is important not to indicate the objective of the Three Movement exercise; otherwise group members have a tendency to serve the result rather than the immediate objective.

Case Example

In a workshop in Krakow, Poland, several women began to discover the body mythology of traditional male–female relationships and social–cultural–historical gender roles. The exploration of gender roles, which was not an objective of the workshop, evolved when the participants were asked to play the opposite gender. The passivity of the women played by men and the aggressiveness of the men played by women immediately struck a cord highlighting a disparity of perceptions and gender roles. Following this thread and continuing the playing of opposite genders, the work evolved into scenario building exercise.

At first, the exercise focused on a contemporary domestic scene and then stepped back generationally to the time of their grandparents. Various scenarios were collapsed into one emblematic collective memory scene for each generation, with participants adding detail and side coaching to the scenarios. Unexpectedly, this process re-defined the workshop objectives and shaped the course of the subsequent work, which went on to explore gender issues and their relation to sexual and emotional abuse in a changing Polish society. One cannot anticipate what the process will provoke or reveal; it is essential that the facilitator be unjudgmental, alert, and responsive. The goal for the workshop leader is to apprehend through one's body, emotion, and mind; to be present and intensely observant so that the necessary information can reveal itself.

PERFORMANCE

After establishing the body/cycle/communication/group/rhythm themes, the work can move into any number of directions, depending on the objectives of the project. At this point, it is important to keep engaging the body. Through the establishment of trust and the use of playful exercises, bodily expressions will become increasingly uncensored and often reveal deep-seated personal, social, and cultural expressions. These exercises, presented without the scrutiny or pressures of "performing," provide a way of easing into the act of performance, like the sociodramatic warm-up exercises (Sternberg & Garcia, 2000) noted in this volume. A group may decide on a culminating performance (Emunah, 1994) based on themes and scenarios that have come up during the exercises. Projects that have sufficient time—at least 2 months of workshops are necessary due to the time, discussion, and exploration necessary—might develop culturally specific warm-ups, such as "Ritual Preparation," which will be outlined below.

The need for performance lives in the dissonance between socially and culturally inscribed roles and behaviors. In our daily lives, we perform variations of what was performed before, what Richard Schechner (2002) calls "twice behaved" or "restored behaviors" (p. 22), and scripted, what Erving Goffman (1959) termed the "presentation of self in everyday life" (p. 28). For Jung (1998), the archetype was fundamental to identity, an individual's "life script." The individual's archetype was for Jung only the beginning of corresponding thought forms, "in myth, laws, social, cultural, political, religious, economic patterns" (Segal, 1998).

Working in urban (indigenous and mixed cultural) contexts, I have often applied a variety of archetypal explorations to explore cultural and social roles. An example follows.

Exercise: Cultural Archetypes

The participants are asked to choose an archetype specific to their culture. Sources will vary, of course. With indigenous people, archetypes are usually derived from dance, ritual, mythology, and daily behaviors. In previous workshops, for example, the Raven and Coyote figures were chosen by Native Americans, Krishna by Indians, the Warrior by Zulus, and the hunter by Inuits.

The leader helps the participant develop the archetype's movement by asking questions such as: How does the character move? How is the body aligned? Bent? Straight? Where does the archetype's energy come from? Where is its center? What part of the body does it lead from? What is its attitude toward the world? Is it happy? Sad? Angry? Explore a variety of emotions. What is it that attracts you to the archetype? How are you similar? Different? What comforts you about the archetype? Frightens you? If the participant's images and ideas about the archetypes are vague ask the participant to expand and extrapolate from what he/she knows. Several different archetype explorations may occur in one session. The facilitator should note which archetypes have a special connection with individual performers. This exercise provides a psychophysical foundation from which performance and/or characters may develop.

Recent archetypal explorations (with mixed and non-indigenous groups, among them the Chicago Director's Lab in 2008) have included the non-gendered: the Lover, the Hero, the Warrior, the Outlaw, the Innocent, the Explorer, the Ruler, the Magician, the Jester, the Caregiver, the Creator, and the Sage. These explorations are centered on defining the archetype through a series of questions and psychophysical responses/explorations. The questions are: What is your core desire? What is your goal? What is your fear? What is your strategy? What is your gift?

The archetype of the Explorer, for example, has brought the following characteristics: freedom to explore the self with the goal of experiencing a more authentic and fulfilling life, the fear of being trapped in emptiness, the strategy of embarking on a journey to seek out new things, the trap of aimless wandering, the possibility of becoming a misfit, the gift of autonomy, the ambition to become and remain true to one's own soul. Eliade (1961) wrote that archetypes reveal a striving to transcend one's own local, provincial history and to recover some "Great Time." I have found that archetypal work provides the participant with an opening toward self-analysis in the context of myths, stories, primary modes of behavior, and social-cultural signifiers can be enacted.

Cultural and archetypal explorations lead to the articulation of a performance vocabulary from which subsequent performance explorations derive. The establishment of a vocabulary is an important step in reiterating and reaffirming a group's shared and collective identity, laying the groundwork for further work.

Exercise: Creating Elemental Forms

In this exercise, participants study one specific group of people—they may choose their own culture or another. Both group and subgroups are identified (see Figure 7.1). For example, if the group decides to study religious archetypes, subgroups may be Pentecostal Baptists, Hindus, Catholics, Moslems, and so on. The study should be limited to those groups that can be studied in person and/or by way of field research and/or media/video. Participants are asked to identify typical movements, gestures, vocalizations, objects, and use of space for their characters. Written and video notation is recommended. This exercise has been particularly useful assisting indigenous people that have been urbanized to revisit and examine their own culture and traditions through movements that may be remembered, but not in the context of their original meaning. Combining and reinventing the new and old can create a performance expression that expresses a particular present need in the context of tradition.

RITUAL PREPARATION

Ritual Preparation is a term that I coined when the processes I used repeatedly resulted in ritual-like actions. Bodily movements, gestures, actions, and vocalizations, combined with rhythm, create a sort of coded expression of a culture (see Figure 7.2). Their charged meanings reveal a living sense of the culture, its place and worldview. To express oneself through this coded language is to actively live the culture. For marginalized indigenous groups, such participation is empowering, for it is a psychophysical model of their way of being in the world.

In my experience, because it is an expression of their culture, the work of recovering and reworking traditional codes serves a social/cultural therapeutic value. The performers need to make it their own by re-engaging and reconfiguring the performance elements into a living example of a culture's vitality. A performance produced by this participatory process can serve as a demonstrable project the group has created, which can be joined by the greater community as audience.

The reaction of a Yup'ik Eskimo audience member demonstrates how one of the audience members—having negotiated the multiple spaces of his modern and traditional world—was able to enter the liminal place of performance.

Figure 7.1. Awakening section at the opening of the Ritual Preparation developed with Tùkak̓ Teatret, a Greenland Inuit group, Fjaltring, Denmark.

Figure 7.2. Praising the sky section at the opening of the Ritual Preparation developed with the Metamorphosis Theatre, St Petersburg, Russia.

The process of Ritual Preparation becomes the group's diagramming of place with the goal of public performance. Ritual Preparation serves to organize previously explored performative elements into an affirmative act uniting self and culture. The participants step out of a contemporary, Western-influenced world and "re-boot" their own worldview by reawakening their rhythms, performance language, and community. All the elements, all the spaces, all the participants coalesce in the place of performance (see Figure 7.3).

Ritual Preparation has been successfully used in a variety of indigenous and non-indigenous settings—with Alaska Natives, in Zambia, with the Zulu, in Korea, with the Sakha of Siberia, with a Slavic group in St. Petersburg, and with a variety of folk and multi-cultural groups in Europe and the United States. Ritual Preparation becomes a sub-cultural forum—a sequence of events and actions not unlike the time-honored performance formations created by shamanic practices and often codified by their traditions. My experience as a field researcher of shamanic and ritual healing practices in a variety of cultures—Sakha (Siberia), Zulu, Miao and Yao (China), Korea, and !Xuu and Khwe Bushmen (lower Kalahari)—has led to the identification of a similarity of pattern, method, and function among shamanic healing rituals, the inspiration for Ritual Preparation.

My role as facilitator is not unlike that of the traditional shaman, whose primary function is "to create a state of interaction, to bring out both his own task as mediator and also the role of the supernormal figures in the ritual performance" (Siikala, 1978). Fundamentally, such an action demands that participants join in the art of social role-changing, a transformation that often entails ecstatic role-taking techniques enabled by rhythmic drumming, singing/chanting, and dancing (codified movements) that bring on a gradual alteration of consciousness (Siikala, 1978).

When working with Alaska Natives, the three-movement exercise yielded many movements derived from social dances. Significant animals, such as raven, walrus, and eagle, were mimed and hunting actions such as spearing a seal or ice floe hopping were shown. Spiritual beliefs such as praising the owner of the universe became part of the gesture system. Depending on the size of the group, a few dozen movements can be presented. The facilitator then leads the group in a discussion to determine how to begin the preparation. Listening to the movement and its meaning is essential, as is associating a sound or rhythm to the

Figure 7.3. The warrior challenge section of the Ritual Preparation developed with the Metamorphosis Theatre, St Petersburg, Russia.

action. The use of rhythm brings the movements to life. As in indigenous ritual and dance traditions, the rhythm is difficult to perform without a performative action and vice versa—they are inseparable and indistinguishable.

The process requires every action, rhythm, dance step, and vocalization to be understood, detailed, and coordinated with other elements. For example, when a tribal dance step is introduced, its context needs to be discussed and learned, comparisons to other traditions noted, and then adjustments and adaptations made to suit the project's needs. The process is community building, becoming a positive and participatory template for not only the subsequent performance work, but for the development of a creative and educational perspective of the world. The process has the goal of teaching that (1) everyone is a creator and has ownership, (2) a new-old process is revealed and experienced, (3) cultural sources are identified, (4) the narrative of the past and future is re-vitalized, and (5) a demonstrable and shared expression is completed. Participants have variously described Ritual Preparation as "a healing" and as "walking with my ancestors" and comments such as "I feel proud of who I am and my culture" and "With it I don't feel so alone now" abound.

Below are examples from the opening sequences of a Ritual Preparation developed in Zambia, with 26 different tribal/ethnic groups, and that of Tuma Theatre, an Alaska Native performance group.

Ritual Preparation: Zambia

The group circles, kneeling in position of reverence. After a minute of silence, the simple low beat of the drum is heard. The participants come alive, shifting to one knee on the ground (reverence position) and then begin to clap their hands, welcoming of the spirit of performance. The drum increases and the participants move convulsively to receive the spirit of performance into their bodies. Hands over their heads rise up to the sky as the initial movement reaches a climax. The participants wipe their feet, twice on each foot, to wipe away any evil spirit that may have followed them. Then the performers perform the recovered Woman's Initiation dance from the Tambuka tribe, with a shuffling step with arms and hands in and out. The group moves counter-clockwise in the circle.

Ritual Preparation: Alaska

Performers gather in a circle around the fire, on their knees, eyes closed, their sticks gathered in the center. A faint drumbeat becomes louder. Slowly the performers pull their sticks from the "fire" and begin to accompany the beat to awaken the earth. The chant begins softly and builds as it is repeated: *new-knumb nah-llun-ghit-dah ma-knee ma-knee ma-knee wee-dall-but* (Yup'ik for "the earth knows that we are here"). The chant, drum, and stick beating increase in tempo and build into a climax that transforms all of the performers into their power birds. Transforming into birds and flying, the drumbeat is frantic at first and then slows into a steady two-beat rhythm as each bird performs a story/dance/song. The birds return and land in a circle and then stand as humans again, awaiting a signal from the drummer(s).

Ritual Preparations take approximately 30 minutes and are physically and vocally demanding, becoming the group's warm-up for each work session. The Ritual Preparation established during my first year with Tuma Theatre in Alaska evolved and changed over the next five years, becoming a touchstone by which old and new members could participate in an evolving body of knowledge. As my own work as a facilitator evolved, I changed from viewing performance as created from an individual vision to a collective vision. Intended neither for commercial consumption nor for a wider audience, these rituals are seen as a collective and community event. Performance is a way of marking completion. Even when no one outside the group experienced a performance—as was the case with my work with the !Xuu and Khwe Bushmen—it was non-etheless a performance vital to the community, a return to ritual origins, whereby a community presented itself to its larger community of ancestors, spirits, animals, and place.

The proof of any ritual performance is its ability to change and enrich the lives of the individuals and their community. Wilma Brown, a Tuma Theatre group member, participated in all of the exercises and explorations noted above. A shy Inupiat Eskimo woman from the isolated village of White Mountain (population 350) when I first met her, she later told me that her brother and uncles had sexually abused her for several years. She had undergone years of individual and group therapy, yet she felt that the retracing of ancient pathways had transformed her. In an interview with Dale Seeds from the College of Wooster, Wilma describes her experience:

Before you could understand what Tuma did for me, I think it's important for you to understand from what world I come. Before I joined Tuma, I had inherent questions about my heritage and place in the universe. I grew up with drinking, drugs, gambling and abuse with a small light of hope and love from my grandparents. Going to college was my escape from tragedy. My rage propelled me through the White Man and I left my home with many questions my people could not answer for me, like where do my people come from? What are my responsibilities here? What is good and what is bad here? I was traumatized in many ways spiritually and emotionally before I joined Tuma. When I joined Tuma, I faced some of my greatest fears about why I felt like a sick person. Tuma and Tom Riccio changed me forever. My world began to open. Wrongs toward my people were being acknowledged, the power of the people who once were was being asked for, and it was safe for me to grieve and ask for myself. I was with Tuma for three years, and with every year, I grew. I became empowered, confident, and learned to focus my rage in a different way. Now I am more expressive and have a deeper understanding of what happened in my people's past and what is happening now and what I can do about it. (Riccio, 2003, p. 7)

CONCLUSION

The deliverers of news services supply us with new evidence every day of the inevitable changes in our lives to come. Global warming concerns groups of people in all nations. Economic changes have filled the news. The technologization and virtualization of reality is a topic of frequent discussion. In many of the places I have worked, groups of people are aware that our earth and its inhabitants are challenging long-established ways of being in the world, into an era that will require a fundamental re-evaluation of who and what we are, of how we relate to one another, our self, and our planet. An emerging consciousness (Macy, 1991) is learning from the place-based systems that have much in common with indigenous cultures (Tarnas,1991). Whether this consciousness is motivated by the necessity of political, environmental, or economic survival, or symptomatic of a larger historical evolution or cycle, is of no consequence. I believe with Macy that our sense of self and connections with others, the environment, animals, and spirit, is undergoing change, shaping a participatory reality sensitized to interdependence and holism. Humanity's wisdom and abilities are being called to task in this process, including, in no small way, performance. The abundance of dance, music, and theater offerings, the explosion of cable offerings, films, and video games seem to me to be, in part, an attempt to explain, comfort, and/or prepare for the global transformation, which concerns us all. Performance, one of the most fundamental personal, social, and cultural expressions, has taken on a heightened significance. In a time of fundamental change a fundamental and grounding resource is being called upon. At its most basic, performance, in any and all of its diverse manifestations, gives form to feeling through a system of signs and codes in an effort to make visible the invisible. Faced with what seems to be unprecedented change, the groups I have worked with are accessing and re-examining historical and cultural resources (much of which were formerly marginalized or misunderstood); among them ritual, shamanism, traditional healing, and indigenous performance focused on harmonizing the material and spiritual worlds.

Performance aids a participant in recreating our world and it can be also a forum to which we look to understand the new indigenous place that is evolving within and around us. My hope is that we are all becoming earthlings and, with that, a more knowing part of a whole that now needs to be called in existence.

REFERENCES

Abram, D. (1996). *The spell of the sensuous.* New York: Pantheon Press.
Damasio, A. (1994). *Descartes' error: Emotion, reason, and the human brain.* London: Penguin Book.
Eliade, M. (1959). *Myths, dreams, and mysteries: The encounter between contemporary faiths and archaic realities.* New York: Harper Collins.
Eliade, M. (1961). *Cosmos and history: The myth of the eternal return.* New York: Harper Collins.
Emunah, R. (1994). *Acting for real: Drama therapy process, technique, and performance.* New York: Brunner-Routledge.
Fox, J. (Ed.). (1987). *The essential Moreno: Writings on psychodrama, group method, and spontaneity.* New York: Springer Publishing Company.
Goffman, E. (1959). *The presentation of self in everyday life.* London: Penguin Press.
Hyde, L. (1983). *The gift: Imagination and the erotic life of property.* New York: Vintage Books.
Kawagley, O. (1995). *Yupiaq worldview: A pathway to ecology and spirit.* Prospect Heights, IL: Waveland Press.
Macy, J. (1991). *World as lover, world as self.* Berkeley, CA: Parallax Press.
Napoleon, H. (1996). *Yuuyaraq: The way of the human being.* Fairbanks, AK: Alaska Native Knowledge Network.

Riccio, T. (2003). *Reinventing traditional Alaska native performance.* Lewiston, NY: E. Mellen Press.

Riccio, T. (2007). *Performing Africa: Remixing tradition, theatre, and culture.* Berlin: Peter Lang.

Riley, J. (1997). *Chinese theatre and the actor in performance.* London: Cambridge University Press.

Schechner, R. (2002). *Performance studies: An introduction.* New York: Routledge.

Schipper, K. (1993). *The Taoist body* (K. Duval, Trans.). Berkeley, CA; University of California Press.

Segal, R. A. (Ed.). (1998). *Jung on mythology.* Princeton, NJ: Princeton University Press.

Siikala, A. (1978). *The rite technique of the Siberian shaman.* Helsinki: Suomalainen tiedeakatemia: Akateeminen kitjakauppa.

Sternberg, P., & Garcia, A. (2000). *Who's in your shoes?* Westbrook, CT: Praeger.

Tarnas, R. (1991). *The passion of the Western mind.* London: Pimlico.

Turner, V. (1987). *The anthropology of performance.* New York: PAJ Publications.

Van Gennep, A. (1984). *The rites of passage* (2nd ed.). Chicago: University of Chicago Press.

8

Empowering the Oppressed and Their (Oppressed) Helpers in Bangladesh and India

HERB PROPPER AND SABINE YASMIN SABA

Authors' Profiles

Propper: *The opportunity to do this work came about through a series of circumstances that were both unforeseen and illustrative of the fortuitous connections that so often arise through the operations of "tele," the foundation of J. L. Moreno's revolutionary group method of sociometry. In brief, it refers to the laws of attraction and repulsion between individuals, the invisible causes of our social choices. (For a detailed explanation, see chapter 2; Ed.) In 2001, as a member of the Executive Council of the American Society of Group Psychotherapy and Psychodrama, where I had volunteered to respond to email inquiries, I received an appeal from a Bangladeshi, Mostafa Kamal Jatra, M.A. (hon.), University of Chittagong. He is the founder and Executive Director of United Theatre for Social Action (UTSA) and was eager to learn more about psychodrama. UTSA is a local, private non-governmental organization with the broad mission of working with the disabled and disadvantaged using social consciousness-raising theater with Bengali folk theater forms.*

I responded by sending him books and articles, which fed his growing passion to bring psychodrama to Bangladesh. As psychodrama must be experienced in live sessions, it was not long before I

*volunteered to travel to Bangladesh to begin a series of yearly Na-
tional Therapeutic Theatre Workshops, which in 2006, gave rise to
the incipient Bangladesh Therapeutic Theatre Institute (BTTI). The
fact that we recognized in each other an opportunity to work together
in such a distant land demonstrates our "tele." In addition to training
in psychodrama, sociodrama, and sociometry, these workshops have
included training in Playback Theater through the work of our colleague, Jen Kristel, MA, CET, and Certified Playback Theater Practitioner. This form uses trained performers to act out stories from the
audience in an effective and powerful form for creating community.*

*After my initial Bangladesh training workshop in 2003, socio-
drama became the primary focus for several years. More recently,
as participants gained increased levels of experience, and in workshops for clinical psychologists, counselors, and graduate students,
it has been possible to include more explicit psychodramas. Currently,
my Fulbright enables me to complete the structures for a thorough
training of Bangladeshi psychodramatists.*

Saba: *I am a Bangladeshi who met Herb Propper by attending
one of his trainings. I had been a theater activist since the age of
fifteen, when I joined the Theatre Center for Social Development and
later the Ain-o-Shalish Kendro, an organization that used theater
to teach human rights awareness. Because many Bangladeshis are
illiterate, theater is popularly used to communicate sociopolitical-
cultural issues. When a politician is delivering a 3-hour speech,
people stop listening and get bored. After the talk, what was said is
often forgotten. But theater continues to occupy an important place
in our culture and attracts a lot of spectators. Not just another
entertainment, theater provides a way to express problems, criticism,
and wishes. Our goal at Ain-o-Shalish Kendro was to use this powerful medium as a tool to create awareness for human rights issues.*

*However, it soon became clear to me that creating awareness
was not the same as creating change. Awareness seemed to be limited
to communication in the workshops themselves. More specific techniques were needed to address problems of oppression, which continued to be reported even among workshop participants. Sociodrama,
I learned, was different.*

*When I got the opportunity to participate in a psychodrama and
sociodrama workshop conducted by Herb Propper in 2003, I was
amazed by this wonderful method. After only one workshop I could
already feel its impact on my personal and professional life. During
the workshop, we shared our most personal thoughts and stories
with each other. the trust and teamwork missing in the awareness*

training was created by integrating socio-psychodramatic techniques. As proof, the group that participated in the first workshop 5 years ago still maintains strong bonds. The psychodrama/sociodrama method has helped us understand ourselves and others better than before (Propper, 2004, 2008).

Herb Propper, PhD, TEP, Emeritus Professor of Theater at the Johnson, Vermont, State College is one of the foremost trainers of sociodrama and psychodrama. He has been active in both *theater* and psychodrama all of his life and has published widely. Founder of the BTTI, he received a Fulbright to continue his work in Bangladesh and India.

Sabine Yasmin Saba, MA, a political activist using *theater* and movement, spends part of her time in the U.S., Britain, India, and Bangladesh, where she is a trainer at the BTTI. Together with Dr. Propper, Saba began to create the BTTI, which has continued to provide psycho- and sociodramatic trainings for social activists, social workers, psychiatrists, psychologists, and others, often working with non-governmental agencies.

INTRODUCTION

This chapter is a descriptive survey of two levels of group work using psychodrama, sociodrama, and sociometry with oppressed populations in Bangladesh from 2003 to the present. One level covers selected examples of trainings in these methods with a number of Bangladeshi private non-governmental agency (NGO) and Mental Health workers, to provide them with new ways of intervention and healing. The second level illustrates examples of field work with several different populations in India. We also include an example of Playback Theater training in Bangladesh.

When one considers Bangladeshi society, the concept of oppression needs to be applied in the widest possible context. Restricting oppression to typical situations, such as armed conflicts, civil wars, ethnic cleansing, genocide, terrorism, and the like, would miss the point. Bangladeshi society is exposed to a significant level of political violence in the form of beatings, machete attacks, guns, and bombs from armed cadres loosely associated with major political parties. Such incidents are routinely labeled "terrorism." For example, in 2004 a university professor/poet and prominent member of a political party, giving a public speech, was attacked by a single man wielding a machete. The political association of the attacker was never made clear nor were his motives; however, the the man was routinely referred to as a "terrorist." Such events create a palpable climate of intimidation among many elements of the voting population.

In addition, there is cultural oppression through denial of basic civil rights to those Urdu-speaking Pakistanis who had settled in what was originally East Pakistan and became trapped there during the independence movement in 1971. In the domestic realm, there is physical, emotional, and legally sanctioned intimidation from a deeply entrenched patriarchal culture. Widows and women whose husbands have "put them aside"—a common legal maneuver in which a husband can simply make a public declaration that stands as a divorce—experience economic and social discrimination. In rural villages, occurences of husbands attacking their wives for slight cause by throwing lye on them, even murdering them, are reported regularly, but less frequently as time goes on. Such acts contribute to a pervasive atmosphere of intimidation and oppression. Finally, a country regularly visited by cyclones, earthquakes, floods, and monsoon mudslides can be appropriately considered to suffer from we may call "the oppression of natural disasters." This is particularly the case for the poorer sectors of the population who are forced to live in flood plains, river banks, or coastal areas in shelters unable to withstand the ravages of wind, rain, and swollen rivers (Propper, 2004).

THERAPEUTIC STRATEGIES

Role Theory (J. L. Moreno, 1977) provides a solid foundation for the development of the general therapeutic strategy that informs the work of the BTTI trainings. (To review specific information about sociodrama, psychodrama, and role theater, see chapter 2.) To address trauma, BTTI makes use of the body of work developed by Dr. Kate Hudgins, clinical psychologist and psychodrama trainer, who created the Therapeutic Spiral method (Hudgins & Drucker, 1998; Hudgins & Kellerman, 2000). Dr. Hudgins has enlarged sociodramatic work by stressing the importance of protecting traumatized groups from becoming re-traumatized. Noting that trauma victim are often so eager to dive into the central problem, she has developed a number of methods to slow down the process. Using several supportive doubles as well as metaphorical protective symbols, she has developed support systems that remind the protagonist(s) of their strengths and resilience before and during the encounter with painful material. Group members select scarves and other symbolic props where they can serve as reminders. For example, a person may select a crystal to represent inner strength, and a green scarf to recall a capacity for joy experienced in spring time, and place it where it can be seen while a trauma is enacted.

BTTI has also benefited significantly from the work of the Jungian psychotherapist Donald Kalsched on archetypal defense structures in trauma survivors (Kalsched, 1996). He begins trauma work by identifying two types of roles, which we may designate as roles of positive strength, on the one hand, and negative or maladaptive roles, on the other. Various socio-psychodramatic techniques are then used to complete the enactment. The next stage of Kalsched's work focuses on action explorations of one or more roles of positive strength, through extended role interviews, psychodramas of interpersonal relationships featuring this role, future projection role-training psychodramas. Here, the protagonist can practice encountering various situations and relationships, as well as intrapsychic psychodramas in which the protagonist builds an internal support system through discovering ally roles which support and strengthen. This "team building" of inner positive roles has proved helpful in supporting traumatized individuals.

Training Examples

The steps of the process will be familiar to experienced psychodramatists (Treadwell, Kumar, Stein, & Prosnick, 1998). However, since other readers may not be as well-acquainted with these forms, explanations of director's choices have been added for the purposes of understanding and clarity. In Bangladesh, participants use Bengali as the primary language of the drama.

Rarely do all the members of a group have fluency in spoken English, and even when they do, at moments of intensity, it is beneficial to ask role-players to shift back to their native language. What is lost in understanding is offset by the enhanced spontaneity the native language affords. A less apparent advantage of using the native language is that it allows the director to focus more fully on body language, vocal tone, and emotional dynamics.

Cyclone Sidr struck Bangladesh on the night of November 15, 2007. Just after the country had recovered from summer floods, the deadliest storm in a decade caused massive devastation and destruction of crops in the southern regions of the country just before harvest. Several thousand people died and probably up to 100,000 were injured. The survivors had little food, medicine or shelter for months to come.

Example: Sociodramatic Vignette: "Hope after Cyclone Sidr of 2007"

This vignette—or short scene—describes a sociodrama that used all the members of a small group in an enactment. Sociodrama, done in this way, can be useful in groups of fifteen or less, where short, compact action is needed, because of time limitations or the newness of the group. In the early stages of group life, the vignette can function both as an introduction to sociodrama and as a warm-up.

On the final day of a 3-day workshop titled "Using sociodrama and sociometry for performers' creativity and social issues" at Jahangirnagar University, the group decided to do a sociodrama addressing the devastation of Cyclone Sidr. A short group exploration of a single abstract role provided the content. It was co-directed by Herb Propper and Danielle Forer, MA, Social Worker and Psychodramatist from the Psychodrama Institute of Melbourne, Australia.

Warm-Up Example: Whole Group/Single Role

The director created an action exploration of the role of hope demonstrating the three-step process of role development outlined by Moreno; namely, role-taking, role-playing, and role-creating (Sternberg & Garcia, 2000). First, each person in the group took on the abstract role of hope, using movement and one or more colored scarves to express his/her perception of its essential qualities. A generous portion of time was allowed for the warm-up to the role in general. Partners were chosen and each pair explored their individual version of the role. Then, as the group reformed into subgroups of three or four, they were asked to shape their individual versions of the role into a sculpture of "shared hope." This technique asks group members to form a tableau and, finally, to find a title that synthesized the role qualities of each member into a common whole, to present to the full group. During such a presentation, group members may be directed to add a song for the whole group to sing to deepen the experience. The "shared hope" warm-up ended with verbal sharing as each member of the group demonstrated a specific aspect of the deep well of emotion related to Cyclone Sidr.

Although many were not themselves injured, nor suffered property destruction, every member of the group was closely related to a person who had suffered serious consequences. On a collective level, the sense of national pride and identity had been negatively impacted. Indications of an underlying sense of national inferiority appeared over and over again.

The workshop leaders had planned further role-training activities for this group. However, continuing with this plan would have left the feelings of hopelessness, inadequacy, and shame stirred up by the warm-up unexpressed. Therefore, the leaders switched from the original plan and began a sociodrama about the loss of hope. A new warm-up was needed for the roles that helped to enact the conflict about hope and hopelessness. The director marked out locations in the working space for three roles: the *group*; *obstacles* to hope; and *hope* itself. In one corner, group members clustered together to take on their sociodramatic role of *group*; the role of *obstacles* was marked by a chaotic pile of empty chairs in another corner; the role of *hope* by a large pile of colored scarves in a third. Drawing on the principle of safety in numbers, the sociodramatic technique of having the entire group play a single role, or using the entire group as multiple role-players for two roles offers important advantages for working with groups who have experienced some variety of trauma. Individuals can avoid feelings of inadequacy and embarrassment associated with being in the spotlight in a single role. The entire group is kept in action at all times. The tendency of group members to become passive audience members is avoided. Even when there are multiple role-players, however, the director needs to pay attention to those who are less outgoing or spontaneous, to prevent the role from being dominated by the more aggressive role-players.

Because the role of *obstacles* was new, the group needed to characterize this role, a collective expression of the obstacles to feeling hopeful perceived by each group member. The action began with the full group, in their sociodramatic role as *group*, making a series of spontaneous statements to the role of *obstacles*. The director used frequent doubling (see chapter 1) and echo-doubling (an emphatic repetition of a group member's statement to highlight it throughout these group enactments. Next, the full group, still in their role of *group*, made a series of spontaneous statements to the role of *hope*. In this spontaneous group expression, the goal was not to produce a series of well defined and logically coherent statements, but rather to stimulate spontaneity. Group members were encouraged to discard politeness and speak over one another, to repeat any overheard thought or feeling if it was also theirs, and to maximize their expressions of feeling. Since there was no audience, there was no observer who needed to hear every word or make sense of what was produced.

Next, through role reversal, the full group took on the role of *hope*, and responded to the statements made by the role of *group*. In a typical psychodrama or sociodrama, it is customary to begin a role reversal by repeating the previous statement to that role by the initial role (Schramski, 2000). However, where the entire group plays each of the roles, such a process would be unwieldy and time-consuming. The solution to this quandary is to rely on each participant's memory for his/her own statements.

Group members, now in their collective role of *hope*, were cued by the director. "OK, *hope*. You've just heard what group has said to you. How are you going to answer?" The group now produced another series of spontaneous responses from the role of *hope*. The co-director then asked the group to add a second role reversal into the role of *obstacles* and back into the role of the *group*, with a series of spontaneous statements from both sides. As the group members played each of the three roles collectively, the directors picked up central themes. *Hope* was characterized by such statements as "There can be a happy future! My family will have a good home! We can rebuild! I want to help!" *Obstacles* were expressed as "Bangladesh will never recover! You're stupid to think things will be better! The government can't do anything! There's no help for you! Why should you have a better life. Cyclones will keep on coming! Nobody cares about Bangladesh anyway!"

To intensify the dramatic action, the director asked two volunteers to take on the role of *obstacles*, while the remainder remained in their role of *group*. The *group* expressed anger and resentment, "You're not helping! Why don't you leave if you feel this way!" The *obstacles* remained cynical and defiant throughout. "You know we're right! Nothing will ever get done! This is what you deserve!"

As a means to begin to break the cycle of emotional oppression, the director created a psychodramatic "cone of silence" around the role of *obstacles*. In this technique, the group members cannot hear what is said inside the cone. In this scene, one of the co-directors took the role of *friendly interviewer*. "Tell me, *obstacles*, just between the two of us—and I promise I won't tell *group* anything you say—what is the secret of your power?" The two volunteer role-players answer, "Our power is actually their lack of confidence and low self-esteem. When they believe in themselves our power goes away." Thanking them cordially, the director removed the cone of silence. Shifting roles from *interviewer* to director, the leader reminded the *group* that they just overheard *obstacles'* secret of power. Group members had now gained enough insight to achieve a shift in the balance of power by nourishing their individual strengths of self-confidence and accomplishment, a strengthening of collective hope.

Had more time been available, the action could have been continued by exploring the impact of this new information. Like psychodrama, sociodrama often stirs up powerful feelings among the participants, even when the action is relatively short. If time does not allow the group members to express and integrate those feelings, it is incumbent on the director to help the group make a plan for post-session processing. In this instance, there was enough time left to accommodate the process.

In the closure of the sociodrama, group members in their collective role of *group* made a final series of spontaneous statements, first to *obstacles*, and then to the role of *hope*, as a way to begin their process of integrating the discoveries made during the action. Finally, group members de-roled from the role of *group* by stepping outside the action space and making a few spontaneous statements to that role.

The sociodrama finished with the sharing typical of sociodrama; a series of statements from each group member about what particular learning experiences s/he would take from this experience. Group members unanimously expressed experiencing greater clarity. A number of group members felt better able to contain the mixture of hope and pessimism. Several group members gained confidence because they felt less isolated. Although some individuals stressed the profound practical difficulties of recovering from the devastation of Cyclone Sidr, a large majority also expressed increased hope for the future and related it to the insight they gained from the *obstacles* role-play.

Example: A Moment I Want to Remember

This example comes from a 2-day workshop, "Introduction to Psycho-drama & Sociometry," in Chittagong (Propper, 2008). The group consisted of nineteen participants, chiefly local private NGO field staff, counselors, and social workers, together with several university students. A series of group-building sociometric exercises, small-group practice in doubling and the creation of a group "Circle of Safety" (Hudgins, 1998) had already been done the morning before our afternoon workshop.

This single-scene psychodrama, also termed a "vignette" was the second of a pair enacted in this workshop. The technique is very simple in both concept and execution, and typically does not require the protagonist to examine deep painful emotions or confront traumatic situations. At the same time, it allows both the protagonist and the group to use spontaneity and creativity and to reveal authentic feelings. Thus, it is an effective way to ease the group gently into the psychodramatic process, creating progressive stages of trust and intimacy. Small-scale enactments of positive past experiences eliciting relatively casual and chiefly pleasant feelings are especially useful in early stages of work with traumatized groups. They allow persons opportunity to reveal something of themselves to one another, thus building positive group sociometry, and to become familiar with the methods of psychodramatic action before revisiting situations replete with strong, painful emotions, such as fear, shame, and grief. The process of living in the general and abstract role of *the person who has a positive experience*, for example, can build confidence and positive ego-strength. To warm up, the full group was asked to find a moment that they would like to remember in the recent past, emphasizing that this moment did not have to be one of great emotional depth or profound meaning, nor did it necessarily have to be light and happy. But for each group member, his/her moment should have some personal significance. The warm-up was followed by a request for volunteers—one of the typical, and often most time-efficient, means for determining choice of protagonist. In response, the first volunteer created a full scale "remembered moment" drama creating the locale of the event with vivid sensory details. S/he then chose auxiliaries from the group for each of the significant roles and role-trained them. In the following actual enactment, the protagonist engaged with the auxiliary roles, showing them appropriate behavior through role reversal when necessary, and expressing his inner thoughts and feelings through soliloquy. There are various choices for closing the action. A common one would be to freeze the action and bring the protagonist into the mirror position, choosing another group member to stand in his/her role. The protagonist would then be directed to speak to the role of him/herself in the remembered moment. If warranted by the situation, a dialogue between the two different positions of the protagonist through role reversal could also be created.

To close the action in this instance, the director chose to use the "psychodramatic photograph" because it is a very simple but effective action piece that can be used as a mini-enactment in itself, or as a warm-up to a larger psychodrama, or, as in this instance, as a means of closure for the action of a vignette. The protagonist was asked to use an imaginary camera to snap a photo of the moment as a tableau or piece of living sculpture, seeing the moment "in the mind's eye," an effective method for creating a strong memory imprint. In the director's interview, the protagonist, S, a social worker in his 30s, revealed that he wanted to remember two interrelated moments. The first was leaving his family home some twenty years previously; the second was returning to live in his family home five years ago. This unusual request required a spontaneous and creative response from the director, who reacted by letting him re-enact both moments, "letting the protagonist be in charge of his/her own drama" (Z. Moreno, 1995). Asking the protagonist to choose just one of these moments—a more typical form—might prove to be a difficult choice and could risk diluting or distorting his emotional warm-up to the drama, leading both protagonist and group into an unproductive circle, and significantly lessen the group's spontaneity (see Figure 8.1).

The initial interview had warmed up the audience sufficiently to allow the director to skip an elaborate setting of the scene. The doorway to his parental home was indicated with two chairs. Another pair of chairs was placed to indicate the doorway of re-entering, 15 years later. S chose two doubles, one for each of the moments. The director then asked him to select three pairs of auxiliaries, to represent the three most important persons for the first of the two moments, his mother and two siblings. To characterize each of these roles, he was asked to "mold" the group of three into a frozen tableau and provide each role with a short essential message that expressed the emotional contribution of each for his departure.

Figure 8.1. Yasmin encourages a performer.

With his double for the first moment at his side, S then re-enacted the moment of leaving his family home. The action was short, starting just inside the doorway, then stepping through it and out into the larger world. In order to allow a deeper experience of the emotional content, he was asked to repeat the action several times in slow motion, during which the auxiliary roles repeated their essential messages. S then explored his feeling reactions with the help of his double, sometimes sharing his thoughts with the double, sometimes reversing roles to become his double to explore and express the inner content of his thoughts and feelings. After S felt he had sufficiently explored the moment of leaving, the director asked him to step outside the action into the mirror position, while his double remained in his place within the action. From here he took a "psychodramatic photograph" of himself in the moment of leaving, completing the action of the first moment.

To allow both protagonist and audience to make the transition of the 15 years between the two moments, the director created a psychodramatic "time bridge." Together, director and protagonist slowly weaved their way through the space between the two doorways, while the director enumerated the passing of years and asked the protagonist to recall silently a few different experiences that happened to him in each segment.

Arriving at the second moment in which he returned to live in his family home after 15 years, S chose three more auxiliaries to represent the most prominent persons for him at this time, and sculpted them into a tableau with a brief, essential message from each.

The one role common to both moments was that of his mother. In another short enactment, the director had S repeat the action of his arrival several times, to enhance the emotional experience. Then, just as before, S stepped out of the action into the mirror position, was replaced in the tableau by his double, and took a psychodramatic photograph of his moment of return.

As a brief closure to this vignette, the director, standing beside S with his psychodramatic camera in hand, summarized the action as a means of helping him begin to integrate his experience. During these moments, the depth of his experience in the protagonist role was evident. His face wore an expression of calm intensity, his eyes slightly moist with tears. The psychodrama closed as group members shared the feelings and experiences stimulated by his work. Many thanked him for his courage and openness. The sharing also marked a clear change in the way the group members viewed S, previously viewed as an isolate, and now viewed as warm and compassionate—an example of the way in which any psychodrama can change the sociometry of the group.

The group members' vocal tone and expression reflected the deep chord touched in this Bangladeshi group whose traditions place primary emphasis on family bonds. In Bangladesh, young adults frequently live with their parents, for both economic and emotional reasons. Those whose families still live in rural villages frequently return for visits and keep in close touch. Another striking example of this bond was demonstrated during the first NTTW workshop in 2003. During the sharing portion of a particular exercise, one young man suddenly began crying profusely, in long inarticulate sobs. The director immediately provided him with several doubles and brought the entire group into a close circle around him, obtaining his consent with nods. When his outburst of tears finally subsided, the group learned that he had forgotten to call his mother at her village home, the night before, to wish her a happy birthday. The guilt and shame he felt from his neglected duty were the cause of the eruption.

FULL-GROUP MULTI-SCENE SOCIODRAMA: TERRORISM

This sociodrama occurred in the Chittagong 5-day workshop "Socio-drama and Sociometry," with 13 participants (Propper, 2004). In the "Single Central Role" form of sociodrama, the action centers around one main role, which interacts with a number of other roles. The action also readily allows the creation of a number of significant internal subroles contained in the central role.

Earlier in the workshop, the central theme of terrorism had been chosen by the group through a lengthy sociometric choice process, which had produced two themes of relatively equal importance. The first theme, "Bangladesh Political Parties," had been explored the previous day through another multi-scene sociodrama.

This enactment began with the director's setting out an empty chair for the central role of *Terrorist*. As a warm-up, group members were asked to make a series of brief statements to the role, focusing specifically on the feelings this role evoked. The director accompanied the group members' expression—spoken in Bangla—with expressive sound and gesture, as well as doubling and echo-doubling to keep the flow. Think-ing that group members might be resistant to taking on a role that would invite negative feelings, hostility, or even verbal attacks from the group, the director asked group members just to try out the role, with permission to drop it when the player wanted to. However, one man took on the role immediately, in a calm, confident and relaxed manner. After thanking him, the director, in the role of respectful, considerate interviewer, asked, "What name shall we call you?" He replied, "Osama bin Laden." A shock wave ran through the group, producing an immediate increase of spontaneity. The director's role interview continued for some time, allowing the role-player, the group, and the director to warm up gradually. To make sure he is viewed as open minded, the director refined his *interviewer* role, making a clear distinction from the "Western Imperialist journalists."

The *bin Laden* role made disparaging comments about being misun-derstood and slandered by the others. After producing an initial defini-tion of the role by articulating *bin Laden's* goals, aims, and motives, the director moved the drama into its action phase by asking him if he would like to talk with some young Bangladeshi NGO workers who were interested in him and his activities, allowing the group members to move into the action.

To deepen the emotional level, the director asked group members to move from provocative questions to expressing their own feelings and views, whether in agreement or disagreement with the *bin Laden* role. The director's goal was to explore the role of *bin Laden* in some depth, working towards a complex portrait, in contrast to the media's narrow and often stereotyped images. Splitting the single role-player from the rest of the group is a risk, with a possible consequence of becoming a sociometric isolate or even a negative star (J. L. Moreno, 1978). Instead, the director chose to bring the entire group into the role of *bin Laden*. As warm-up for this role shift, group members were asked to take their time in order to feel their way into the role gradually, bringing each individual's own projected feelings, attitudes, and motives into the role, and to decide which part of bin Laden they felt they wanted to express. Group members produced roles such as the *Islamic revolutionary*, the *guerilla fighter, champion of disempowered Muslims*, and *military strategist*, to be interviewed by the director.

The most spontaneous and evocative response came from a man who identified himself as *the hidden part of bin Laden's heart*, providing the group a profound look at the inner landscape of the role. The director asked, "Are you aware of this hidden part of your heart?" He reflected for a few moments. "Yes, I am." "Do you ever acknowledge that part of you?" Again, he answered after some reflection, "I know it's there. But I don't admit it very often, even to myself. That would be a distraction from my mission." "And your mission is...?" With a slight smile, he said, "To oppose the Western Imperialist powers. To wipe them out." Although other group members, playing other parts of the *bin Laden* role, were equally rock-firm in their commitment, the presence of this deep inner role, with its potential for compassion and vulnerability, shifted the emotional tone of the drama.

After a tea break that offered a natural suspension of the action and allowed the group members time to process the action, the group was ready to shift focus. The director suggested continuing the drama by moving it into the external, social, and geopolitical arena.

Some participants wanted to create the broad role of oppressed *Middle Eastern Muslims,* the people whom the actual bin Laden professes to serve. To specify this collective role of *oppressed peoples*, five role-players took sub-roles of *farmers, manufacturing workers, slum-dwellers, housewives,* and *religionists*, a term coined by group members for those who believed strongly in a religious creed. With this general category, a potential group conflict between sects was avoided. In Bangladesh, where more than 80% of the population is Muslim, the role-players were referring to the fundamentalist minority Muslims, who make up the most disadvantaged sectors of the population; the broader category of *religionists* avoided the stigma.

When three group members asked if they could remain observers, the director, wanting to keep the entire group in the action, responded by asking them to create a common role. Spontaneously, they created the role of *journalists*, which they refined as *CNN reporter, BBC reporter,* and *Al-Jazeera reporter*, injecting more depth to the drama by adding the dimension of cultural perspectives and values. In the same way, when the *oppressed peoples* role-players were asked to develop their roles with more specificity; they became *students, farmers, rural villagers, low-wage urban workers,* and *women*.

Meanwhile, the original *bin Laden* role-player had decided to continue in that role. To help the role-player understand the risks of negative transference and projection from the other group members, the director used the interview to remind the others of their responsibility to separate the role-player from the role. Further, other group members were invited to join this role in order to minimize negative transferences. However, the director's caution was rejected once more, as everyone in the group seemed content to stay with the role configurations already established.

To begin the action of the second half of this drama, the director asked each of the sub-roles of the *oppressed peoples* to tell *bin Laden* what they needed and hoped for from him. *Bin Laden* was to reply in kind. A lively interchange ensued, as various sectors of *oppressed peoples* declared that *bin Laden* was not helping them enough, diverting too much of his attention toward terrorist military operations.

The deep-seated recognition of their nation needing basic resources came into play. *Bin Laden* acknowledged that he wanted to work more directly to improve their economic status. He attempted to shift the blame for shortchanging *oppressed peoples* onto the Western Imperialist USA and its allies.

When this conflict reached an impasse—as the argument started to become repetitive and the role-players' energies waned—the director brought the *journalists* into the action. In sharp exchange, the *journalists* attempted to point out contradictions between *bin Laden's* platform and his behaviors. *Bin Laden* needed cooperating *journalists* to help get his message out to the world, but questioned the objectivity of the *CNN* and *BBC reporters*. The *oppressed peoples* expressed resentments towards the *jounalists* for ignoring them, and asked them for more in-depth reporting so that the world would get to know their personal stories.

During this portion of the action another unexpected role emerged, taking the group's focus into deeper dimensions. The same person who had produced the role of the hidden part of *Osama bin Laden's* heart, and then the role of *CNN journalist*, spontaneously took the role of *Buddhist*. He confronted *bin Laden* about the contradiction between the latter's love for the people and his use of violent means. After some time, the director observed that this issue would not soon be resolved within the group, a situation often seen in a sociodrama that deals with complex and controversial themes. The goal of such a sociodrama—important for the director to communicate—is limited to allowing participants an opportunity to explore conflicting beliefs, examine values, and gain awareness of opposing views without necessarily reaching a consensus.

To validate his perception, the director shifted the level of action from the roles themselves to the role-players by directing the role-players of *Bin Laden* and *Buddhist* to step to one side of the actual role. Asked whether each role had sufficient opportunity to state his position fully and to hear the position of the other, both agreed. They were then asked to reverse roles, briefly and silently, to simply stand for a moment in the position of the other, his moral/philosophical adversary, and then return to his own role. This way of expanding the technique of role reversal enlarges the perspective of the role-players and the entire group. This exercise is repeated by the entire group.

Closure was achieved by having *bin Laden* and *oppressed peoples* reverse roles, make brief statements and then, returning to their own roles, make concluding statements. *Oppressed peoples* final statements came from each of the five sub-roles that had been created. As the most neutral role, the persons playing *journalists* were given an opportunity to make final statements to their role as *journalists*. Statements such as

"Like you, I like to observe; but, unlike you, I couldn't remain neutral" were made by each role-player to the role he no longer embodied.

De-roling was accomplished by setting out empty chairs for each of the *journalist* and *oppressed peoples* sub-roles. Each role-player was given an opportunity to address his/her role, describing similarities and differences, and, finally, to back away from the chair to complete the separation from the role. As *bin Laden* was the most complex and emotionally charged role, the director asked the role-players to take plenty of time in their process of separation and distance. To avoid possibilities of lingering identification and projection, the director then asked the group members to cluster around the person who had been the major *bin Laden* role-player, addressing him by his actual name and naming some of his own personal qualities. Finally, he was welcomed back into the group with words, hugs, claps on the shoulder, nods, and smiles.

The "Terrorist" sociodrama is an example of the more elaborate de-roling process required by a profound drama, in which the role-players have spent considerable time and deep, emotional energy. Because of the depth and complexity of this sociodrama, the director chose a two-step sharing process first done in small groups, where the need to compete for attention is lessened. Participants were asked to focus on what they have learned in the full group, each participant naming two or three things s/he had learned both from experiences in the sociodrama and from the small group sharing.

Although the director could not comprehend many of the verbal details and nuances of the group's Bengali, the general consensus was that the experience had been meaningful and full of important learning for the participants. A majority of group members observed that their perception of terrorists was more nuanced. While they held fast to their values of rejecting violence as a solution to social and economic oppression, they could appreciate that terrorists could also have worthwhile motivations. With few exceptions, the group—consisting mostly of educated, middle-class students—also noted that their desire to improve the lot of their most disadvantaged people had been strengthened by playing the various *oppressed peoples* roles. Some drew distinctions between the celebrity foreign terrorists (such as bin Laden) and the local terrorists (members of violent political cadres or crazed individuals, deserving unmitigated scorn and pity). Finally, they acknowledged the insight, spontaneity, and courage of the person who had injected the

Figure 8.2. Children: Post-cyclone workshop.

Buddhist perspective of non-violence into the action. Their commitment to be open to a diversity of religious views was reinforced. While all group members were Muslim, they were generally liberal and varied in their degree of religious practice, as evidenced, for example, in the relative minority who took extra time off to attend prayers during Friday lunch break.

WORKSHOP WITH CYCLONE-AFFECTED, TRAUMATIZED BANGLADESHI CHILDREN AGES 5 to 12 YEARS

For young children and adolescents, the night of the storm was a terrible, traumatizing experience. The storm hit them in pitch black night and when the day broke, the survivors found that they and their families had lost not only their shelter, but also their animals and other income-generating assets such as fishing boats and nets. The children and adolescents were heavily traumatized by the experience (see Figure 8.2).

An organization called *Working for a Better Life* had arrived after the cyclone, giving out food and providing psychological first aid to the stricken families and orphans. This group asked Saba to conduct a workshop for the children, most of whom were shy and withdrawn, suffered from nightmares about flood and drowning, developed sleeping disorders, and no longer played with their peers.

Initially, the children did not want to talk about their experience. Using spectograms, Saba helped the warm up by asking them to choose whether they liked sweet or hot foods, chocolate, or fruit. In another, they chose their favorite color. Their spontaneity increased immediately. Colors and food and, later, birth order and the number of children in the family—these were easy, normal topics that transformed the quiet, depressed group into a group of playing children. In order to help them express their personal experiences of the cyclone, the leader then placed an empty chair in the middle of the room and said, "This chair represents the cyclone. Speak to it, and tell it what it did to you." This exercise transformed the group. Children described the water coming relentlessly, members of the family scattering, some dying, and the destruction, dislocation, and chaos that resulted. In a doubling exercise, the leader asked the children to choose partners and asked one to talk about how s/he behaved on the night of the cyclone, and the other to try to show what that person might not be expressing. The children who said things like, "It didn't bother me, I just ran up the hill and I was fine," were partnered with others who said, "I was shaking the whole time, I was so afraid." Others who spoke about being afraid were partnered by children who said things like, "But I did what I could, and I survived."

To help further increase the children's spontaneity and energy, a game they loved, the "killer game," was played. The children, standing in a circle, were asked to close their eyes, and the one who would be the killer would be tapped on the shoulder by the leader. The killer would then use his/her eyes to kill when the time came. Then, they opened their eyes and were asked to move around the room without talking, trying to determine who the killer was. After a few minutes of moving around, the victim was given the direction to die and to imagine what kind of death it was. The children died dramatically, either shot and dropping quickly with a scream, or groaning and stumbling to their deaths. The children had no difficulty with this gruesome drama—

obviously enjoying the chance to play out hostile, negative roles and show their mastery in an energetic, comical way (see Figure 8.3).

In order to encourage the expression of withheld feelings, the director placed an empty chair in the middle of the room in the role of *a person they could talk to*. Saba asked the children to tell the chair what happened that night. Direct questions, Saba had learned, stimulated the children's fear of strangers and of authority. The empty chair gave permission to play. Many of the children reported scary dreams at night—the "black" was taking over, water everywhere, walls collapsing, parents disappearing, children searching for their relatives, lots of blood, and people dying. Other children took the opposite role: "Nothing really happened to me. I can handle this. I'm brave."

In the next part of the workshop, Saba used a version of Playback Theater to elicit the children's stories in more detail. Saba then directed a group of four children to show what happened in the teller's story, either as sculpture or with sound and movement. Two dramas emerged illustrating the experience of the cyclone. First performed for the groups themselves, they were enthusiastically received and later repeated and presented for an invited group of 300 children who had not been able to participate in the workshop.

The work was successful. The children themselves and workers from the *Working for a Better Life* organization reported that many of the children had recovered their ability to play, were more optimistic, and were less in denial about their experience.

PLAYBACK THEATER TRAINING: CYCLONE SIDR WORKSHOP, CONDUCTED BY JENNIE KRISTEL

Invited by Herb Propper, Kristel, a trained Playback Theater conductor, began working in Bangladesh in 2003 and repeated her visit seven times in the past 7 years. She sees her role as both a teacher of a particular technique and as a collaborator who feels it is important for the Bangladeshis to create a local form of Playback Theater that is centered in their own cultural norms, religious affiliations, and societal outlook.

A mix of 28 students, staff, and faculty attended. Most spoke some English; there was interpretation for those who did not. Kristel focuses extensively on role-training to help participants become accustomed to understanding different roles and to be able to take on a variety of emotionally challenging roles sequentially.

Figure 8.3. A cyclone survivor expresses his joy.

In beginning the training, Kristel asked the participants to draw a safe place, a place that they could go to in their imagination at any time in the workshop. She also encouraged each participant to partner with one other person who would remain their "ally" throughout the workshop. Kristel soon learned that most participants in this particular workshop had not experienced personal trauma. However, the participants expressed eagerness to learn techniques that would give them much-needed tools to provide help and support for the victims.

Bangladeshi parents expect their children to take care of them in their old age, and to accept their parent's choices regarding marriage and other life decisions. Themes of family connections most energized the group, and participants shared many stories about parents' expectations of them.

The warm-up used a life time line. Placing cloth on the floor to denote each person's life, group members marked important personal events from birth to the present. Powerful experiences were shared through stories and fluid sculptures, a group form that uses sound and movement to "play back" a person's experience.

One story told toward the end of the day stands out because it affected the teller and the group as a whole, most of whom had been caught by the struggle between the old traditions and the call to modernity. "S" told the story of his family and the connection he had with his grandfather, who had passed away a few years previously. As a young child who understood that mother had to work long hours, he nevertheless felt abandoned. S remembered feeling hungry and dirty throughout his childhood. As a young adult, however, his grandfather's emotional support enabled him to go to university and pursue this dream of being a psychologist.

In coming to the teller's chair, S had trouble voicing this story. His crying made it difficult for the conductor (Kristel) and the actors on stage to hear him. For support, Kristel invited him to ask his ally, "T," to sit with him and me during the telling and acting of the story. T's presence clearly helped S to continue to participate and share his story. After S had chosen actors to play himself, his mother, and his grandfather, the conductor reminded the actors that, instead of graphically recreating the scenes of abandonment, which could retraumatize the teller, they needed to be sensitive as they played the scenes he described, finding a balance of truth and highlighting details. Working with frozen and fluid sculptures and simple dialogue, the story was played back sensitively, using scarves and simple props to explore the powerful metaphors of the mother's lack of communication with S or his siblings. In the final scene, when the teller's actor met with his Spirit grandfather at the university, the actor expressed S's gratitude and appreciation for his grandfather's support of his dream. S was deeply moved, slightly tearful, but calm as he watched the interaction between the actor S and his grandfather. Returning to the audience, his ally at his side, he saw that many others were crying. The story had united the group in a common experience of struggle and transcendence.

A playback performance is often followed by a short interlude of music, which can soothe nerves, calm emotions, and aid participants to reflect quietly and integrate the story. After that is over, the conductor usually invites more stories to be told. As time was short, however, Kristel asked the group to think of a common Bangladeshi lullaby they could sing together. Afterwards, the participants shared what the story meant for them in their own lives. Finally, fluid sculptures reflected the themes of the day and the transformation of the stories.

Our last example takes place in India and was conducted by Saba, who has been trained entirely by BTTI workers.

CASE EXAMPLE: THE *HIJRAS* PROJECT, NEW DELHI, INDIA

Hijras, generally known in the West as transgenders, have been part of South Asian society for thousands of years (see Figure 8.4). They are born as men but become marked as women, often early in their lives because of a noted difference in sexual organs or because they behave in a way that is considered feminine in the community. Marked because of their different gender identity, they are a despised and neglected minority, even lower than the *Untouchables*. The negligence and discrimination that these people experience from their families and the culture causes them to suffer severe victimhood.

The massive social isolation of the *Hijras* creates strong feelings of fear, shame, and low self-esteem. The major goal of sociometry in this project was to enable the *Hijras* to deal with their isolation. As group leader, Saba found ways of empathizing with this community by tapping her own experience. Outside of the group, using her imagination and the information she had gathered, she role-reversed with the *Hijras*, placing herself in the role of the outcast, the victim abandoned by both

Figure 8.4. The drum serves as a warm-up for the *Hijras*.

the culture and his/her own family. She imagined what it would be like to be marked as different and unwanted from early childhood.

In most groups, role reversal is an easily available tool in the group itself. In this group, marked by their sense of inadequacy and abandonment, Saba feared that an active role reversal could have engendered resistance. Later, she shared the parts of her own life she felt she had in common with the group: the way she herself had been disrespected and put down as a woman in Bangladesh, leading to a feeling of constant fear, watchfulness, and protection of her body. For a while, Saba, had wanted to hide as much of her body as possible, to escape unwanted touch and comments from male peers and elders. Although her experience represented a much lesser version of the *Hijra* experience of social discrimination, Saba's sharing provided a way to lessen the gap between group members and leader.

Asking the *Hijras* to open up about their feelings was a challenge. Having a history of rejection and marginalization throughout their whole lives, *Hijras* as a group mistrust outsiders. A variety of sociometry exercises established common bonds (Hale, 1981). In spectograms and locograms, the *Hijras* shared the foods they loved or hated, their favorite colors, their family structures. As they moved about the room finding others with similar tastes, they began to form a more and more spontaneous and creative group. Next, Saba asked group members to create a map of India using parts of their colorful clothing to mark the villages or cities they came from. The map was used to find others from their native villages, the age at which they left home, how much contact they had with relatives, and what kind of living situation they had now. In the small groups that centered in the various villages, Saba asked the participants to interview each other, to talk about the special qualities they remembered about their place of birth, to share their own talents. As the group shared, the atmosphere lightened. It then became possible to use locograms to express more painful material. Locograms using four chairs were used to address various living situations. One chair represented the *Hijra*'s current situation. In addressing one of the four chairs, she might be talking with a parent, a partner, a shelter house for *Hijras*, or with the street, if that's where she lived. Slowly, trust for the leader was gained and spontaneity began to increase.

As the participants began to share stories and enactments of their lives, several members played scenes of their home lives, in which the *Hijra* lived in a family as a kind of second wife. She—and she is always identified as "she"—had to cook, clean, and take care of the children under the thumb of the first wife, the "real" woman.

During the workshop, one of the participants tearfully shared her feelings about her mother, whom she loved a lot but couldn't see anymore. Suddenly—stimulated by her openness—all the other participants joined in and expressed their emotions. Not having any connection to their original families anymore, most of the participants declared initially that they had few memories of their relatives. The sudden confrontation with the feelings of their peer broke a dam, releasing the past and allowing necessary grief to surface. As confidence grew, the *Hijras* enacted problems accompanying the spread of HIV/AIDS and other sexual illnesses among them, adding to their public shame. When they heard denigrating labels such as *chokra* and *hijra*, several related that they got angry in return, yelling and throwing shoes. Practice enactments increased the *Hijra*'s choice in such a situation, as less aggressive ways of reacting were rehearsed. Slowly, the group played out their feelings of anger and despair. Group members began to weep openly. The realization that they were all in the same situation had finally brought them together as a group.

When the workshop was over, it was clear the *Hijras* had rediscovered their own strengths. The hopelessness and resignation in the beginning was replaced by a lively spontaneity. Most of the group members gained in understanding of when and how they had played the victim role but were now ready to experience more positive ways of standing up for themselves without throwing shoes or being consumed by anger. Afterwards, one of the members commented, "I'm fine. I feel so much better in this group. We, too, have things we can be proud of. We're strong. We've survived." Another continued, "I wouldn't wish being a *Hijra* on my worst enemy. My role as *Hijra* is real, but it is not my only role. I am working on a role that is more accepting of my current situation with compassion for my suffering. I don't want to be angry all the time, wishing that I could give my role to my worst enemy. I can be good to myself and help myself heal."

CONCLUSIONS

We hope the foregoing discussion and descriptions offer some insight into the healing power of Moreno's methods applied to the conditions of disadvantaged persons in Bangladesh and India. These methods have already begun to take root and are being used to good effect in limited instances, particularly with the trauma of natural disasters. The emergence of the BTTI is providing a framework to develop local NGO workers and professionals as givers of psychosocial care. It is also an important part of the effort among therapists, counselors, and NGO aid workers to raise national consciousness about the importance of mental health issues, which have not been given much attention to date. With the infusion of additional training expertise and the cooperation of local universities and professionals, the benefits can increase and flower.

REFERENCES

Hale, A. (1981). *Conducting clinical sociometric explorations: A manual for psychodramatists and sociometrists.* Printed privately by the author.

Hudgins, M. K., & Drucker, K. (1998). The containing double as part of the therapeutic spiral model for treating trauma survivors. *International Journal of Treating Action Methods, 51*(2), 63–74.

Hudgins, M. K., & Kellerman, P. F. (Eds.). (2000). *Psychodrama with trauma survivors: Acting out your pain.* London: Jessica Kingsley.

Kalsched, D. (1996). *The inner world of trauma: Archetypal defenses of the personal spirit.* New York: Routledge.

Moreno, J. L. (1973). *The theatre of spontaneity* (rev. ed.). Beacon, NY: Beacon House.

Moreno, J. L. (1977). *Psychodrama, Vol. 1* (4th ed.). Beacon, NY: Beacon House.

Moreno, J. L. (1978). *Who shall survive? Foundations of sociometry, group psychotherapy and sociodrama* (3rd ed.). Beacon, NY: Beacon House.

Moreno, Z. T. (1995). *On surplus reality.* Unpublished manuscript.

Propper, H. (2004). *National Therapeutic Theatre Workshop 2004; II. Chittagong Workshop.* Unpublished manuscript.

Propper, H. (2008). *Trainer process report: National Therapeutic Theatre Workshop '08.* Unpublished manuscript.

Schramski, T. (1989). *How to role reverse.* Unpublished manuscript.

Sternberg, P., & Garcia, A. (2000). *Sociodrama: Who's in your shoes* (2nd ed.)? Westport, CT: Praeger.

Treadwell, T. W., Kumar, V. K., Stein, S. A., & Prosnick, K. (1998). Sociometry: Tools for research and practice. *The International Journal of Action Methods; Psychodrama, Skill Training, and Role Playing, 51*(1), 23–40.

9

Re-Reconciling Culture-Based Conflicts With "Culture-Drama"

JON P. KIRBY AND GONG SHU

Authors' Profiles

Jon P. Kirby: *My journey to Ghana was prompted by my religious order. After spending some 13 years in training to be a missionary I was asked to choose where I wanted to spend the rest of my life. I had always fancied myself "a real missionary," deep in the Amazon, where I could study anthropology. Well, things don't often turn out as we expect. When my turn came to go into my superior's office to find out my "desideratum," the word "Ghana" was sounded. That fateful moment still rings in my ears. The comforting presence of a much-loved colleague, Fr. Kofi Ron Lange, who was on leave from Ghana at the time turned me around. Through his efforts, I became the first SVD missionary in Ghana to be given a full 6 months just to study the language. Soon, I was seeing the world from their perspective. And what a wonderful vision that was. Later, my anthropological studies provided the means to deepen this relationship which kept me in the wilds learning from the people. And it is here that culture-drama has its true roots, for it is merely the knowledge of the people intensified and made explicit.*

Gong Shu: In 1979, when I was an expressive arts therapist using art therapy and psychodrama at the House of Affirmation, a psychiatric residential treatment center for religious (an African term for church-affiliated workers), my work brought me in close touch with missionaries from various parts of the world. Culture drama was used since then to help resolve conflicts among the residents. I was first attracted to go to Africa because of my work with a Ghanian religious. The Provincial of this religious appreciated my work and requested that I go to Ghana in 1989. He wanted me to help resolve the conflicts among the missionaries coming from various parts of the world as well as the conflicts between the missionaries and the local religious communities. He scheduled six workshops for me to do in one month's time, starting from Accra in the south to Wa in the north. In these workshops, I was able to help the groups realize how cultural differences contributed to the miscommunication, through the processes of culture drama which I have continued to develop in various parts of the world, among them: Singapore, Malaysia, Taiwan, and Mainland China.

Jon Kirby, director of the Tamale Institute of Cross-Cultural Studies, participated in the last of my six workshops in Ghana, which ranged from Accra to Wa. We discovered that we were kindred spirits and he joined me in my work both in Ghana and other parts of Africa, developing Culture Drama as a cross-cultural discipline of Anthropology and Psychodrama.

Fr. Jon P. Kirby, PhD, SVD, is a Catholic priest, a theologian, and a social anthropologist. Beginning in 1972, he worked in Ghana for 36 years as a missionary, an anthropologist, a cross-cultural trainer, and, since 1989, as a culture-drama facilitator. He has taught at Ghana's University for Development Studies, and, for 25 years, served as the founder-director of Tamale Institute of Cross-Cultural Studies (www.ticcs.org), which is a research and teaching facilty for applied ministry and development. In the United States he has held positions at Catholic Theological Union, Boston University, and Washington Theological Union and is a member of many professional organizations, including Anthropos Institute, the American Anthropological Association, the African Studies Association, the American Academy of Religion, the American Society of Missiology, and the United States Catholic Mission Association. He has published widely.

Gong Shu, PhD, ATR, TEP, LCSW, is an internationally known psycho- and sociodramatist who has received both the Hannah Weiner Award of the ASGPP and the Outstanding Achievement Award in Traditional Medicine. She has published widely and is known for her work in Asia, Europe, and the United States. Gong Shu is also the founder of the International Zerka Moreno Institute, with branches in St. Louis, Taipeh, and soon China, and is a founder of the Center for Creative Development.

INTRODUCTION

The middle-aged man, eyes rolling and rigid with fear, was dragged off the bus by his accusers as they sounded the alarm: "Konkomba! Konkomba!" Before he reached the bottom step he was swept away by the roiling mob and an instant later dispatched by five or six flailing Dagomba cutlasses. At the edge of the crowd, barely able to contain his shock and terror, stood another man who, despite his efforts to add to the murderous refrain "Kill him! Kill him!" seemed strangely out of place. His demeanor furtive; his eyes cautiously darted to his Dagomba neighbors, then down to his torn "canvas" shoes, and at the sight of the bloodied machetes raised high in victory, he nervously tried to reduce his large frame to nothing. He too was a Konkomba, and if the slightest hint of his true identity, like the unbidden sweat beading up on his forehead, ever broke through, he dared not think what would happen.

Hundreds such scenes occurred across Northern Ghana in the days following the outbreak of the infamous "Northern Conflict" of February and March 1994—scenes that, due partly to the overshadowing Rwanda-Burundi affair and partly to a well-orchestrated governmental cover-up, hardly garnered the attention of Southern Ghana, let alone the rest of the world. Nonetheless, it was estimated that up to 20,000 people lost their lives and more than 200,000 were deprived of their land and all their earthly possessions and were forced into exile as refugees (Bogner, 2000; Katanga, 1994a, 1994b; Kirby, 2003; Pul, 2003; van der Lingde & Naylor, 1994). They remain so to this day and the cities where these dramatic events unfolded are even now more segregated tribally than was Johannesburg at the height of apartheid.

This describes the opening scene for the culture-drama workshop that unfolded in March 2002, 8 years after the conflict (Kirby, 2002). The 20 workshop participants, who belonged to the two major conflicting groups, Konkombas and Dagombas, had all experienced events like these, and, for this reason, they had to be individually chosen and well prepared. Nevertheless, it was with extreme care and trepidation that my colleague, Dr. Gong Shu, and I coaxed and cajoled them to engage in the process of full recall and re-enactment—the first steps along the road to reconciliation. For we were all too conscious of the terror, lurking beneath the surface, that could be unleashed at any false step.

DESERT ISLAND SCENE: DRAWING TOGETHER

This opening scene had been preceded by a "warm up" portraying the survivors of an imaginary shipwreck who had found themselves cast up on a small desert island represented by a large sheet. Here, as they paint their marooned lives on the canvas, the very jostling for space conveys the need to live together in harmony or not at all. After some time we survey the final product noting the barriers and deep divisions. Even the more creative attempts to bridge the communities through shared services like farming, animal husbandry, schools, and training centers are incapacitated by the fact that all the Konkombas are on one side of the island and the Dagombas on the other.

Following the desert island warm-up, we are ready to begin. All are a blank except for the palpable fear that unites us. Finally, a voice intones: "I don't know why I agreed to this workshop. It doesn't do any good to keep going over and over the same thing, bringing up those terrible experiences." It echoes across the room as the other participants signal their agreement. Shu cajoles them into naming the scene they fear most. "It is the bus scene." Here is where we begin.

THE BUS SCENE

Still unconvinced, but absolutely committed to building peace, the group fearfully begins constructing the scene. Eight folding chairs arranged two by two with an aisle between are our "bus." The "mob" brandishes rolled up magazines as their weapons. One adds a touch of realism reminding the mob to wear the magical amulets used for protection in "wartime," while others stoke an imaginary bonfire of discarded tires which is used to block the roadway.

Soon after the role-play begins, we ask them to "stop" and to switch places. The technique of role-reversal is one of culture-drama's mainstays, and we use it throughout the workshop. We explain that the Konkombas are to play the role of the Dagomba mob and the two Konkomba victims are to be played by Dagombas. Still murmuring their dissent, they regroup and take their positions. As they settle into their new roles, Gong Shu and I advise them to stop the action if they find that anything seems "wrong" or "out of place." We refer to this as raising "red flags" but actually they just interrupted the scene whenever they had a question or didn't agree on something.

Hardly do they begin again but "red flags" go up and action is stopped. First the Dagombas speak. "It's not like that," two of them insist. "You have to really shout, "Konkomba, Konkomba!" It's not loud enough; not forceful enough!" Another chimes in, "No, not that way! Grab him like this! Use all your strength." Then it is the Konkombas' turn to advise: "You, there. This is no joke. You are the victim. Look, they are going to kill you. You are behaving too proudly. You are helpless!" He then shows the Dagomba how to look like a helpless victim. The Dagomba attempts to follow his advice. Again he fails, but is encouraged by the Konkombas.

At this point Gong Shu intervenes by explaining her version of the technique of doubling. Other versions are mostly verbal but hers is also physical: "No, don't just tell him, stand behind him and hold him. Move him along, make his arms your arms, his legs your legs. Move as a Konkomba would actually move. Let him feel it. And you the Dagomba, let yourself be moved by this person who is showing you how to behave. After all, he is the Konkomba. He knows how Konkombas act doesn't he?"

Incredulous, he looks around the room to the faces of the other Konkombas in the group, to scan them for the slightest indication that this is a plot to make him look silly, or worse, to make all Dagombas look foolish. But he doesn't see what he is looking for. His resistance deflates as he thinks about his feelings that he will later share with the whole group. We summarize them as follows:

> This way of acting is much different than I thought Konkombas would behave. It is not the way I would behave. But is it really the way Konkombas are? I feel strangely dependent on this Konkomba leading me around. Yet I trust him. He could not have made this up to embarrass me. As I look around at the others, I can see they are all in agreement. This is not something they pre-arranged. It is spontaneous. This Konkomba really wants me to know the way he feels, the way he acts and sees things. He is on my side. For the first time in my life I trust them.

They go back again to their scene work, but now they are more circumspect, learning as they go along. Each step becomes a test waiting to be rejected or confirmed by the other group—the group whose life experience they are trying to act out misstep by misstep. Gradually it dawns on the participants that they really do not know the other. And to learn about the other, they are obliged to learn about themselves. In scene after scene, it becomes clearer how alone and isolated we really are, on our separate cultural pathways. Long-accepted but unsteady, perhaps even faulty, judgments relegate these "others" to lesser or imperfect versions of ourselves. At this point the "hidden self" leaps out and can be recognized, named, and accepted for what it is. At this point it may be negotiated or changed. One can begin to ask how much I am willing and able to change *my own* cultural pathways in ways that accommodate the other's ways of thinking and believing, valuing and behaving. Each side needs first to negotiate with themselves before the "transformative" work—the work of forming a new way of being together—can begin. Here is the magic of culture-drama: it gets to those darkened and powerful areas of our cultural unconscious, the areas that move us along without a question or a thought. In the same instant it cracks open our pre-suppositions about ourselves and the other.

HISTORY OF CULTURE-DRAMA

When Shu, who was well known for her work with Catholic priests and brothers in the United States, was called in to help with discussions, she was convinced that the problem was not that they were ill but that the conflicts were due to cultural differences. She felt the solution was simply to get these culturally mixed groups to engage in leisure activities together instead of just sitting around watching television (Kirby, 2003; Shu & Kirby, 1992). This goal was greatly aided by teaming up with the co-author, Jon Kirby, who is an anthropologist with a great deal of experience working with different culture groups in Ghana. Together they developed the unique method of "culture-drama."

CULTURAL PATHWAYS IN CONFLICT

Notwithstanding individual differences and personal problems, the cultural perspective focuses exclusively on collective differences and issues—the European perspective versus the Ghanaian perspective. Here, "conflict" is understood in terms of oppositions in the groups' "cultural pathways" rather than the differences between individuals. The importance of this perspective can be illustrated by showing the differences between the two culturally embedded notions of European charity versus African hospitality.

The Europeans complained that the Africans were not "good" community members and were not behaving as "good" members of the religious order ought to behave. The Africans, even more vocal, complained that the Europeans were "not even good human beings!" They were "just bad!" But neither group was able to explain what they meant, or offer concrete examples. It was at this point that we usually asked them to stop talking and begin role-playing.

THE COMMON ROOM SCENE

The primary focus of community conflict is the "common room," the very place where we are running the culture-drama session. Actors are chosen, two from each group, and the first scene is set by moving around some of the furniture. It is a visit from a friend of one of the African brothers.

The scene begins with a knock at the door. The African brother gets up to answer the door. A long litany of greetings in the local language along with interspersed laughter fills the room. We intervene to explain the rules of role-reversal and how to interrupt with questions and observations. Hesitantly they begin again in reversed roles. But it is not long before they are interrupted. "We don't do it like that," says the Ghanaian to his European colleague who is trying to imitate what has just transpired. "You can see your brother through the window, wave to him as you approach the door. Don't let him just stand there; begin welcoming him in with enthusiasm."

One of the Europeans begins to address the Ghanaian who is playing the part of a European sitting down reading the newspaper with a scowl. "Why are you wearing such a mad face?" he says. "Is that supposed to be me? I don't behave like that, do I?"

"Yes, that's you," they all respond in unison.

There is a pause. He thinks it over and responds, "Well if I do behave that way it must be for a good reason."

"Show us, don't talk about it," we insist.

Over the course of two more interruptions, they work their way through the greetings and cross the threshold to the common room. They are now seated and a round of introductions begins: "Welcome to our home," says the European (playing the part of a Ghanaian).

Immediately "red flags" go up from the Ghanaians. "You must give him water before any official welcome!"

Action resumes. But when the actor opens the fridge he finds it full of food; no water.

Once again "red flags" go up. "Um-humm! You see? Every time we put water in the fridge you remove it and replace it with your cheese. Now you see the problem. When you do that we can't welcome our friends properly. So we remove the cheese and put the water back."

THE ANALYSIS

Culture-drama enables the participants to concretize their unarticulated, implicit pathways and, through the enactments, get to the roots of the problem. The full meaning of the cultural "event" is conveyed by the total context, including the use of space, objects, and the actions, much more than simply by words. This is the principle of "action insight" which will be described more in detail below.

The scenes convey the cultural meaning. The "community room," the "fridge," and the "water" are all essential components of the customary practice of welcoming in Ghana. For example, one "conflict" arises from the different and conflicting cultural expectations concerning "hospitality." The different expectations and uses of the fridge become clear in the scene. But these rest on deeper foundations. The meaning and use of food versus drink is different in each culture. In Africa, much more than in Europe, food and drink are rigorously required components of hospitality and fridges are part of this cultural complex.

SOCIAL CONTEXTS OF HOSPITALITY

In Africa, the cultural meaning of fridge is intimately linked with "drinks" and the initiating of hospitality. Of course, until quite recently, there were no fridges in Africa. In the past this "welcome water" was kept cool in clay pots. Cool water brings cool, or peaceful relations.

Although food is the consummate mark of hospitality, it can be offered only after the relations have first been initiated through drink. Rituals follow the same pattern. Libations precede the "sacrificial food." But food, unlike drink, is never served cold. It is always freshly prepared and hot. The sharing requires a "sit-down meal" with all the social trappings including an overnight stay. In Africa, "food" normally refers to the starchy staple which spoils quickly, even if refrigerated, and therefore needs to be entirely eaten at a sitting. There are no leftovers for the fridge. Therefore, "food" is not associated with fridges in the same way that "drink" is.

Accordingly, fridges are not limited to the kitchen, as they are in Europe and America, but are found in areas where relationships are initiated; where people meet, sit, and talk. For example, offices are usually equipped with small fridges located within easy reach of the desk. African hosts are required to welcome into their living space all and sundry by offering the primary requisite of cold water. The appearance of the fridge in the workplace, especially in the boss's office, enables the "big man" to welcome a continuous flow of visitors, business associates, and fellow workers.

THE HOSPITALITY RITUAL

Throughout Africa, water is the primary symbol of hospitality. It is absolutely necessary in forming and sustaining relationships, and relationships are needed to sustain life. If this "action chain" is broken, as the great popularizer of culture, Edward Hall, has so clearly demonstrated (1966), peoples' unfulfilled expectations lead to fear and confusion, which in turn lead to flight-or-fight. Thus, "welcome water" can never be refused. It must always be accepted, or at least acknowledged, because hospitality binds all, enemies included, at the most basic level of our common human identity. Similarly, its influence extends beyond relations in the "seen world," between people in everyday life, to relations in the "unseen world," with spirits and ancestors. Here too, it is the first step in establishing and sustaining relationships.

To sum up, fridges are for water, water is for relationships, and relationships are for promoting and sustaining life. In Africa, spiritual and physical life are one. If water, and by extension, the fridge, are repositories of life, they are also symbols that foster spiritual energy or are conduits of creative life. Thus, they involve a religious obligation and a moral necessity. To the African, this is unquestionably something that God fully endorses and requires of us, for as proverbial wisdom would have it, "The stranger is God" (Lange, 1998).

From this perspective it is quite logical and consequent for Africans to wonder how their European brothers and sisters, who are at times referred to as "holy religious," can presume to interrupt or short-circuit what is understood to be "God's holy activity." It is not any wonder, therefore, that the Africans said, "as for them, they are just bad!"

THE EUROPEAN VIEW

Not so for the Europeans. Their meanings and expectations are primarily constructed around a much narrower concept of community. The "common room" of a religious community is a cloistered inner sanctum for the common life of its members; not the open "meeting room" at the entrance to African compounds. Only members of the order (the religious group) or other clerics and intimate associates are admitted. In the minds of Europeans, breaking this code is equated with not being a good religious.

During the scenes it became clear that the Europeans did not think it was appropriate to admit "outsiders" to their common room, especially the African friends of their African religious brothers. The African members of the religious community saw this as "wicked," given their understanding that "God's rules" are more important than any man-made book of rules. The fact that the Europeans did not seem to accord others the minimum recognition of their human-ness also led many to say: "They are not even human," or "They are racist," or the greatest sin of all, "They are selfish."

CULTURAL MEANINGS AND COMMUNAL HARMONY

Before enacting the drama, the participants were only able to voice their most general feelings that the other group somehow "had the wrong idea" or that "they were doing things all wrong." When the Africans referred to the Europeans as "inhuman" the meanings behind these statements were implicit, buried deep inside the cultural pathways, connected to the meanings embedded in "water," "fridge," and in their conception and use of communal space. Culture-drama exposed these meanings, helped to foster acceptance and a more concrete, honest, and open dialogue leading to greater understanding, more give-and-take, a broader way of interpreting the community rules, and, eventually, to a more harmonious community life.

With sufficient time, culture-drama could serve as a vehicle to synthesize adjusted views, beliefs, and behavior and, in this way, lead to a new "peace culture." We offer an example of this below.

THE NORTHERN CONFLICT

Many political analysts oversimplified the 1994 "Northern Conflict" as one over scarce resources between two groups—the Konkombas, who were pictured as violent and "wild invaders" from neighboring countries, and the better-known Dagombas, who were generally regarded as the cultured leaders of the North (Mahama, 1989). The conflict itself was mocked and made light of by the government-controlled press as the "guinea-fowl war" because the spark that ignited the blaze was a quarrel between a Konkomba and a Dagomba over the market price of this animal. In actuality, the conflict covered most of the North and involved its peoples in a full-scale civil war.

The peoples of northern Ghana, like those of other countries stretching across the West African Savannah belt, are of two traditional political types. One type has chiefs and is politically structured as a "traditional state system" (Eyre-Smith, 1933; Goody, 1954, 1967/1969, 1971; Staniland, 1975; Wilks, 1961, 1971) comprising a bureaucracy that extends hierarchically over their own clans and subordinate peoples having different customs and languages.

The other type is without rulers or any formal structures of governance outside the extended family system (Kirby, 1986; Tait, 1958). Although these non-chiefly or "acephalous" groups in northern Ghana are usually referred to as "the minorities," they actually outnumber the "state system" peoples three to one. They are only the "minority" when it comes to political and economic power.

CHIEFLY VERSUS NONCHIEFLY PEOPLES

These two groups of peoples—the structured and unstructured, chiefly and non-chiefly—have been at loggerheads from the time that peoples of the Western Sudan discovered the concept of state in ancient fifth-century Gana (Middleton & Tait, 1953). The Mole-Dagbon groups, of which the Dagombas are a sub-group, entered the area that is now northern Ghana in the 13th century as raiding break-away factions of other state groups further to the north (Wilks, 1971). Increasingly these groups came to be associated with literate Muslim clerics and gradually the Muslim calendar, clothing, art, customs, and beliefs became a part of their culture (Levtzion, 1968). From the seventeenth to the turn of the twentieth century, the powerful Asante coerced the northern state societies, including the Dagomba, to capture and deliver thousands of slaves, along with foodstuffs and livestock each year, which they gathered from the surrounding non-chiefly peoples. In the early twentieth century, under British colonial rule, the three northern chiefly groups were put in charge of the other 40 to 50 non-chiefly groups thus making "official" and normalizing this predatory relationship (Ferguson & Wilks, 1970; Tait, 1961). After Ghana's independence, under Nkrumah, this relationship continued (Ladouceur, 1979; Staniland, 1975).

Under the British administration the northern royals of the "major tribes" were educated to provide the system with clerks and administrators. But beginning in the 1950s, the British opened the North to missionaries, with the result that mission schools, hospitals, and other services were, for the first time, offered to the "minorities." These services continued and expanded after Independence throughout the 1960s and 1970s. By the mid-1970s the non-chiefly groups could boast of a larger educated elite than the chiefly groups, and by the end of the 70s full awareness of their repressed political and economic condition had led them into overt political opposition.

Ethnic conflicts, involving one or more of the chiefly groups against one or more of the non-chiefly groups, erupted in 1979 and continued until December 1993 when the non-chiefly groups demanded their full and equal rights, their own land, and their own chiefs. This was promptly rejected by the three chiefly groups, and within weeks the entire north was engulfed in armed conflict (Katanga, 1994b).

After a month of fighting, the combined chiefly groups had been roundly defeated by the non-chiefly peoples, and everyone feared an imminent attack on the Dagomba-controlled main cities of the north, Tamale and Yendi. The army was called in by the "majority groups" and they attacked the "minorities" with overwhelming ferocity. Unwilling to fight government forces, the non-chiefly forces simply "disappeared" into the bush leaving an "occupied North" under military law for more than a year. Only very slowly did the North come back to life.

In the aftermath of the war there were a number of unsuccessful peacebuilding efforts by the strongly biased government and by NGOs (Assefa, 2001). Gradually things calmed down. But up until now the war has never been resolved. For example, even now, in 2009, 15 years after the war, the non-chiefly peoples, especially the Konkomba, are not permitted to own property, hold jobs or reside in the two main urban centers of the North.

THE GHANAIAN WORKSHOP

The festering discontent, the division, and the deeper structural issues of the conflict between the "chiefly groups" (especially the Dagombas) and the "non-chiefly groups" (especially the Konkombas) were for the first time addressed in our 2002 culture-drama workshop. The workshop, comprising ten of each ethnic group, was sponsored by Catholic Relief Services, Ghana, at a conference center in the south, some 500 miles from where the fighting took place. For one intensive week, in complete seclusion, they worked toward building a lasting peace for themselves and the whole of Northern Ghana (Kirby, 2002).

Some of the major enactments centered on different points of view concerning "big-man" versus "small-man," "masters" versus "subjects," the role of "chiefs" versus "Earth shrine custodians" on the question of land tenure and ownership, and other areas of conflicting expectations, especially those regarding "freedom" and "constraint" (Kirby, 2002, 2003). The objective was to establish a genuine trust and interdependency so as to build from their conflicting pathways a number of basic shared pathways toward a new culture of peace (Kirby, 2007). Besides the "bus scene," which was the first, there were four other significant scenes which we will now describe.

The Chief Scene

The Konkomba playing the part of the Ya Na (King of Dagbon) was visibly moved. His eyes widened in a look of pleased disbelief as the Dagombas placed the chief's hat, the final touch of the Dagomba regal attire, on his head. He was asked to play the role of the Ya Na, the "King of Dagbon," ruler of the most important ethnic group in Northern Ghana. No Konkomba could possibly know the many taboos, the refined postures and forms of etiquette that go with being King of Dagbon. The preparation for the role contributed to the conciliatory process. The regalia of the chief was so important, and so hemmed in by restrictions and taboos, that simply getting access to it, to say nothing of actually using it in a role-play, required much tact. The effect of having real artifacts was tremendous.

As we were about to begin, the Konkombas intently watched the faces of the Dagombas for any reaction. There was something more than role-playing here. But not only were their worst fears demolished by what they saw, they were emphatically moved. The way the Dagombas helped the Konkomba, who played the role of the Ya Na, to act "kingly" and to wear the regal attire, and the way they tutored them on how and when to sit, stand, and move about, to direct their courtiers and to "look regal," immediately dispelled the greatest fears of the Konkombas concerning their belief that the Dagombas looked down upon them, considered them beneath their dignity, unfit to rule, and unable to be chiefly. As the Dagombas vied with each other to help the Konkomba actor to be a "proper" Ya Na, this fear vanished.

Credibility was also greatly increased by the fact that one of the Dagomba participants was, in real life, the "Mionlana," a very powerful chief, next in the line of succession to the Ya Na. It also soon became clear to the Dagombas that the Konkombas did not hate them or even the idea of chieftaincy. They too could be moved by its power and dignity. But it was simply not a part of their culture.

The Marriage Dispute Scene

These powerful currents increased as the role-playing continued. The scene was set for the trial of a marriage dispute. Konkombas, like other non-chiefly peoples, have long been forced to submit to the judgments of Dagomba chiefs in cases of dispute-settlement. Most of these involve quarrels between Konkomba families over their claims to women, livestock or land. It was not unusual for the chief to settle such disputes by punishing both families with a fine and taking the woman as his own wife.

The Action

The scene is set. A sturdy coffee table serves as the King's dais. He sits above a throng of buzzing advisors as the disputing party is led into the makeshift court. "This man stole my wife and hasn't given me any compensation," the first man says.

Then action stops and some Konkombas intervene: "It is not simply a question of compensation. You Dagombas don't have the bridewealth system, but we Konkombas do."

"That is true. We Dagombas do not 'sell' our women," interjects a Dagomba.

"Neither do we," say the Konkombas in quick response. To acquire a wife, a man must work on his in-law's farm for seven years. This strengthens relations between the two families. If a wife is stolen by another man, everyone gets upset. A simple compensation does not cover the husband's time and trouble. Nor will it win him a new wife. The bad relations and consternation extend to all three families. The ancestors themselves demand vengeance and, in the vendetta that ensues, many will lose their lives.

Better informed about the heavy weight of his loss, the Dagomba acting the part of the jilted Konkomba says, "Please, chief, my wife has been stolen and our families are at a considerable loss." According to custom, this is translated to the chief by the "linguist" or spokesman of the court.

The chief then summons the defendant, "Let the other Konkomba man come in to speak." They bring in the other Konkomba (played by a Dagomba). But before he can utter a word the "red flags" go up.

A Konkomba says, "No, he wouldn't act like that. A real Konkomba would not know all the proper etiquette used in the presence of a chief and would embarrass himself." He then shows the Dagomba how a Konkomba would actually behave. Everyone laughs at the spectacle. "You see," says a Konkomba, "we are at a distinct disadvantage in the courts of the Dagombas; we are out of place. They don't know our customs and their laws don't help us."

The action continues. The Ya Na (played by a Konkomba) is urged to pass judgment but finds it difficult.

The real Dagombas advise him: "After consulting with my elders this is what I am going to do: I am giving you both a fine of one sheep to pay. As for the woman, take her away to my house where she will not cause any further trouble." All laugh at the cleverness of the Ya Na in confiscating the woman.

But some Dagombas are not of the same view. "It would not be as simple as that," they say. "The Ya Na would first discuss the matter with his elders sitting there in front. He would then call the woman and ask for her view. Finally, he could fine them for causing trouble and for ignoring the woman's view; and, yes, he could take the woman as his own wife. But this is not out of selfishness or lechery." They go on to explain that each village under a chief's authority is obligated to send him a wife, establishing a link of responsibility to her family. This is to their advantage. In this way she becomes an unofficial spokesperson for her family and village. Eventually her village will have a stake in chieftaincy and her sons may rise to the level of the chieftaincy held by their father.

The Konkomba, playing the role of the Ya Na, then explains his hesitancy, "We Konkombas do not tell others what to do. Every man is to be free as God created him. I cannot presume to tell another man what to do. He would certainly understand this as a wicked attempt to take away his freedom. If he does not resist, the ancestors themselves will rise up to assert their independence and punish him."

All begin to understand the differences in their perspectives. Then the facilitators interject: "But now you are a Dagomba chief. You are not a Konkomba. Do what you must do." The Ya Na pronounces judgment and all agree to it, even the Konkombas. Great relief and a hint of pride show in his face. It is a wonderful thing to have power! The real Dagombas in the group give him a round of applause and the Konkombas are thinking: "We too could do that; we too could be chiefs. It would be a good thing."

Culture-drama is a door to discovery. Konkombas learn that chiefs are not "so bad" after all. It becomes clear that, in many ways, the Konkombas are not equipped to make use of the benefits of appeal and support that the institution of chieftaincy could provide, and they discover that many of their grievances are not so much against the system itself as against its abuses. The Dagombas, in turn, learn the full consequences of the selfish judgments made by some of their chiefs. Above all, both sides learn to trust each other.

In both systems "respect" (jirima) is the most important quality or virtue, but it is understood differently in each. The understanding of the Dagombas is shown in this proverb: "The chief's guinea fowl is the one in the bush" (Lange, 1998). It means that a good chief, in the name of hospitality, would be expected to give away to visitors all his household's guinea fowls, leaving only the wild guinea fowls in the "bush" for his own supper. Much of the anger of the Dagombas toward the Konkombas is based on the mistaken belief that Konkombas are not respectful to their chiefs. The "chief" scene taught both sides that what each thought about the other is not true. Each is, indeed, quite "respectful" but in very different ways.

The Market Scene

Two women, one from each group, chose the marketplace as the location for their conflict, because the market is the public arena of women. The Konkombas are mostly subsistence farmers. The men produce the "food," which includes yams and grains, while the women produce the vegetables used in making the "soup." The main meal is "TZ" (tee-zed), a kind of thick porridge of sorghum, millet or maize covered with soup.

Dagombas, on the other hand, are mostly traders. The Dagomba women traders meet the Konkomba women producers at the Konkomba markets. Together, the women set up the village market scene with great efficiency. Various market items are situated around the room—a table of tomatoes here, okra there, dried fish, rice, sorghum, beans, and so on, are all in their own corners. Konkomba women take up their positions as the sellers and Dagomba women as the buyers. Because there are not enough women a few of the men are recruited as market women selling various commodities. As soon as the action begins they change roles: Dagombas do the selling and Konkombas the buying.

The Action

A Konkomba playing a Dagomba trader starts off. "Greetings to you and the market! I hope you are fine. I like your tomatoes. How much for them?"

The Dagomba playing the role of the Konkomba seller responds saying, "They are five for 500 cedis."

"Here, get your money," says the trader. Then the order to stop the action is given by both groups.

The Konkombas say they wouldn't behave like that in real life. Rather they would say: "They are five for 500 cedis, but if you buy some I'll reduce the price and give you some extra."

The Dagombas say they wouldn't behave that way, either. They would press for a better bargain saying, "Oh! Now don't make a fuss. There are plenty of tomato sellers. Give me a good deal and I will always buy from you. Here take 400 and give me 10 tomatoes." Then they would snatch up some extra besides and put them in their basin. Finally they would say, "Take these to the truck for me. I'm going to see the rice sellers."

The Konkomba woman, who is acting as the buyer, tries but she can't bring herself to speak or act as she has been instructed. In particular, she finds it impossible to snatch up the extra tomatoes.

The Dagombas urge her on saying, "Try. Go ahead and do it."

She answers, "I can't! I just can't."

The Dagombas are amazed. "Why can't you do this? It is not difficult."

No response.

Then the Dagomba, who is acting as the Konkomba seller, offers a demonstration. She places her hands on her hips and says, "No, you can carry the tomatoes back to the truck yourself and give me the full agreed price or you will be sorry you ever came here."

Again, the real Konkombas intervene to correct her: "No. As a Konkomba you can't say that! You have to do as she says. Give everything to her and take them to the truck."

Then the Dagomba, who is playing the Konkomba seller, is dumbfounded and objects, "What do you mean? I can never do that."

The real Konkomba woman then takes on the seller's role again and shows the Dagomba woman how a Konkomba would really behave.

The Dagomba woman playing the Konkomba seller then asks, "How can you do that? Don't you respect yourself?"

The Konkomba says in reply, "This is the way we respect ourselves. If someone wants it so much you must give it to her. You shouldn't try to stop her. That is what we have been taught by the ancestors. You must allow her to be free." In both the "market scene" and the "chief scene" the Dagombas and the Konkombas found it nearly impossible to act out the role of the other. This was not because they didn't see or understand what was being asked of them but because the particular actions or behavior they were being asked to enact were simply inconceivable in their own culture. Their accustomed cultural pathways literally prevented them from acting in those ways even if it was "make believe."

The resistance was challenged by a Dagomba who didn't understand why the Konkombas should suddenly "lash out" at them when they "were only doing what they always have done." For example, in the market scene, a participant insisted that the Konkombas had the chance to refuse to give the Dagombas what they wanted but they just couldn't do it. "This is only cowardice," he said. "And then later on when they suddenly turn on you, this is absolute madness."

At this point Shu confronts the man and, to his great surprise, starts pushing him, thrusting him back, again and again, until his back is against the wall. "How does this make you feel," she says, using the drama therapy technique of "action interpretation" (Johnson, Sandel, & Eicher, 1983). Finally, with his back against the wall, he pushes back. "Aha," says Shu. "Now you know how it feels to be pushed against a wall like the Konkombas have felt for centuries." He was silent after that.

The Earth Shrine Scene

At the most basic level of identity, all of Africa is divided up into thousands of territorial parcels, demarcated by rivers, mountains, forests, and natural formations, each of which is presided over by a particular "Earth Spirit" that is responsible for the fertility and well-being of all within its territorial domain. Both Dagombas and Konkombas have the same proverb stipulating the relationship that exists between this spirit and the people: "The people know the 'Earth' [Earth spirit] and the 'Earth' knows its master" (Lange, 1998).

Although non-chiefly peoples, like the Konkombas, do not have chiefs, they do have spiritual leaders who form the link between the "Earth" and the people (Froelich, 1954). When the Dagombas entered what is now the Dagomba Kingdom (Dagbon) as raiding parties from territories further north, they killed these leaders and usurped their office (Cardinall, 1920/1960; Kirby, in press). Part of the conflict concerns this disruption and its continuation in various forms up to the present time.

To set the scene, one participant locates a stone that can serve as the shrine's "altar," where sacrifices are made, and various objects associated with "Earth" shrines, such as a clay pot and an iron bell or "gong-gong," are used to call the spirit. Dagombas play the parts of the Konkomba "Earth shrine custodian" and his elders, while the Konkombas play the role of Dagombas who are forced to go to the Konkombas to appeal to the shrine for rain.

The Action

The local Dagomba chief and elders (played by Konkombas) approach the house of the "Earth shrine custodian." "Ko, ko, ko! Knocking, knocking!"

"Who is it?" asks the custodian.

"It is Suleman, the chief of Damon."

"Oh, come in, chief. You are most welcome." Water is offered and the chief is asked his mission.

"I am here to ask for rain. All our crops are failing. We don't know what to do. Can't you intercede for us with the 'Earth'"?

The "Earth" priest (acted by a Dagomba) wears a tattered old smock. It is ludicrous in comparison to the Dagomba chief's magnificent robe. He sits on a smooth flat stone, obviously ill-at-ease playing the role, with his back up against the crumbling mud hut. He responds to the request, "Ok, I will help you. Bring me a black goat and a white fowl."

The Konkombas interject: "No as the 'Earth shrine custodian,' you must first assess the extent of the problem. You must send three men to find out from diviners exactly what is blocking the rain. It could be something simple requiring only a small sacrifice. But it could also be something very serious like 'spoiled Earth.' "

Both sides understand the meaning of "spoiled Earth." It is a condition of intense disjuncture leading to the "death" of the earth, rendering it infertile, dangerous, and unfit for cultivation or habitation. The most important cause of "spoiled Earth" is the spilling of human blood on the earth (Kirby, 1999).

All present realize that no ritual healing of the "Earth" has occurred in eastern Dagbon since the war. Worried eyes still look to the east for rain at the beginning of each rainy season. But no Dagomba dares talk about it because doing so would grant a certain prior authority to the non-chiefly Konkomba peoples whose ritual experts are in charge of the "Earth" shrine. Soon the results are in. As everyone fears, the diviners reveal that the "Earth is spoiled."

The "Earth" priest calls the Dagomba chief to hear the diviners' verdict. "Well, as you know, the diviners tell us that the 'Earth is spoiled.' This is very serious. You can't just ignore it. You must make it better. This requires a special sacrifice."

"What should we do? We are willing to do anything," say the Dagomba chief and his elders, played by Konkombas.

At this point the Konkombas intervene telling the "Earth" priest (played by a Dagomba) to say: "We must all gather at the 'Earth shrine' and perform the 'burying of the blood' ceremony." They instruct the Dagombas to sacrifice fowls and a black goat, saying that each party must bring some of the weapons that were used, especially the bows and arrows. The animals are to be sacrificed and the blood of the sacrifices will be buried along with the broken weapons of both groups. They explain that this ritual will put an end to the infertility and pollution. The "Earth" will come back to life and it will enable the people to come together as before. From this time onward, no one may ever speak of the war again. It will be as if it never happened.

Step by step they enact the ritual. This time the Konkombas, in the roles of the Dagombas, take charge. They are proactive, doing things which the Dagombas would never have thought of doing, like making a representative of each side hold the goat while it is being slaughtered. The Dagombas are full of questions which the Konkombas eagerly answer. By the end of the ceremony all feel that they actually worked together to solve their common problem.

CULTURAL TRANSFORMATION: BUILDING A NEW WORLD TOGETHER

The night before the last day of the workshop, like static electricity before a summer storm, a great euphoria filled the air. Quite spontaneously, the participants felt the need to "do something." One said, "We have been suffering too long. Let us break down the walls that separate us. Let us 'reintegrate' Yendi." Since the war no Konkomba has been allowed to live in Yendi, the main city of Dagbon. This has caused a great deal of hardship for each group.

The scene is set and the two groups switch sides. This time the Dagombas, who are playing the parts of the Konkomba leaders, are the more vocal. They start the scene by gathering all the Konkomba clan heads and heads of the major households for a meeting in their capitol, Saboba. One speaks in behalf of the others: "We have all been suffering because we cannot go to Yendi to sell our goods, or to come and go as we please like we did before the war. Let us go to the Dagomba King and speak with him."

Immediately the "red flags" are shown by the Konkombas. "No, you can't just call a meeting like that. No Konkomba elder would come. We are all independent of one another. Calling a meeting like that is an unacceptable presumption of power."

The Dagombas, playing the parts of the Konkomba elders, are shocked into realizing that something as simple as calling a meeting, which they find extremely easy to do, is fraught with difficulties. It is almost impossible for the Konkombas. All begin to realize that the first initiative must come from the Dagombas.

The next scene is at the palace of the Ya Na, the Dagomba King. The King, played by a Konkomba, speaks to his elders thus: "You are wondering why I have called you today. It is because I want to have your advice about the Konkombas. It has been 12 years since the war. We need to improve our markets. Do you think it is time to bring the Konkombas back to Yendi?"

The Dagombas interrupt the scene, explaining to the Konkombas some of the intricacies of Dagomba diplomacy. "No, the Ya Na wouldn't do this. The initiative must come from the elders. He must feel that there is no opposition from them before he will come out with his view." Gradually, a way is found. It is one that navigates the intricacies of the Dagomba court, that organizes the Konkomba elders, that subdues other political agendas, that prevents the youth of both sides from causing trouble, and that builds up a healthy anticipation among all the people. By the end of the day all the workshop participants are literally jumping for joy.

In the final scene, step by step, they reintegrate Yendi. They are astonished at what has been accomplished. A few of them express their amazement:

> If we had the authority to do so we could integrate Yendi right now. We know exactly what we would need to do. We have looked at every angle, every potential and real danger. There were many problems we could not have anticipated. But by working together, we have gotten to know about them and have overcome them right here in this room. This is why the

government is powerless. They really do not know what to do. But we know. We know how to solve our problem.

Return to the Desert Island

In the final scene, they return to the "desert island" and are asked, once more, to paint their world and what it needs. Their new masterpiece is a collage of unity. They are no longer separate—Konkombas on one side of the island and Dagombas on the other. There is a harmony of action, of colors, and in the use of spaces. There is a flow between the various services and self-portrayals. They have given symbolic expression to their newly unified "peace culture."

SOCIODRAMA AND CULTURE-DRAMA

There is a fine line separating sociodrama and culture-drama. In the understanding of the authors, and in the briefest of terms, sociodrama is to a society as culture-drama is to cultural groups. Sociodrama, as a therapeutic genre, aims to address the unhealthy, neurotic or chaotic relations of a social group (Moreno, Blomkvist, & Rutzel, 2000). It presumes a general accord or common language among the individual members of the society. Not so with culture-drama. Here, different culture groups assign different meanings to their worlds. When they come into contact with one another, the clash and mutual misinterpretations lead to conflict between them. Our so-called "culture wars" are an example of this, as are the increased ethnic and religious tensions around the world today. Culture-drama offers a way to deal with these problems.

Culture-drama uses many of the techniques and methods of psychodrama—especially role-reversal and doubling—and it follows a similar process toward integration (see Vargiu, 1977), but it is not concerned with individuals or societies as such. It is rather concerned with bridging and integrating the two or more cultures and their worldviews. It focuses on interpreting one cultural group to the other; and, in the process, opening up greater self-understanding and mutual discovery for each—especially around points of conflicting expectation. It is precisely this discovery of a conflicting point of expectation, for example, the cultural meaning of "fridge" for Africans, or "Earth shrine" for Konkombas, or

"Chief" for Dagombas, that opens the possibility of learning that different groups do have quite different worlds of meaning, that these worlds are organized, logical units, and that they are accessible and understandable. Knowing them and acting accordingly affects our relationships. Fridges are important because of water, and water is important because of the all-important rule of hospitality.

Culture-drama is, therefore, therapeutic, not simply for the individuals in a society, nor for the society itself, but for different cultures in relation to one another. It offers peoples of different cultures the possibility to consciously re-form, adapt, and change behavior in relation to our changing times and circumstances, and to the mounting friction engendered by living in close proximity to other cultures—a problem that has intensified in our global era.

In their evaluation, the participants showed their appreciation for this new approach to resolving conflicts and went back to their homes with great enthusiasm for the method, new insights into their cultures, and renewed hope for a "peace culture." All the participants came to appreciate the role culture plays in helping them to understand themselves and the other better. It helped them to begin to address the core issues beneath their feelings of enmity with the other group, to resolve these issues, and to begin new ways of living together. Furthermore, it did this in ways that were accessible to them. "We could use our own languages and ways of doing things. This made it real. The real issues came up without us thinking about them and the way we interacted let us see a new way through the problem." The enactments helped the participants learn that true peacebuilding is not just a matter of discussion and negotiations. It is also necessary for each side to experience and understand their own cultural pathways and those of the other.

But it goes a great deal further than mere understanding. When the participants traded places they actually experienced what it was like to live in the "shoes" of the other. They were able to feel the sentiments of their brothers and sisters from inside their culture and the discussions helped them to understand this. The "action insight" or dialogue of action brings about a kind of "conversion" to the perspective and world of the other. One becomes a "guest" in that world and is led around to see its beauty and grandeur, its meaning, and good sense.

Culture-drama works in the space between worldviews and it negotiates these worlds rather than individual contracts. It works to transform the historical, social, and cultural structures at the heart of conflicts (Lederach, 1997). Instead of each side struggling with the other to score points, participants end up acting and speaking for each other. This leads to compassion, which, in turn, leads to acceptance, forgiveness, and positive action. Finally, by confirming each other in a natural give and take, participants are able to build new pathways and, in some limited but authentic ways, they actually put those transformations into practice.

In summary, the importance of culture-drama is evident in these ways:

- It is a method for discovery of one's own culture and that of the other.
- Through empathy gained in "action insight" it builds a new foundation of trust and confidence in the other group and in one's own group.
- It opens possibilities for learning and "playing" with new cultural meanings.
- It offers a hope-filled vision of a new cultural integration.
- It offers a vehicle for bringing the two groups together to build a new "peace culture."

MOVING TOWARD A "PEACE CULTURE"

The workshop in Ghana was a unique experience for everyone. Its uniqueness brought its own brand of difficulties but gradually, as the participants began to experience its integrating effects, the enthusiasm of the group increased. One participant confessed: "It took us some time to get used to the new approach, through acting, but it turned out to be much better than just thinking and talking about the issues." After getting into the act, another reported: "I feel much closer to my Dagomba brothers and sisters now because I can see and feel things that I didn't see and feel before." Another one felt that dramatizing reversed roles helped her to see the issues more clearly. She said, "We could actually feel the sentiments of the other party. The drama helped us to say and do things we couldn't have said or done back at home. This has brought us closer together." It is our hope that in our converging world with diverging cultural meanings culture-drama can bring us all closer together.

REFERENCES

Assefa, H. (2001). Coexistence and reconciliation in the northern region of Ghana. In N. M. Abu (Ed.), *Reconciliation, justice and co-existence.* Oxford, UK: Oxford University Press.

Bogner, A. (2000). The 1994 civil war in northern Ghana: The genesis and escalation of a "tribal conflict." In C. Lentz & P. Nugent (Eds.), *Ethnicity in Ghana: The limits of invention* (pp. 183–203). London: Macmillan.

Cardinall, A. W. (1960). *The natives of the northern territories of the Gold Coast.* London: Negro. (Original work published 1920)

Eyre-Smith, St. J. (1933). *A brief review of the history and social organisation of the peoples of the northern territories of the Gold Coast.* Accra: Government Printer.

Ferguson, P., & Wilks, I. (1970). Chiefs, constitutions and the British in northern Ghana. In M. Crowder & O. Ikime (Eds.), *West African chiefs: Their changing status under colonial rule and independence.* New York: Africana Publishing Corporation and University of Ife Press.

Froelich, J.-C. (1954). *La tribu Konkomba du nord Togo.* IFAN-Dakar.

Goody, J. R. (1954). *The ethnography of the northern territories of the Gold Coast west of the White Volta.* London: The Colonial Office.

Goody, J. R. (1967/1969). The over-kingdom of the Gonja. In D. Forde & P. M. Karberry (Eds.), *West African kingdoms in the nineteenth century* (pp. 179–205). Oxford, UK: Oxford University Press.

Goody, J. R. (1971). *Technology, tradition and the state,* Cambridge: Cambridge University Press.

Hall, E. (1966). *The hidden dimension.* New York: Doubleday.

Johnson, D. R., Sandel S. L., & Eicher, V. (1983). Structural aspects of group leadership styles. *American Journal of Dance Therapy, 5,* 24–45.

Katanga, J. (1994a). Stereotypes and the road to reconciliation in Northern Ghana. *Uhuru, 6*(9), 19–22.

Katanga, J. (1994b). *Ghana's northern conflict: An ethnographic history.* Unpublished manuscript.

Kirby, J. P. (1986). *God, shrines and problem-solving among the Anufo of northern Ghana.* Anthropos Institute: Collectanea Instituti Anthropos, Vol. 34. Berlin: Reimer.

Kirby, J. P. (1999). The earth cult and the ecology of conflict-management in northern Ghana. In J. P. Kirby (Ed.), *ATRs and development* (Culture and Development Series, No. 3). Tamale, Ghana: TICCS Publications.

Kirby, J. P. (2002). *"A cobra is in our granary": Culture-drama and peacebuilding, a culture-drama workbook.* CRS-Ghana Peacebuilding Project. Tamale, Ghana: TICCS Publications.

Kirby, J. P. (2003). Peacebuilding in northern Ghana: Cultural themes and ethnic conflict. In F. Kroger & B. Meier (Eds.), *Ghana's north: Research on culture, religion, and politics of societies in transition.* Frankfurt: Peter Lang.

Kirby, J. P. (2007). Ethnic conflicts and democratization: New paths toward equilibrium in northern Ghana. *Transactions of the Historical Society of Ghana, New Series, 10,* 65–108.

Kirby, J. P. (in press). Ghana's "witch camps" and the culture of rights. In S. Tonah (Ed.), *Ghana at fifty: Papers commemorating the fiftieth anniversary of Ghana's independence.* Sociology Department, University of Ghana, Legon.

Ladouceur, P. (1979). *Chiefs and politicians: The politics of regionalism in northern Ghana.* London: Longman.

Lange, K. R. (1998). *Dagbani proverbs.* Dagbani Proverbs and Scripture Project. Tamale, Ghana: TICCS Publications.

Lederach, J. P. (1997). *Building peace: Sustainable reconciliation in divided societies.* Washington, DC: United States Institute of Peace.

Levtzion, N. (1968). *Muslims and chiefs in West Africa: A study of Islam in the middle Volta Basin in the pre-colonial period.* Oxford, UK: Clarendon Press.

Middleton, J., & Tait, D. (Eds.). (1953). *Tribes without rulers.* London: International African Institute.

Mahama, I. (1989). *Ya-Naa the African king of power.* Accra, Ghana: Privately published.

Moreno, Z. T., Blomkvist, L. D., & Rutzel, T. (2000). *Psychodrama, surplus reality and the art of healing.* London: Routledge.

Pul, H. A. S. (2003). *Exclusion, association and violence: Trends and triggers of ethnic conflicts in northern Ghana.* Unpublished MA Thesis, Duquesne University, UMI Dissertation Services.

Shu, G., & Kirby, J. P. (1992, May). *A methodology for using sociometry, sociodrama and psychodrama for resolving conflict arising from situations of cultural change in Africa.* Presented at the ASGPP 50th Anniversary Conference, New York.

Staniland, M. (1975). *The lions of Dagbon: Political change in northern Ghana.* Cambridge: Cambridge University Press.

Tait, D. (1958). The territorial pattern and lineage system of Konkomba. In J. Middleton & D. Tait (Eds.), *Tribes without rulers.* London: Routledge and Kegan Paul.

van der Lingde, A., & Naylor, R. (1999). *Building sustainable peace: Conflict, conciliation, and civil society in northern Ghana.* Oxford, UK: Oxfam.

Vargiu, J. G. (1977). *Synthesis, a psychosynthesis workbook, Vol. I.* Redwood City, CA: Synthesis Press.

Wilks, I. (1961). *The northern factor in Ashanti history.* Legon: University of Ghana.

Wilks, I. (1971). The Mossi and Akan states, 1500–1800. In J. F. A. Ajaji & M. Crowder (Eds.), *History of West Africa, Vol. I* (pp. 344–386). New York: Oxford University Press.

10

Teaching Family Dynamics Using Sociodrama and Psychodrama at Sichuan University, Chengdu, China

ALAN LEVETON, EVA LEVETON, AND MARTIN NEWMAN

Authors' Profiles

This chapter explores work which began in 2004, when we (Alan Leveton and Martin Newman) had an opportunity to conduct a one-day experiential, systems-oriented workshop for a class of graduate students in Pedagogy and Psychology at the Sichuan Normal University in Chengdu, China. In a school strictly run on the authoritarian model—professors lecture, students take notes and exams—our workshop was an opportunity for the students to experience a radically different form of teaching. The students' enthusiastic response led to an invitation to return and conduct a more extensive course. In 2006, we two and Eva Leveton—whose book on psychodrama had just been translated into Chinese—returned to conduct a 5-day workshop that would explore the dynamics of family life using socio- and psychodramatic techniques for a class of 40 graduate students.

Alan Leveton, MD, is past Clinical Professor of Pediatrics and Psychiatry at the University of California Medical School. In private practice in San Francisco, he has published widely, combining hypnosis and experiential work with family therapy. Together with his wife, Eva Leveton, he made the educational film *Children in Trouble, Family in Crisis*, a 5-hour film demonstrating work with families in Crisis Counseling at the U.C. Davis School of Criminal Justice.

Eva Leveton, MS, MFT (ed), has taught family therapy and psychodrama in the United States, Europe, India, and Africa for the past 50 years. The recipient of the Zerka Moreno Award for Distinguished Work in Psychodrama, Sociometry, and Group Psychology, she has written three books: *A Clinician's Guide to Psychodrama; Adolescent Crisis: Approaches in Drama Therapy*; and *Eva's Berlin, Memories of a Wartime Childhood*. She is an associate professor on the faculty of the Drama Therapy Program and the Somatics Program at the California Institute of Integral Studies.

Martin Newman, MA, MFT, is in private practice in San Francisco where he sees families and individuals and he also teaches at the Wright Institute. He was the family therapy supervisor at the South Alameda County YWCA, in Castro Valley, CA, and the Claremont Center for Family Counseling, San Carlos, CA, and is currently on the Adjunct Faculty at the Wright Institute in San Francisco, CA. He is a past consultant to several San Francisco family service agencies.

INTRODUCTION

The family, the basic unit of Chinese society, survived attacks during the 20th century by reformers, who saw its traditions as the main source of the country's weakness; and the Communists, who wanted people to identify with class and state rather than family. Both groups succeeded in making the state less like the family, and the family less like the state. Neither managed to subordinate the family permanently to the state as a focus of loyalty and obedience (Chin, Ng, Phillips, & Lee, 2002: Fuligni & Zhang, 2004; Hutchings, 2001).

This chapter explores work which began in 2004, when Alan Leveton and Martin Newman had an opportunity to conduct a 1-day experiential, systems-oriented workshop for a class of graduate students in Pedagogy and Psychology at the Sichuan Normal University in Chengdu, China. In a school strictly run on the authoritarian model—professors lecture, students take notes and exams—our workshop was an opportunity for the students to experience a radically different form of teaching. In 2005, in an open lecture to graduate students, M.N. presented and discussed the basic concepts of family therapy and introduced them to an experiential way of working. The students' enthusiastic response led to an invitation to return and conduct a more extensive course. In 2006, Alan and Eva Leveton and Martin Newman returned to conduct a 5-day workshop that would explore the dynamics of family life using socio- and psychodramatic techniques for a class of 40 graduate students. The students, primarily from rural communities, were expected to return to their villages to teach and deal with psychological issues that might arise in a school setting.

Sichuan University, founded in 1938, is the largest university in Sichuan Province awarding Master's level degrees in Psychology and Education. Its Web site proclaims "all the faculty staffs follow the educational policy issued by the Communist Party of China. They uphold the socialist approach to operate the university" (2009). On campus, the Communist Party is represented by sculptures of the leadership, large billboards with patriotic themes, and frequent announcements over loudspeakers exhorting students to attend classes promptly, to study well for the sake of the state, while men in army uniforms patrol the gates and the grounds.

The model of teaching used in Sichuan Normal University follows strictly traditional lines: the professor sits at the head of a large rectangular table backed by a blackboard while the students sit around a very large table, taking notes. Students have little opportunity to ask questions; there is no communication between students in this hierarchical, formal classroom setting.

The University is located at the edge of Chengdu, a city of eleven million, showing marked signs of westernization. Kentucky Fried Chicken, Taco Bell, and McDonald's outlets and other familiar Western companies are well represented. Particularly prominent were the Starbucks franchises, always crowded with young Chinese paying U.S. prices. Expansion has been surprisingly rapid. In 2004, we observed that the streets were evenly divided between bike lanes and car lanes. By 2006, the bike lanes were greatly reduced and the car lanes choked with modern cars, often driven by a single woman with a child in the backseat. Modernization has its costs, one of which is a more or less permanent miasma of smog. Chengdu records less days of sunshine than any comparable Chinese city. The impact of Western materialism and its clashes with traditions on our students would be clearly demonstrated in our workshops.

THE CHINESE FAMILY:
THREE GENERATIONS OF RAPID CHANGE

In the traditional China of Confucianism, the family towered over individual and community. The father was seen as all-powerful, his sons dutiful and obedient. Women mattered much less. Their birth was not always a cause for joy, their young lives a preparation for an arranged marriage and removal to their husband's home. There, the new bride was expected to obey her husband and his father and to serve her mother-in-law. Her main duty was to produce sons to sustain the family lineage, inherit the property, and provide for the parents' old age (Hutchings, 2001; Z. Zhang, 2001; Y. Zhang & Goza, 2007).

The first major challenge to the traditional family structure, the generation of our students' great grandparents came from the May Fourth Movement of 1919. At that time, protests broke out in Beijing against the Versailles Peace Conference decision to deprive China of Germany's World War I privileges in Shandong, awarding them to Japan instead. Controversies raged in newspapers, journals, and university classrooms across the country as debate about the future took an autonomous, unofficial form it had seldom known before and has not seen since. Capitalizing on this foment, the Chinese Communist Party was founded in 1921.

With the Communist Party's power in 1950 came a focus on Land Reform with its profound effect on rural families. Class labels were affixed to the rural population and peasants were encouraged to hold "speak bitterness" meetings recalling past oppression. Landlords were humiliated at public trials and executed by the hundreds of thousands. The landed-gentry—sustainers of a rural tradition dating back to ancient times—were wiped out (Hutchings, 2001). At public trials, exposure of family life carried the possibility of being denounced as "bourgeois" or "counter-revolutionary" by one's neighbors with a punishment of execution or imprisonment. Since our work would involve our students depicting aspects of their family life in the public, classroom setting, we were concerned that remnants of this history would impede their spontaneity.

Another important change in family structure occurred with the passage in 1950 of the Marriage Law, freeing women from arranged unions and allowing them to work and acquire property of their own

(Hutchings, 2001). The consequences of this change in women's status would be evident in one of the sociodramas of our first workshop.

Anxiety about the slowness of agricultural output with land reform and collectivization of labor led Mao to initiate the "Great Leap Forward" in 1958. The Leap brought two phenomena to the countryside: People's Communes, in which collectives were merged and life in them subjected to military-style discipline and a mass famine, the consequence of ludicrous industrial policies and the neglect of simple farming (Hutchings, 2001). Women, engaged in the nationwide production drive, handed over their traditional household chores to kindergartens and canteens (Hutchings, 2001). It was estimated that between twenty-three and forty million Chinese died in the famine. The collectivization of farmers was accompanied by an emphasis on group and Communist Party conformity, sacrificing traditional values for political ones.

Just as recovery was beginning with the reluctant restoration of more traditional household farming practices, Mao initiated the "Cultural Revolution" of 1966–1976 (Schoenglass, 1996), the brunt of which was felt by our student's grandparents. The Cultural Revolution was an attack on expressions of individuality of every kind, highly destructive of family life, particularly in the cities. It was a revolt of the young against the old; of children against parents; of students against teachers. Re-education, rustification, persecution, and imprisonment split families up, often for years at a time (Hutchings, 2001). No one was safe—except Mao.

Anyone with a Western connection, however remote and insignificant, was at risk. Those who had followed the Party all their lives, as well as those who had absolutely nothing to do with politics were pursued with equal vigor. Mao and the radicals taught that China was besieged by outsider enemies and at the mercy of fiends within. Such official paranoia created an efficient environment for the violence of Communist politics, the blind worship of a leader, and the petty hatreds of past feudalism to do their work (Hutchings, 2001).

The next radical intervention in family life, one that would most directly impact our graduate students—most of them in their early twenties—was the One Child per Family policy in 1976, used as a method of limiting population growth and improving living conditions. In 1979, two thirds of the population was under age thirty, and an unchecked surge in the population of "baby boomers" born between 1950 and 1960 would certainly have added to the burgeoning population. The policy was enforced vigorously in the cities and with government employees who were completely dependent on the Party (Y. Zhang & Goza, 2007). Limits were relaxed in some rural areas—our students' villages not among them—and among minority populations who were permitted to continue traditional and primarily tribal lives. The one-child policy also created a shift in the gender ratio, the number of male to female births. In industrialized countries this ranges from 1.03 to 1.07. In China, the ratio has risen to 1.17. Sonograms have been made illegal to prevent women from aborting less desirable daughters. But abortions and abandonment of females continue to be a major problem (Hesketh, Liu, & Xing, 2005).

PSYCHOTHERAPY IN CHINA

Psychotherapy, as we know and practice it in the West, is a relatively new idea in China. The first mental health clinic was established in Kunming in 1994 and the approaches were mostly cognitive and behavioral in line with the training values of Chinese society. According to Y. Zeng (1991), the development of psychotherapy in China can be divided into four stages. From 1949 to 1969, Chinese psychiatry came under the influence of Russian neuropsychiatric models with priorities focused on maintaining public order. Mental illness and other forms of deviance were cast as problems of wrong political thinking by the leaders of the Cultural Revolution, in 1966–1977. Re-education, rather than mental health care, was the treatment of choice. From 1978 to 1986, political and economic reforms supported the revitalization of Chinese psychiatry and its reengagement with Western scientific communities. National professional meetings and international exchanges and clinical research resumed, and new periodicals and professional journals were founded.

The fourth stage, from 1987 to the present, has witnessed a blossoming of the mental health field in China. This growth has been fueled by the government's recent acknowledgment of the social burden caused by mental health problems; a variety of state-sponsored initiatives have improved access to psychological services in the country's hospitals, schools, and prisons (Y. Zeng, 1991). Contemporary forms of psychotherapy have been developed to include Chinese cultural beliefs and philosophical and healing traditions. *Taiji quan* and *qi gong*—two Chinese somatic practices well known in the West—continue to be practiced along with newer therapeutic methods.

Psychodrama itself was introduced in 2003 when M. Wieser and X. Deng conducted a 2-day psychodrama workshop in Nanjing demonstrating role reversal, empty chair, doubling, soliloquy, enactment of fairy tales and family counseling (Deng & Wieser, 2003). This well-received workshop was one of the first teachings of experiential techniques. Since China opened to the West and implemented the one-child policy, there has been an enormous shift of emphasis to the gratification of individual desire.

Depth psychology approaches have made few inroads with the needs of the majority of the population, partially because of issues of cost and adaptation to Chinese culture. Psychotherapy as we know and practice it in the West is a relatively new idea in China (Q. Zeng, 2005).

THE LEADERS: WORKSHOP #1

Alan Leveton, MD, is a psychiatrist who taught family therapy in the Department of Pediatrics at the University of California School of Medicine in San Francisco as an Associate Clinical Professor of Pediatrics and Psychiatry for 28 years and in various settings in the San Francisco Bay Area since 1966. Martin Newman, MA, has cotaught seminars with Alan Leveton and supervised Master's level clinicians in conjoint family therapy for a number of years.

Case Examples

These examples will discuss in more detail some of the work accomplished in the 2004 and 2007 workshops. Since we had information about the prevailing pedagogical style, we began with a strong message of change and a role assignment: we asked the students to get rid of the large tables and arrange circular seating. The students were told that the instructors would give them the opportunity to play the role of our California graduate students. They would be expected, as our students were, to participate actively, to get out of their chairs and move around the room and interact with each other and us. "In the United States, all the students are expected to participate actively in our work. We know that this is not expected of the Chinese. Therefore, we will ask you to pretend that you are American students from now on [much laughter]. All right?" The students agreed enthusiastically, and, in fact, eagerly cooperated. They would be exposed to an example of experiential learning.

Sculptures

Presently, cultural preference for sons has led to concerns about the overvaluation of boys who become fawned over like "little emperors." Then, because they have failed to acquire social skills, many of the boys face the possibility of not being able to marry and start families (Hesketh et al., 2005). In this context, we decided to begin with an active exploration of family systems. The first exercise was a variation of the family sculpture, in which we asked students to help us to sculpt a typical one-child, one-son family, as a living sculpture done in such a way that a passerby would be able to draw some conclusions about that family's life from what they observed. As this was a non-verbal task, we asked their permission to mold their bodies and facial expressions.

Case Example 1: One-Child Family Triangle

When we asked for a volunteer to portray a 7-year-old boy, to our delighted surprise, several students eagerly raised their hands and one was quickly chosen. He was invited to pick a "Mother" and she a "Father" to complete the family constellation; they did so without difficulty.

Our suggestion that the students become Californians had succeeded. It seemed to us that rather than the restrictive behavior we had been warned about, these students were eager and ready to work experientially.

The boy was molded crouched down and clinging behind his mother who stood facing his father. We molded their facial expressions so that the boy looked frightened, the mother, worried and protective, and the father, angry and impatient. They were told to imagine what this sculpture—designed by us to elicit comments about the one-child family and authoritarian relationships—demonstrated about a particular family dynamic. The rest of the class was encouraged to stand and circulate around this sculpture and make statements about what they observed. Their response was lively and accurate. In this one-child-per-family culture, they immediately understood that the mother was babying her son and that his father was frustrated and indeed could not even see or reach the son, hiding behind his mother. The role-players reported what it felt like to be in the sculpture: The mother felt she had to protect her son from her frustrated husband. The husband felt his authority was undermined; he missed contact with his child and felt angry with his wife. The son felt ambivalent about the attention he was getting from his mother and frightened by his father's impatience and the tension between his parents.

After the role-players rejoined the group, we asked them to reflect on what they had seen and experienced and how they could relate their observations to their everyday life. We directed them to the usual sociodramatic sharing of what had touched them in responding to the sculpture. Students identified with the dynamic of the sculpture and talked about their ambivalence about being special (if males) and their loneliness without sibs or cousins.

In conclusion, there was an enthusiastic and interactive discussion about their concerns that the one-child family system and its high valuation of sons were leading to the "little emperor" syndrome of overprotected and pampered male children, a complaint substantiated by Zhang and Goza's (2007) research.

Case Example 2: The Working Woman

The second demonstration also used sculpture. One of the department's professors had asked us to help prepare for an upcoming seminar about the place of women in the structure of contemporary Chinese society. We had already perceived a current of anxiety in the group, felt by the women students, mostly in their 20s. As noted above, the paucity of available women and the shift from a traditional multi-generational family structure to a desire for a "Westernized" and materialistic lifestyle created additional challenges for these women students. We were initially puzzled and somewhat daunted by the breadth of the professor's request, and decided that another sculpture would serve to concretize the problem.

A female student volunteered quickly. We asked her to stand in the center of the circle of chairs. In advance, as we planned this sculpture, we decided to bring a number of 4-feet-long, light ropes to the workshop. Several roles were proposed. Our woman would have a Husband, Child, Mother, Mother-in-Law, Best Woman Friend, and Boss making demands on her. In turn, each role-player was asked to tie one end of the rope around her waist, and express his/her demands vociferously as s/he tried to pull her in her/his own direction.

The Boss said, "Could you stay late and type up the minutes of the Committee meeting? I have to have it today." The Child cried plaintively. The Husband complained, "I never see you and when I do, you are always tired." The Mother-in-Law criticized, "Your house is so messy, there is no room for us!" And the Girl Friend whined, "We never even have time to have tea together anymore." Each role-player, in turn, spoke his/her line(s) and pulled on his/her rope. They were directed to say their lines in a variety of ways—singly, in concert, loudly, softly—all the while tugging the protagonist this way and that. The enactment ended with robust and knowing laughter. When the role-players regained their seats, they were invited to share their personal, emotional reactions as they watched the scene.

The discussion that followed illuminated the students' instant understanding of the dynamic and started a robust interactive discussion about the hard lives of women, who were now expected to be able to juggle careers, children, marriage, and friends without complaining and without help. The husbands' lack of help with housework, cooking, and children was widely blamed, yet the girls agreed that they would never want to go back to the old ways.

After the workshop, the students surrounded us, saying how much they had learned and how much they enjoyed being in our "California" class. The chairman of the department, Professor Bading Nima, invited us to return and teach again for a longer time.

2 YEARS LATER

Two years passed before our next visit to China, to conduct a 5-day workshop called "An Introduction to Family Dynamics and Experiential Methods." Our workshop faculty was joined by Eva Leveton, MS, MFT, an Associate Professor in the Psychology of Drama Therapy Department Master's Track of the California Institute for Integral Studies and the author of books on psychotherapy and psychodrama. Her *Clinician's Guide to Psychodrama* has been translated into Chinese.

To orient ourselves, we began our work with an interview of two psychology professors, Drs. Chan and Shao Ling. Asked for a story about their students, Professor Chan recounted visiting Lhasa, the Tibetan capital, instead. He felt it was a tale that centered on the question of identity in the face of changing values—so relevant to our students' concerns—and we decided that this story would provide a good *Leitmotif* for our work. It goes as follows: Professor Chan, walking around the the main square of Lhasa, encounters an eight-year-old boy, who is crying. Asking him about his trouble, the little boy tells him that he and his parents came to the capital by walking for miles and miles of mountain paths by doing full body prostrations, a Tibetan Buddhist practice which is done so as to gain merit. "My father told me," the little boy said, still crying, "that after all this I would be able to become the flower I was meant to become but," and here the boy cried harder, "I don't know what I want to be! I don't want to become a flower!"

The Class Work

Again, we stipulated that we wanted to teach in a room with a circle of chairs and an open space in its center. We requested a class of up to 20 students; however, we counted 40 on most of the days as the enthusastic reports about our work got around. Their average age was 25 years and the male–female distribution was approximately equal, unlike our teaching experiences in the United States, where classes are predominately female. All were from the culturally dominant Han ethnic group. These graduate students were enrolled in the Departments of Education and Psychology at a level equivalent to our Master's programs; most came from rural areas and were only-children having grown up under the one-child rule. They were on scholarships studying educational and psychological methods and expected to return to their villages to teach or counsel. They wanted to learn to deal with problems in both the classroom and with families. As we discovered, many did not want to return to the countryside as intended by their program but had dreams of moving to Hong Kong or Shanghai.

Our workshop ran for 5 days from 10 a.m. to 5 p.m. Fluctuations in class size reflected other class commitments and a series of academic tests that coincided with our scheduled time. Most of the students had completed 7 years of English language instruction which had emphasized reading rather than conversational skills. One student with excellent spoken English served as our translator.

A Note on Methods

Our teaching relied primarily on enactments of family and social scenes to produce examples from which we could derive teaching points and introduce concepts of the systems approach to understanding family dynamics. We continued to develop the use of sculptures throughout the 5 days. The students were ready to role-play and engage in role reversal. At times some students were facile enough in English to use that language. At other times the material was so emotion laden that we felt the full impact of the scene would be better experienced by the students in their own language. Even when Chinese was being spoken, the affective meaning and charge of the material was readily apparent from the non-verbal emotional music and gestures conveyed in the enactment. Sculpting was particularly useful as a demonstration of what was being explored because it is kinetic, involves movement and touch, and stretches the boundaries of culturally prescribed classroom decorum in a way that is playful and non-threatening. Within the structure of sculpture, sociodrama and psychodrama were easy to introduce.

The First Meeting of the Class

There are 40 graduate students from the Departments of Psychology and Education. Their average age is 25 and the class is evenly divided between men and women. Except for some chairs at the edges of the room, it is empty of furniture, and students and faculty sit in a circle. After introductions, we tell them that we will be teaching through enactments of stories. We will begin by showing them an enactment of a story told to us by Dr. Chan, who was unable to attend the class. Professor Shao Ling volunteered to help enact Professor Chan's story from the previous night. Eva Leveton acted as the overall director of the enactments, with occasional help from her two coteachers, who provided help with small-group work and led when they were more familiar with a particular scene.

After stating that the main protagonist in our enactment is a small boy, E. L. asks the class who should act his role. The class seems to be in total accord: Professor Shao Ling! It should be stated that of all the professors, Dr. Shao Ling seems closest to the students. He is young, athletic, and given to practicing his *Tai Ji Quan* moves outside of class, and always ready for a joke. Asked to give him a name, several are suggested, but the vote, with much laughter, goes to "Little Nima!"—the name of the Chairman of their department! It is clear to us that the students are ready to play. Professor Shao Ling, in the role of Little

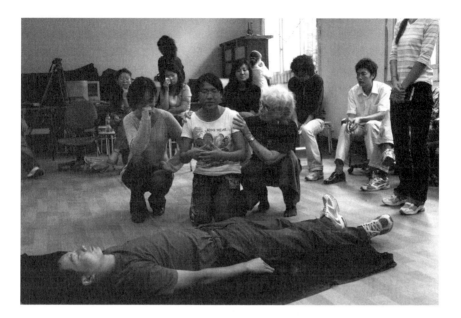

Figure 10.1. Eva Leveton assists grieving student.

Nima, picks students to portray the boy's mother and father. They learn about their strenuous climb. The Chinese use the word "kow-towing" to describe these prostrations, which the three role-players perform in front of the class, in our stage area. They fall to their knees, extend their arms and hands to the floor and slide the full length of their bodies, then draw up their feet and stand while moving their clasped hands from head to heart to solar plexus. They have advanced one body length toward Lhasa. We had been warned about a cultural prohibition about touching a floor which isn't very clean, and showing the soles of their shoes, which in some circumstances, is a gesture of disrespect. However, watching their Professor Shao Ling enter the role-play with humor and enthusiasm supported the playful tone in the classroom, and we did not meet the anticipated resistance. Again and again, these students, used to such different teaching methods, surprised us by joining our challenges so easily (see Figure 10.1).

In our scene, the boy becomes tired and sits down, refusing to go forward. "Why do I have to do this?" "Because," his father replies, "When we get there you will have peace and harmony." "You will become the flower you were meant to become," says his mother. The boy slowly gets up and sadly prepares to continue, asking morosely, "But what kind of flower will I become?" He then mutters to himself that he never, ever wanted to be a flower. The question remains unanswered so as to provide a stimulus for further work with the students. Our plan is to reprise it at the end of our 5-day workshop, when the question of their own identity will be most relevant.

The students are delighted by the enactment, by Shao Ling's charm as he enacted an 8-year-old boy. Having demonstrated how we will dramatize a given story the class is then divided into six groups, with the instruction that each group is to agree on one story that we will use in our teaching. We will be available to help them to begin the story with a sculpture, unless they want to try it by themselves. The following stories are all derived from the small-group work.

The First Story

Scene one: In the schoolroom: A male student, acting age 10, is being criticized by his teacher. He doesn't understand his math assignment and has not handed in his homework. The teacher is impatient and judgmental. The boy lowers his head in shame, unable to speak (see Figure 10.2).

Scene two takes place in the kitchen of his grandparents' farm where he is being raised. His grandmother is cooking at the stove with her back to him. He asks his grandmother for help with his assignment. She looks angry and sad and turns to resume cooking. The director gives her an instruction, "Say to him: 'You should understand this. You are going to school. I did not go to school.'" As the grandmother says her sentence, the director instructs the student to react by changing his body posture. "If you feel good, show it. If you feel bad, you could show it in your body, getting smaller, going further away, whatever fits." As the student plays the role, he seems to shrink in size, distancing himself from the grandmother, crying, and saying, "I don't know where I can go. My grandmother doesn't understand me. I hate school. I want my parents!"

Scene three: His parents, who have returned to the farm from their jobs in the city, talk with his grandparents. Parents: "How come he isn't doing well in school?" The grandparents are angry and defensive: "You have gone off to work in the city and left us with your son. We

Figure 10.2. Martin Newman demonstrates.

didn't go to school. How can we help him?" The father replies: "If we didn't work and send money to you, how would you live?"

The boy is crestfallen and silent.

The director summarizes the enactment: "The child is sad, the grandparents are at a loss, they don't like what is happening. Their old-age is being disturbed. They had thought they would be taken care of by their children and didn't expect to have the responsibility for raising their grandson. The boy doesn't know what is happening. He doesn't know how to help himself. Because of the one-child policy, he is lonely. The nearest neighbor child is many miles away. The teacher doesn't know how to help this boy and he is mad because the boy won't do his work. These are unhappy people. The parents feel guilty for leaving, but they have to work. The grandparents are bitter."

Sharing

Although we know that the psychodramatic concept of sharing implies empathy, we want to stress its importance for these Chinese students who had so little experience in speaking openly about their feelings. Our intent is to increase the students' empathic understanding of the situation. Countering the initial response of the students—to ask further questions, to make generalizations—the director gives further instructions. We explain that we are using a different way of teaching. "To help families," Dr. Leveton explains, "we must learn to use ourselves, our hearts as well as our minds. A small but important part of understanding any problem is to look for traces of it in yourself and your family. If you can do this in a group that will respect your privacy and not hurt you—such as ours—the experience can enrich your intellectual understanding and help you understand your clients. I want you to begin by sharing your own feeling reactions to what you have observed instead of abstractions or further questions. I could see that some of you were thinking, 'I know this boy, I know this grandmother. I know how they feel.' Let's start with that."

The Students' Responses

Male student: I know how he feels. When my mother and father leave me I feel very sad. I want to go with them. But that is impossible. When my father leaves me, I am unhappy. Nobody helps me, so I don't study. I always feel not in the mood. My spirit is always low. My grandfather and grandmother can't help me so I just can't do the work. I don't have any friends. I have nowhere to go for help. Maybe I will do something bad, maybe steal something. I don't know.

Female student: I love my parents and I love my grandmother, I can't complain, I can't complain. Even though I am sad, I can't say it, as the child in my family.

Male student: I feel sad for this boy, when I was young, about 8 years old, my father and mother left me. I had no one to talk to. There were no other children to play with and my grandparents kept complaining that they had already raised their children. They didn't want to be raising me. I was too much trouble.

With this first class exercise an important principle was established: rather than passively receiving didactic lecturing, students were expected to participate in the enactments and to respond to them with a personal sharing. Once our communication was clear, the students continued with empathic sharing for the entire workshop.

Our instruction also served to remedy an absence of directness and contact between family members in the enactments. The situations being portrayed did not allow the communication of feelings of abandonment, guilt, or resentment. The high value placed on family harmony, a desire to protect the feelings of other family members, acted to suppress the expression of feelings. Listening as class members, shared their feelings gave support to the role-players as they spoke more expressively in the role-plays as well—speaking about feelings with their classmates was an unexpected and new experience—and fostered group closeness and trust.

Case Example 3: Left and Bereft

Scene 1: In this psychodrama vignette, the protagonist was a shy, thin, and sad-looking 25-year-old man, Liu, who volunteered to tell a story from his childhood. He has picked players to represent his father and grandparents. The scene plays in a room in his grandparents' house in their village during a harvest festival.

> He plays with his father, time flies. He is happy. After dinner, father gets ready to return to his job in the city. The son begs his father to stay. Sobbing, he clutches at his father's clothes, crying "Don't go!" until his father promises to stay. At bedtime he reads his son a story. The boy falls asleep on his father's lap. When he awakens, his father is gone.

Scene two: Liu confronts his grandparents angrily:

Liu: "Father tricked me. How could he lie to me like that? It's not fair!" (He has a temper tantrum.)

Grandmother: "Don't be upset. Your father will come back in a few days." But his father doesn't return and the more he asks for his parents, the harsher his grandparents' treatment becomes. Grandfather hits Liu upon hearing that he has been yelling and stamping his feet.

Scene 3: The director suggests an intervention. "In psychodrama, we have something called surplus reality. There, you can experience things that might not be possible in the real world. So, if you wish, you and your father can have a conversation now to talk about how you felt." The protagonist and his father have a long conversation in which the father apologizes for tricking his son and explains that his working in the city is essential because his money is necessary for the support of the family and there is not enough paying work on the farm. Liu accepts this though he remains sad.

Sharing

Female student: "I have no words to say how this makes me feel. We didn't have permission to express anger and sadness in our family. When my parents went to the city to work, I didn't understand it. I felt too bad and I couldn't show my unhappiness. I was angry at my grandparents all the time. They didn't want me. But I couldn't show my anger. The nearest child my age lived with his grandparents on another farm far away so I had no one to play with."

Male student: "There was no discussing these matters of decision making. Now I understand that my parents had to find work. The grandparent's life on the farm was very poor. There were crop failures and no chance to make money. Maybe it was necessary, but because I couldn't ask questions, even when my parents were with me, I was constantly worried that I would wake up and they would be gone and I would not know when I would see them again. My grandparents were always angry and impatient with me and I couldn't say anything to them. I had no brothers, no sisters, no cousins, and no close friends." As he received group support, Liu, who had been somewhat isolated, became more fully integrated into his group and the class.

Case Example 4: Caught Between

On the fourth day, one of the women students demonstrated her new learning by setting up a sculpture for another psychodrama vignette without the help of the instructors. This showed an increasing sense of independence and confidence that was developing in members of the class (see Figure 10.3).

Scene 1: Fen, a 27-year-old female student, arranged a sculpture depicting an impasse between herself, her mother, and her stepfather. Her mother was moving towards her stepfather while Fen was trying to pull her mother away from him. She was so intent on disrupting her mother's second marriage that

Figure 10.3. A double helps Fen express her grief.

she sat on the floor and wrapped herself around her mother's leg. Her mother could not move. Fen explained to the class that her father had died some years before and that her stepfather had been abusive toward her and the rest of the family.

In this scene, directed by Alan Leveton, she chose another student to play her dead father. A crimson cloth covering computer terminals became his burial shroud. He lay on the floor, his face covered and then uncovered as the protagonist was told that "in surplus reality, it is possible to talk with the dead." She knelt by her father, crying, telling him how much she missed him (see Figure 10.4).

With Eva Leveton acting as a double, she articulated her feelings of love, something she regretted not having said to him while he was alive. They spoke tenderly and quietly in Chinese—Eva's words translated—which was more natural in the scene. Her father responded softly, saying how much he appreciated her loyalty and love for him and firmly released her: her loyalty should be to her mother. Fen paused to assimilate the communication and then thoughtfully inserted herself at her mother's side in the sculpture without attempting to divide the family.

Figure 10.4. Fen's torn loyalties.

Sharing

The students were touched by the loving communication between the dead father and his daughter. Several talked about their sadness that emotional words were not used in their families: "I have never told my mother that I love her" or "I never told my father how much he means to me." (To Fen:) "Even though we have been roommates and I have known your story, I have never felt it this way. I feel so much closer to you." And the recognition that a new kind of communication was happening in the classroom: "I am talking with my classmates about personal matters in such a different way. I knew some of these stories but this is the first time I heard them with feeling. I was so moved."

Closure

On the final day the director, Eva Leveton, directed the class to return to the story of "little Nima" and his pilgrimage with his parents to Lhasa. The questions about whether he wanted to be a flower at all and if he had to be, what kind, were addressed to the students, used here as a metaphor for personal development in the face of parental, and perhaps traditional, demands.

In talking about little Nima's question, the students seemed to express a yearning for something missing in the other stories. In the great natural world of the Chinese landscape, the little Nima's family had been seeking spiritual transformation and meaning, qualities that were expressed in some of the students' answers to the question posed to him.

Each person in the circle had a different idea "what kind of flower I want to be." Some continued the metaphor of the flower: "I would like to be a snow rose and amaze everyone with my beauty....I would like to be a berry bush and stay firmly planted in the ground."

Others chose metaphors of transcendent freedom: " I would like to be a bird, flying high on the updrafts near the mountain....I would like to be the mountain and welcome everyone....I would like to be the sky without boundaries...." Still others wanted power: "I want to be a snow leopard, the king of the Himalayas." Our translator was moving and eloquent as she danced around the circle touching each of us: "I would like to be a little river that can touch and connect everyone." Thus, the crowded room with its circle of chairs and echoes of family life and its struggles had expanded into the possibilities of beauty and stability, of freedom from parental demands, and of the vast space and the constant protection of the great eternal Himalayas.

CONCLUSION

Experiential methods as exemplified in socio- and psychodrama offered the Chinese students an opportunity to access deep emotional wounds and create a setting for healing. Group cohesiveness was fostered through vignettes in which revelations about family life could be contained and through the support of empathic connections. The students expressed their gratitude for the change in teaching methods: "It was the first class I've ever had where each student could contribute." They repeated the gains they had made in relating to each other, reporting that they now greeted each other and were able to talk more meaningfully about their problems, which had not happened before in their 4-year course.

These are small changes, as those of any short, introductory class must be. The methods used facilitated viewing problems of children in school, marital problems, and generational differences in a new and useful light. A beginning was made in accessing the emotional content of family interactions, usually absent in the Chinese families. Many of the students as well as the professors who occasionally looked in on our class seemed to be hungry for new approaches and open to novel pedagogical methods. As China continues its rapid transformation, social and personal problems not encountered before will continue to require innovative ways of dealing with them. Our systemic orientation teaches us how difficult it is to modify a system if everyone involved in the problem is not part of the solution. It is our belief that active methods will serve to discover and rehearse new processes, skills, and understandings.

REFERENCES

Chin, Y., Ng, A., Phillips, D., & Lee, W. K. (2002). Persistence and challenges to filial piety and informal support of older persons in a modern Chinese society: A case study in Tuen Mu, Hong Kong. *Journal of Aging Studies, 16*, 35–153.

Deng, X., & Wieser, M. (2003). *Techniques of psychodrama and application in practical fields.* Nanjing, China: Southeast University Psychological Counseling Centre. Available at: https://elearning.uniklu.ac.at/moodle/file.php/655/2.Basics/Culture/China/Nanjing/Techniques_of_Psychodrama_and_Application_in_Practical_Fields.doc

Fuligni, A., & Zhang, W. (2004). Attitudes toward family obligation among adolescents in contemporary urban and rural China. *Child Development, 75*, 180–192.

Hesketh, T., Liu, L., & Xing, Z. W. (2005). The effect of China's one-child family policy after 25 years. *New England Journal of Medicine, 353*, 1171–1176.

Hutchings, G. (2001). *Modern China: A guide to a century of change.* Cambridge, MA: Harvard University Press.

Scheonglass, M. (1996). *China's cultural revolution, 1966–1969. Not a dinner party.* Watertown, MA: Eastgate Books.

Sichuan University. (2009). Available at http://web.sicnu.edu/aboutsnu-1html

Zeng, Q. (2005, April). Letting a hundred flowers bloom: Counseling and psychotherapy in the People's Republic of China. *Journal of Mental Health Counseling.*

Zeng, Y. (1991). *Family dynamics in China: A life table analysis.* Madison, WI: University of Wisconsin Press.

Zhang, Y., & Goza, F. (2007). *Who will care for the elderly in China? A review of the problems caused by China's one-child policy and their potential solutions.* The Center for Family and Demographc Research. Bowling Green State University, Working Paper Series 05.

Zhang, Z. (2001). China faces the challenges of an aging society: The third story. *Beijing Review, 44*, 12–15.

Afterword

EVA LEVETON

Trauma leads to lasting pain. Whether it is a cyclone, HIV, the one-child family in China, tribal conflict in Ghana, the disenfranchisement of Middle Eastern women, or the transvestite prostitutes of China, all those affected by such events will lead lives marked by scars covering dreadful wounds. The authors of the preceding pages have made it their business to help. Carrying little or no luggage—some colored scarves, some sticks, a hat or two, drums, crayons, pens, and paper—these authors have travelled the world creating greater awareness and compassionate understanding of some of its worst conflicts. Individuals come together in ever-widening circles, moving, singing, and speaking to each other in new ways. Each member of the circle has a chance to stand where s/he has not stood before. Each person of the group can find ways to speak to others that might never have occurred to them. Sometimes the circle dissolves into a stage area with an audience. On stage, the participants are transformed. They may play aspects of themselves they haven't shown before, or take the roles of others with whom they were in conflict. They can transform into objects, into scenery—a person may be cast as a telephone or as the sun. Rhythmic movement lends energy to the participants. Sensitive leadership helps them express something new.

The central message of the work described in this volume is: "Change is possible. Let's see what we can do to make it so." In Ghana, enemies come together, ready to continue their age-old wars. To their mutual surprise, they exchange long-held views of each other for better informed, more complex, and, in the end, kinder perspectives. In China, students who felt isolated, not only in the one-child family, but in the impersonal Chinese educational system, learn to express and share their pain. Germans and Jews, suffering from the legacies of the Holocaust into the third and fourth generations, approach each other gingerly, and end with rituals that help to bridge the seemingly unbridgeable gaps. Immigrants and teenagers express their rage and their creativity, energized by the opportunities given to them in these groups; with scarves, photographs, books of memories, and puppets, they rebuild worlds. Viet Nam veterans share their experiences, create a play and a kind of communication that didn't exist before for these soldiers, who are used to keeping silent about their experience. The play creates new understanding, but we learn that there are limits to healing the profound wounding of war. The inevitable burnout of those working with deep trauma—all of the authors fall into this category, although we are addressing HIV workers in particular—is lightened by shared ways of expressing grief and hopelessness.

What can we conclude about this work? My caveat about all theories of human relationships—"It all depends"—applies here. In our case, we learn that the leaders need to be unusual people with a tolerance for difference, whether it is expressed by living in or being from another country and culture or by the singular traumatic experience affecting the group. Leaders must learn ways of entering a new and different culture, much in the way that the medieval monks who travelled across Europe and Asia spreading their knowledge did. They must have a compendium of theories, methods, and techniques and they must know that there is no key to their use. "It all depends"—on the depth of the problem, on the past experience of the group and the leader, and on the composition and preparation of the group. The group's history with other leaders may hold the key to resistance, the depth of their pain may make some members reluctant to join, there may be interpersonal undercurrents that are hard to detect but that interfere with the group's positive "*tele*" (see text that follows). Success or failure may even depend on the weather. Flexibility, combined with knowledge and experience, is probably the most important lesson in leadership to be drawn from these pages.

The reader will have noticed that many techniques have been added to the complement of methods used in classical socio- and psychodrama. In addition to many auxiliary techniques—using the camera, scarves, masks, assorted objects, written materials, and drawings—one technique stands out: sculpture. It is used by so many of the authors so consistently that it deserves a place, along with doubling and role-reversal, in the essential methods of psycho- and sociodrama. With sculpture, we have added "the body" in a way that none of the more verbal techniques had. In addition, many of these authors make use of ritual. Although improvisation remains the mainstay of the therapeutic work discussed here, ritual requires repetition of an important, often spiritual or transcendental part of the drama. Using rituals to open a workshop, such as the passing around of a candle to be lit, or marking a closure by speaking or singing a poem developed by the group, allows for a deeper communication and/or promotes a feeling of completion and pride.

In all of the groups discussed here, feedback to the leaders tells us that what helps is the existential quality of the work. Many of these groups have experienced attempts to resolve problems by talking. Committees set up to solve problems by seeking information and forming discussion groups are accepted as evidence of good will and often provide much-needed financial assistance, but seldom lead to a felt change. For that, action is a necessary ingredient. It is one thing to talk about the difference between chiefly and non-chiefly tribes, but quite another to reverse roles and experience the ways of the other. Alienation and rejection based on perceived difference can disappear in an enactment that gives both parties a chance to represent themselves with energy and dignity.

Second, Moreno's vision of a world based on *tele*, the invisible bonds that connect or sever relationships, is validated by the work of these authors. We are seldom conscious of our own racist tendencies, be they inherited or learned. Privilege exists without announcing itself. Deprivation is often explained as inevitable. Experiential techniques create awareness. Enactments, with their possibility of extending the emotional range of our perceptions, help us to see the humanity in each other. Difference remains but the threat diminishes. Conscious choices become enlarged and the exclusion of others less facile. The world becomes smaller, a large tribe rather than a crowd of faceless millions.

Third, the techniques described in this book help us understand each other on a deeper level through sociodramatic and sociometric techniques. Small groups, like the Indian transvestite prostitutes, each of whom feels alone in a hostile world, learn what they have in common and recover their pride. Children, traumatized by natural disaster, learn to play again. Jewish people severely wounded by the Holocaust learn to see past their own wounding to the vulnerability of the Germans who suffered in their own way from World War II and its consequences. We all know about likenesses and differences in our world, but we often tend to deny rather than explore them. These techniques allow exploration—not without risk, of course, but with the possibility of a widening of the view, a lessening of pain, and an appreciation of similarities.

Lastly, the methods described here contribute to the lessening of pain. The comfort of circling, of locating ourselves in our own space, of working on a project together, of viewing what we have made— whether in the form of enactments, mask-making, singing, drumming, poetry, or theater—lifts spirits. The participants in these groups often enter with a combination of skepticism and fear. After the workshop has ended, many leave with a lesser burden and with an appreciation of common bonds and of the depth of experience that affects not only themselves, but those whom they had formerly perceived as threatening.

Our title promised healing. Healing is an ongoing process. It is not completed in the work of these pages, but that work represents a beginning. Significantly, many of our authors suggest that their work is a prelude to a group's action toward a more successful solution to its problems. Successful action arrives through concerted effort, at a later time. Healing, in our terms, means that groups cope more success-fully with the problems of difference, war, illness, and natural disaster. It means that individuals learn to appreciate rather than repudiate difference. It means that acute pain is diminished, energy recovered, and new perceptions are gained. The healing process is life-affirming. It instills hope, not through endless discussion or debate, but by creating situations which potentiate communication on many levels—personal, social, political—and nurturing the energetic potential that resides in each group. Engaged in this work, the victims, often silent and de-pressed, regain their voices and, together with others, learn to be more fully engaged in making their world a better one.

Index